WINTER CARPING

by
Derek Stritton

First published in 1991 by
Angling Books Ltd.
1 Grosvenor Square,
Sheffield S2 4MS

British Library Cataloguing in Publication Data

Derek Stritton
Winter Carping
1. Carp Angling
1 Title
799. 1'752

ISBN 1 871700 353

Produced and Typeset by
Angling Publications Ltd. and Steve Wilde of One and Only

Printed by
Gibbons Barford Print Ltd.

ACKNOWLEDGEMENTS AND THANKS

I have always wanted to write for a number of people. For my children, Claire and Stephen, frequently deserted for my fishing; for my old Dad who introduced me to angling many, many years ago, when Essex rivers ran clean and clear and carp anglers were silent men with cane rods, potato baits and a far away look in their eyes.

There are also thanks to many anglers with whom I've spent time across the years, and particularly those with whom I've spent winter sessions and seasons: Jim Twitchett, Tony Howells, Greg Peck, Jeff Ducker, Fred Wilton, Bob Morris, Cliff Webb, Alan King, Robin Monday, Dave Campbell, Bob Chambers, Alan Webb, Mark Edwards, Bob Sloane, Brad Bradbrook, Brian Cannon, George Cansdale, Terry Seaborne, Roland Meldon, John the Fridge, Mick Nolan and Tottenham Bob, to mention but a few.

Thanks to Angling Publications and Tim Paisley in particular, for offering me the opportunity to write this book and then being prepared to publish it. To Bob Morris for his special contribution. To Martin Locke for his lovely winter carping shot on the front cover. To Barbara and Lynn who patiently typed the original script from my awful handwritten pages. And a final thanks to a special lady without whose support and encouragement the book would never have been written.

Late November 27¹/₂lb for the author.

CONTENTS

WINTER'S COMING

SETTING THE SCENE

It had been one of those beautiful, golden, late October days. The sunshine filtering through the trees earlier in the day as I'd driven through the Essex countryside had given lie to the frost I'd had to scrape from the windscreen of the car before starting my journey; but now I knew, as I gazed through the window across the open courtyard of the old country house, that the day had reached its peak. Not the slightest drift of breeze to even disturb the leaves which would only need the slightest persuasion to release their grip on life and fall to the ground. It was the perfect day for the carp fisher... and yet...

Returning to the moment, I looked around the table. The conversations continued much as they had before – six highly paid adults had taken six hours to perform a task one could have done in half the time, including two longish tea breaks - and here we were, no nearer to a conclusion.

I looked across the courtyard again; the clock on the tower looked as weary as my mind was beginning to feel as the minute hand hung forever between 2.45 and 2.50 p.m. I paused and wondered for just a moment that, whether it was possible or not, I just had to try.

Making as much noise as possible, I reached for my Filofax and thumbed frantically through the pages, paused, and gasped.

"Excuse me, I'm very sorry, I've got to leave now – just remembered I've got another appointment. I'll get back to you as soon as I can".

Then, picking up my briefcase, Filofax and jacket in one well practised swoop, I made my way towards the door.

Back in the fresh air of the courtyard, I was stung both by the beauty of the day and by the foolishness of my own actions. Oh what the hell...

Minutes later, driving frantically towards the flat, I knew time was of the essence. The earliest the feeding spell had been during the past few weeks was around 4.15 p.m., with the latest starting time being 5.30. I needed to be there as soon as possible. The drive home, change of clothes, loading of gear, was completed and the drive to the lake made only marginally uncomfortable by the need to suck 5 boilies in order to thaw them out for threading onto the rigs on arrival! Baits were cast and free offerings in position by 4.05 p.m. and I was able to settle back and enjoy the final embers of the day.

Such times can be very important in the lead in to the early months of winter, for a feeding period tracked at this time can be fairly consistent for a longish period, prior to major temperature changes. Across the years of winter carp fishing, I have found that I have been able to identify periods of feeding activity which have been consistent for long periods – but more of this later...

In a perfect world my story of the session would unfold with a screaming Optonic, singing line and a carp in the folds of a landing net. Alas, in truth, by 8.30 p.m. I was reloading the car, wondering what might have been and concerning myself with the effects of my rapid departure from the afternoon's meeting.

As I settled into the driving seat, started the car and turned on the headlights, I paused for a moment and closed my eyes. Opening them I was brought back to stark reality as my headlights shone into the church graveyard and illuminated a crucifix headstone!

This brief, but true, account records the events of a day in late October, 1989, something over 22 years after I first started carp fishing. That a 43 year old man can behave so impulsively may well surprise you. However, such is the passion and yearning which carp fishing creates that those who are truly afflicted will seek to be out there doing it whenever an opportunity can be created.

I hope that in the chapters which follow I will manage to convey some of that passion to you.

Footnote: The opening section of this book was written beside a damp, foggy lake in early December, 1989. Somewhere in the middle of it I was interrupted and landed my largest ever carp, a mirror at 35lb – and in winter too. The passion continues...

WHY?

It was a clear, still, freezing night. Even the coils of rolled up silver paper which acted as indicators hung motionless on the line. My hands, numbed by the cold, pulled the old army blanket closer to my chin, the moistness of my breath hung in the air and yet my inner warmth was that of an August day. It was 1.15 a.m. and I'd just hooked, landed, and returned my first ever intentionally caught winter carp, a plump, 8¼lb, scattered mirror carp. There was no one around to share it with, just me, but I didn't care; I'd tried so hard to catch that fish. The simple rig had been recast and now I snuggled back to enjoy it all.

Carp fishing has come a long way since that cold night on the 29th November, 1969. Whatever would today's modern carp angler have thought of my soft, ten foot, hollow glass rods, Ambidex reels, half ounce leads and sausage meat and maggot cocktail baits – as well as my frantically unreliable Heron buzzers and indicators made from silver foil? Indeed, how would he have coped with the inadequacy of my cold weather gear, or the alertness required and the need to be at the rods even on the coldest nights?

When I first set out to attempt to catch carp all the year round, it was not because of a pioneering instinct, nor because I was hyped up by the writings of those who'd done it before me. It was for much simpler reasons – that I couldn't satisfy my need to fish for, or catch, carp during the normally short summer season. I also became quickly aware in those early days that even some of the most popular and crowded summer venues would contain few anglers during a winter's day and none at all during a winter's night. For this reason, and because I began very slowly to realise that I could, at the right time, when luck was with me, catch the odd carp or two, I acquired the affliction of being a year round carp angler.

Certainly, in today's hurly burly, hyped up world of carp fishing, it is still possible to be the only angler present on what are fairly busy summer waters during many a winter's day or night. We've all learned from the Press reports and the writings of others, across the years, that carp can be caught with some consistency in winter. However, that's not a good enough reason to spend your winters fishing for them; you've got to really want to do it and enjoy it.

However did we used to survive? Dave Campbell at Nazeing in the late seventies.

Some of today's modern writers will often make it seem that catching carp in winter is as easy as in the summer – I suspect that their findings are based on very little actual fishing time or experience. I believe fishing for, and catching, carp in winter can be a far slower and harder process and is clearly carried out in much less pleasant conditions than summer, and much more in the long hours of darkness, but caught indeed they can be.

The sort of success which can be experienced can probably best be illustrated by describing two seasons of really concentrated winter fishing in 1984/85 and again in 1986/87 when, along with my friend, Alan Webb, I fished a shallow, 10 acre estate lake.

The water, though never overcrowded, was fished by a number of carp anglers throughout the traditional summer season, but in winter was always quiet. This primarily occurred because those who had fished there on occasions, in winter, had been relatively unsuccessful and had, therefore, either abandoned their efforts or focused them elsewhere.

Alan and I agreed that we would fish as frequently as we could from November to March both years and our efforts tended to focus on two nights a week and the daylight hours. If we could manage a further night each week, we would fit it in, often leaving the water at 6.30 a.m. to go to work.

During both winters, by careful baiting with regular visits to keep a steady trickle of bait going in, and regularly working hard on location, we caught a large number of carp up to 29lb and, despite the odd blank, the only real sessions where no action occurred at all were those when the lake froze over around us. During the entire time few of the other club members realised what success were were having and frankly, because we loved the solitude of it all, we never told them.

I believe it is still possible in today's razzmataz world of carp fishing, to have success like this in reasonable peace, if one chooses the venue correctly and is prepared to work at one's fishing.

In more recent years, I have not found the need to fish as intensively for my winter fish, and for the past two seasons much of my fishing has taken place during the daylight hours, for much shorter periods, but I've still managed to catch a good number of carp.

WHERE? VENUE AND LOCATION

Under the heading 'Where?' there are two major considerations: choice of venue and the choice of fishing area on that venue (if indeed this option is even open to you on some of today's crowded waters).

Firstly, what kind of water do you wish to fish in winter? The range of choice may be limited anyway to the range of options open to you, or the area in which you live, but for the purpose of this chapter I'll assume you do have some choices, and try to take you through them.

I can still remember reading the advice of some of the early winter carp fishers who always advised fishing the more prolific waters in winter – those containing as many fish and as little natural food as possible. Some writers referred to them as hungry waters and I suspect, in the early days of winter carp fishing, that's where those anglers who were at it spent most of their time.

The situation has now changed considerably. There has been a major shift away from the belief that you were 'special' to fish for carp in winter and, as a consequence, you will find some of the better known big fish waters as busy in winter as they are in summer, even if they are hard and understocked. Big fish still get caught in winter, often at their heaviest weights. For example, the 35 pounder written about elsewhere in this book, I had caught earlier in the summer at 32lb+ and, certainly, other big fish venues produce their big fish at slightly inflated weights during the winter months.

So, the waters you choose to fish should have much more to do with your own personal desires and requirements than anything I can tell you. If you just wish to catch fish and be in with a chance of some action in winter then, yes, you should choose a well stocked, hungrier, type of water – preferably one which is fished by others – as this will ensure a regular supply of anglers' bait as a food source to keep the fish active and on the look out for food.

Alternatively, you can take the slightly harder route and introduce small quantities of bait on a regular basis throughout the winter, whether you're fishing or not.

If, on the other hand, you're looking for a big fish, then your choice is made for you in that you'll generally have to opt for a harder water where big fish can be caught.

Although my strategy has changed in recent years – it used to be that I'd opt for a water where there was a chance of action and big fish – there are lots of waters around these days containing a fair head of fish, numbers of which are twenty plus (still a big fish in my view), on which any committed carp angler could spend a winter or two.

The choice of venue may also be affected by a number of other factors;

Derek with a brilliant looking common caught straight after the thaw in late February 1991.

shallow or deep bottomed gravel pits, or silty old estate lakes. Some anglers will advise only fishing hard bottomed gravel pits, but some of my most successful winters have been spent on shallow, silty, soft bottomed lakes.

The other waters worth a thought in winter are the ones which contain a few very hard carp, full of natural food and so much weed in summer that you can hardly get a line in. Sometimes in winter such a water will throw up a surprise when natural food has decreased and the decline in weed allows for a more natural presentation.

The strategy I now employ in winter is to try for a big fish at the beginning and end of the season, i.e. through October, November and early December, when I usually move on to an easier water, returning to try for a biggie during the last couple of weeks of the season. I'm fortunate enough nowadays to have access to both types of water on a reasonably private basis.

Probably as tantalising and undeniably as important, is the location of fish on the venue of your choice in winter. In offering advice here, I'm drawing on a range of experience across the years. There are no obvious answers, but maybe, dependent on the type of waters you are fishing, some of my suggestions will help.

To begin with, I prefer not to start to fish a new water in winter – I like to have some understanding of it before then. When I understand how it behaves in summer, I find it a much easier prospect to make judgement in the winter.

If I am going afresh, I try to start out in September at least. I'm not a believer that one should automatically look to be fishing in areas other than those where one would expect to find fish during the summer months, and my first port of call at the start of a winter campaign would always be the same areas as I would seek to fish during the summer. However, I have noticed on some waters an almost imperceptible movement of fish during the winter months and, on at least one, a very obvious movement.

At this point I should go back many years to my old garden pond, which my father made for me and designed on the basis of a bath or sink, in that it was deeper at one end than the other. I can remember watching the small carp and tench I kept in that pond on many occasions during winter months. During the summer period, the fish were spread all over, but by midwinter they seemed to always gather in the deeper area and lie very close together. Any movement would be within a very defined area – almost winter quarters! I would not wish the readers to believe, at this point, that I am advocating that all carp in winter move to the deeper areas, as this is clearly not the case – however, the movement within an area is something which I believe to be of importance.

During the early mid seventies, I spent considerable time, both in summer and winter, fishing Leisure Sport's big lake at Darenth in Kent. During the

A November double from Darenth Big Lake in the mid-70's. Fishing the Darenth waters in winter taught Derek a great deal about carp location during the colder months.

summer months carp could be located in a variety of areas, but once the real winter was upon us, fish could only be reasonably located in what was known as the 'open water end', still a largish area of water, slightly deeper than the rest. But, more interestingly, the fish would congregate in particular parts of that open water, sometimes caught from the Willow Swim, sometimes the Little Willows, sometimes the High Bank or others the Road Bank area.

When empty, the Willows Swim was always claimed first – no action would occur; a disappointed latecomer who couldn't get the swim would often move in next door, cast out and sometimes get fish – the fish were in the area but had moved slightly.

From this experience I developed a strategy of fishing the going area, but moving my baits steadily throughout the session if no action occurred, to fish just beyond the normal area, both in terms of range and also marginally to the left or right of the expected spot. Sometimes this would result in takes when none had occurred earlier.

There are a number of other areas which would attract my attention in winter, if they existed on a water I was fishing – you will know whether they exist on yours.

Decaying weed beds or lily pads particularly have a way of attracting or holding fish in winter. One of the most successful winter periods I've ever spent, in the early eighties, came about because a friend of mine remarked that while spinning for pike in an area of the lake known as the Pads Swim, he had foul hooked two carp in quick succession. I had, meanwhile, been successfully blanking elsewhere on the lake until this information came my way. I was there, and fishing, at the first possible opportunity and it began a period of great success. Fishing at quite short range – 20/25 yards – just beyond where the pads would be in summer, and surprisingly having to strike at small lifts on the line or bangs on the rod top, even though I was rigged up.

Another area worth a try in winter is where overhanging trees or bushes jut out over the back. If they exist on islands, they can accumulate a large number of fish. However, such features do not only exist on islands, and bushes, even within the margins, are worth looking at if you can actually see into them. I once spent several weekends in winter casting across a bay, fishing to the far side. When I reeled in I would toss my cast off baits back into the margin to my left and on one occasion, when I was sitting peering there, I actually saw a small disturbance under the overhanging bush. Retrieving a rod, I merely stopped winding and allowed the lead to fall under the bush which overhung to my left where the disturbance had occurred. Twenty minutes later I was putting the net under a 26lb 12oz mirror carp. That bush became a good area, particularly successful when I switched to another part of the lake and cast across to it so as not to disturb the fish.

There are three other areas I would recommend. Try the gullies between

Don't ignore the shallow areas.

gravel bars, because they can be killers during the winter, as can the areas of gravel located between patches of silt, either on a distant island where there may be trees which regularly shed their leaves over the years. The area in between may actually be gravel, whilst underneath them may be soft and silty. Try them; if it's gravel, give them a go.

Finally, don't ignore the shallow areas of your lake if it has some. They may just give up the goods when you least expect them and sometimes in the coldest of conditions too. Scan them frequently while you're fishing and look out for movement in those areas. At the first sign, always give them a try.

RATS, CATS & BOB'S TALE

Have you ever noticed how the rats – the four legged variety that is – that frequent our lakes these days and sound like small pigs as they blunder through the bankside undergrowth, unseen in summer, actually assume the stature of fully grown elephants in the winter when you can actually see them. I must confess to having something of a dislike of rats, the origin on which can be traced back to the earliest days of winter fishing.

A lake in South Ockenden in Essex, surrounded by a rubbish dump caused by the backfill of another pit, had a population of rats the like of which I've never seen before or since in over twenty years. Such a population was just about endurable because of the lake's carp, had they not included some of the true leviathans of the rat population. The five foot sixers I can handle, but when they come in the Frank Bruno mould, that's where I draw the demarcation line.

In those very early days, back in the late 60's, early 70's, my naivete, tackle wise, had to be seen to be believed. On a windy night when first the silver paper coils and, in later years, the washing up liquid bottle top indicators, began to swing about in the wind and couldn't be restrained by my feeble angled knitting needles stuck in the ground, I would weight them down with the bait of the day (or night – as it was on most occasions). If ever the fad changes from carp fishing to rat catching I can personally guarantee the effectiveness of combinations of sausage meat and rusk, cat food and groundbait or, an absolute killer, trout pellet or fish meal paste.

I remember with true revulsion one night when the wind was blowing a gale and I was feeling really chuffed, with the silver paper indicators well weighted down with the sausage meat mix. The swim had been an absolute hive of activity. Some clown had fashioned the front of it with a piece of corrugated iron, bent over at right angles to the bank, which had the effect of amplifying the sound of any rat crossing the area to the equivalent of four adult females in stiletto heels clonking down a silent street. When the rat activity had abated, at around 2.00 a.m., I had drifted into one of those aimless drowses that takes you nowhere in terms of rest, but puts you on another planet in terms of disorientation, when suddenly one of the buzzers was screaming.

Out from the army blanket, blunder around; yes, the line's pouring out from the spool. Close the pick up and wind as fast as you can; the rod doesn't bend but there's an horrendous squealing noise somewhere up the bank as the mother and father of a ginormous rat tries to regurgitate my silver paper and sausage meat mix. Trouble is, I'm so excited I don't stop winding until it's almost under my bloody nose...

My nerves still jangle at the thought.

Then, of course, there was a time when I forgot my bedchair and decided to sleep on the floor. It'd be O.K., I'd be too cold and uncomfortable to sleep. Have you ever woken up eye to eye with a rat at 2.00 a.m. only to leap in the air in fright and realise that there were about twenty of them around you? I'd stick with the modern day Fox bedchair if I were you!

A small Hertfordshire pit and it's now the late seventies. Yours truly is quite a sophisticated state of the art winter carp angler. High protein boilie baits, proven elsewhere, isotope indicators fitted into the washing up bottle tops – clipped on the line between the butt and the second ring. The rods are up so high in the rests than not even the Frank Brunos of the rat world can reach them, and so confident am I that I'm fishing two evening sessions a week, as well as weekends, and feeling confident of catching carp in three to four short hour sessions. There are no rigs; the hooks are in the baits and I'm experiencing a lot of action from carp. There are twitches on the line, short lifts and, sometimes, out and out screaming takes in the shape of reel spinners, which spin the handle so fast they can skin your knuckles if you miss it and the bail arm crashes against your hand as you pick up the rod. But the rats are still there – a newer variety – they climb trees to eat the berries, primarily because this is a clean water and there is no rubbish for them to scavenge amongst. Nonetheless, it is very unnerving as you sit in your garden chair, next to the rods, and hear the rats gnawing on the berries behind and above you.

It was such a night, very still and cold, that I sat on my garden chair beside the rods, explaining to my old mate, Dave Campbell, that any minute now I'd be away on the left hand rod, rats gnawing on the bushes behind me. Suddenly, out of the blue and with no warning, Dave jumped back with a look of absolute horror on his face and I felt sharp claws impaling themselves in the back of my neck. To say I leapt in the air would be like doing a slow motion replay – I flew – grabbing frantically at my neck and screaming at full pitch. Guess what? The imagined rat was a fully grown, fluffy Persian cat that belonged to a family that lived in a house bordering the lake, which had been attracted to me by the movements of my head. When I wrestled him off, he was actually purring – inside I was screaming!

In the vicinity of the small Hertfordshire pit was a chicken farm which had attracted a community of feral cats which fed voraciously on any recently departed battery hen lobbed out from the sheds into which those poor hens were crammed. The noise of the cats fighting at night was sometimes horrendous, but the most frightening thing of all was to be woken in the middle of a winter's night to see one of these large creatures trying to drag your food out of the bivvy while you are trying to sleep or, alternatively, have one come screaming through your swim with another in hot pursuit. I was later to rescue one of them and tame it at home; problem was, no matter how tame it became, after a rainy night the back garden looked like a battle field of half eaten lobworms where the cat had been to feed.

Bob's tale is something else. At least it has real connection with winter carp fishing and it involves the capture of true winter carp.

On the same Hertfordshire place as the former stories had occurred, there were two lakes and, during certain times of the winter, I would fish what was called the 'Roach Pit' or, as it was sometimes called, the 'Boys' Lake'. It was during one of my sessions here that the following true story occurred.

I was fishing in the same style as I often employed here for winter evening stints. Two rods fished standard style – buzzers, ledgers and boilies – but because I also had a cheating rod out and only two were officially allowed, the third rod had a float on; it was one of those operated on a hearing aid battery with a light emitting diode in the tip. The rod was being fished in the margin to my right, a small boilie side hooked with some diced sausage shaped particle protein baits around it. The rod was propped up in a bush so no one would

The Boys Pit in winter.

know I was cheating. It was around 9.00 p.m. and a pretty frosty night – January 1978.

The only other angler on the complex was Bob and the rattle on the car park gate told me that he had had enough. I heard the door of his Volkswagen car close and waited for the engine to roar into life. Instead, I was surprised to hear him arrive in the swim behind me. We had a brief discussion and it transpired that Bob's session had been as uneventful as mine up to this point in time. It was really cold and frosty and we got into one of those carp fishing conversations which go on for ever, and which would probably still be going on now if the bush immediately to my right hadn't started to shake. Bob looked at it as if divine intervention had just occurred. Me? I knew. The little red light in the margin had gone and I was away on the cheating rod. I jumped up, grabbed the rod as it began to disappear, and was into a fish. Bob knew what was going on at this point and had got the landing net and come to help. As soon as the carp was near the net, I realised what had happened; the rubber band on the float, which kept it at the required depth, had broken and the float had slid down near the soft shot, which was close to the hook.

Bob netted the carp and carried it up the bank whilst I got a weigh sling, dampened it and gathered some scales. I arrived as Bob was unravelling the net and I saw him jump back and gasp.

"****ing hell!" he shouted. "This carp's got a fag in its mouth!"

The red diode float had slid down and was sticking out close to the carp's lip. I fell about with laughter and so did Bob when he realised. A true story this, but I wouldn't embarrass the said Bob by asking him to confirm it; only a supporter of Tottenham Hotspur could make such mistakes!

SHANGRI-LA
AND OTHER
EARTHLY
HEAVENS

I think it was the winter of 1972 when Tony Howells, Jim Twitchett and I were making our regular weekly winter pilgrimage to Shangri-la in Essex. Three of us and our winter carp gear were all packed tightly into my old mini van, which had over 60 thousand miles on the clock and a non-existent heater. By the time we'd travelled 58 miles to get there, the inside of the van was running with condensation. Poor old Jim – he always got the 'bum seat', in the back with all the gear. It's a wonder he could walk when we arrived by the lake, usually around 2.00 a.m. Saturday morning.

It was all so exciting in those days – we felt as if we were on a great adventure and the banter and conversations which took place on route always shortened the uncomfortable journey. Seems so strange in this day and age to liken a journey of 58 miles to a 'great adventure' when guys are going off all over Europe and other continents to fish for carp, but adventure it was.

It was nearing Christmas and this was likely to be our last visit for some time. Because we all wanted to fish the same area, we trebled up in the big swim from which there was a 60/70 yard cast to the rushes and a bay on the far bank. Tony was on his usual sausage meat mix; Jim and I were on trout pellet paste. Hooks were inside the bait, a tube slid down the line to prevent it from cutting the bait as we cast and a crust pad on the bend of the hook to hold it on.

The only other angler arrived at the lake around 7.00 a.m. the following morning. It was Brad Bradbrook, whom I was to get to know well in the years that followed, and with whom I spent a number of winter trips in the late seventies.

Around 10.30 a.m. on Saturday morning, I got an early Christmas present in the shape of an 11lb+ mirror. I was delighted – first fish for about 6 weeks – but a true winter carp. The three of us had a little celebration in the shape of a cuppa at three, and then settled down to see out the session. We certainly didn't expect any more action, or rather, I didn't – Tony was always expecting something to happen; he was so keen he'd drive us to despair with his imitations of a buzzer going off and swoosh noises for strikes. He had a saying which was taken from a puppet show of the day, "anything can happen in the next half hour". It was late afternoon and I was enduring this for seemingly the 99th time, when my buzzer did sound. I was out of the chair like a shot. The plastic ring indicator had moved about two inches and stopped. I pulled it back and moments later it twitched up two inches again and stopped. I wound the bobbin up to within two inches of the butt ring and Tony gently teased it down while I stood behind the rod ready. It twitched and I struck like lightning – unfortunately, before Tony could get out of the way. The rod caught him full smack on the forehead and at the same time I lost my footing because of the force of the strike, and fell backwards. So there we were, Tony on the floor, knees up, holding on to his forehead and groaning; me flat on my back with a rod being wrenched up from my hand by a carp trying to reach the bushes and Jimmy falling about with laughter at what was going on.

Had I known what was on the other end at that point I'd have died. On the bank, I couldn't believe my eyes.

"The carp don't grow that big in here" I said.

By my winter standards of the past, it was huge at 19lb 12oz, a mirror and, I believe, at that time, a lake record.

The photo call that day was really special, even if I do look dazed in the pictures. Tony had a wonderful bump on his forehead, but he was pleased for me.

"The carp don't grow that big in here."

I could tell a million stories about his escapades on winter sessions, but that would be a book in its own right...

It's December 1989 and I am still learning some of life's inequalities, having spent about twenty years in a job where it's hard to cheat on time; I am seconded to an office post where no one really knows where, or what, you're at for most of the time. I'm under pressure to produce a report, but you can write a report anywhere – so I decided to go somewhere quiet and finish it. I'd also just been given the opportunity to write this book, so I could really crack on... Where better to get the atmosphere for writing than beside a carp lake?

Driving to the lake did not fill me with much optimism. It was a particularly foggy day and the closer I got to the lake, the foggier it got. Arriving in my chosen swim was an adventure in itself, having almost lost my way across the field.

The next problem would be to locate the chosen area with the baits. I was fishing in a large bay which opened out into a larger area of the lake. I was intending to fish two baits in the far margin area and one in the mouth of the bay. This was a pretty difficult winter water by most standards – slow going in summer and generally as uncooperative in winter, but with rich rewards on occasions. The placement of the bait was pretty crucial.

One was being dispatched across the bay to an overhanging bush, the

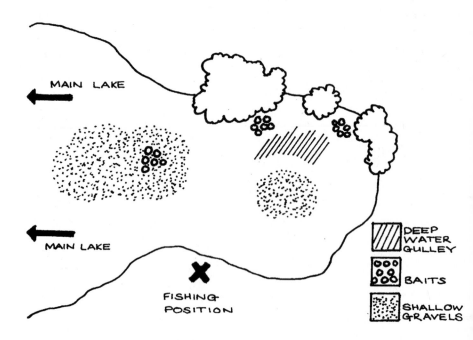

26

closer the better; another to a deep corner with some clear gravel between silt; the third to a gravel area in the mouth of the bay. The rods were set up with soft anti-tangle tube, 9 inch Silkworm hook lengths, short hair rigs with bent hooks and negative buoyancy, H.N.V. boilies which had no polystyrene in them and three bait stringers attached.

The first rod was ready to go but I couldn't see the other side of the bay in the fog. I aimed in the general direction and waited for a splash. It didn't come and the silence indicated that I'd located the bush alright, but above the waterline, rather than below it. Some heaving and straining did nothing, so I decided to walk round and see if I could disentangle the mess in the bush.

After some precarious moments, climbing in the bush and almost swimming in the lake, I managed to untangle the mess, stringer and all, and drop it in the margin, rather than try to cast it again. Perfect position.

Back round in the swim, I dispatched the other two baits without adventure and fired half a dozen free offerings to each to add to the three stringered ones. I couldn't account for the accuracy – most of them were guesses in the fog. It was around 9.00 a.m., having had a cuppa, that I began to write my report and follow this with the opening chapter of this book. By the time I'd finished writing, with my work punctuated by regular cups of tea and sandwiches, the paper was soggy and wet and the gear wet and damp.

It was around 2.00 p.m. and I was just sat wondering whether to try a recast when the take was heralded by three bleeps on the Optonic as the indicator dropped back.

I was up and winding down into a heavy, slow moving fish, which was wanting to find its way back into the bush. I had to put on excessive pressure to prevent it getting there and at this point began to regret all the heaving and straining I'd done with the bush earlier. The remainder of the fight was pretty dogged – the type I really don't like because I kept thinking I was going to lose it.

Eventually it was in the landing net and my efforts to carry it up the bank told me I had something special. Unravelling the net made me really smile and with the scales registering over 35lb, I was really chuffed.

The problem now was with a photograph. I reeled in and drove down to the local pay phone and phoned Alan Webb who worked about thirty miles away. Despite the fact that he was due at a Board meeting in an hour, he agreed to come and take the pictures. Although the weather ensured they were not perfect, I was pleased to have them as, to this day, that carp is my biggest ever.

With the scales registering over 35lb, I was really chuffed.

March 14th 1978 was a sad day. It was the end of what had been an absolutely brilliant season and yet somehow it was incomplete. Here I was, sharing my Hertfordshire lake with good friends – Dave Campbell, Bob Chambers and John the Fridge. We had all caught during the previous night, so this really was the dying embers.

During 1977/78 I'd fished harder than ever; having pulled away from my Kentish venues, the stakes were not so high. There were no twenties here and I spent the entire season chasing the common, a nineteen pounder, the biggest in the lake; I wanted her badly. I'd caught around 120+ fish and still no common. It was 3.00 p.m. and I was beginning to pack up when the reel handle of my Mitchell 300 was spinning frantically. The fish was hooked and found a snag I didn't even know existed in the Gate Swim.

Dave, who had been by my side so often that season, was there to net the fish when she eventually came clear.

"It's the 19" he said.

And, for sure, it was. The perfect end to a perfect season. The 19 was mine and the smile in those car park photos says it all.

FAILINGS REWARDED

I can still, at the ripe old age of 43, remember back to the days when I was late to arrive at secondary school. My recollection of the time is primarily because of the unfortunate 'lines' I had to write in an attempt to prevent me from being late again…

"Unpunctuality and procrastination are similar transgressions". God only knows how many times I set that line to paper 50 times across a period of 5 years but it was certainly enough for me to remember the words and the aching fingers, even to this day. Whilst I learned some things from that tedious punishment, other problems have remained with me to this day – and probably always will.

For example, having completed the arduous task, I realised it was better to be really late than just late; the prefect responsible for the handing out of lines would not be waiting in readiness for me at the front door after 9.20 a.m. Therefore, it was better to pause at Robertsons, the local tackle shop in Prince Regents Lane, if I was going to be late – and be really late – rather than risk the lines.

Procrastination was a word which always held a form of fascination for me, as no matter how many times I wrote it, I never really knew what it meant until many years later. To procrastinate actually means to put things off; to leave until tomorrow what one could easily do today. Sadly, for me, this has always been a problem and one which, despite all those lines written in my formative years, I never really learned from…

It was November 1990 and I was feeling really pissed off. I'd bloody well done it again – had about two months to get myself organised to get to the Carp Society Conference in Birmingham and left it, as usual, to the last moment. Never mind, I could get it sorted.

My own car was going through its final death throes and, having conked out quite a few times on motorways, was not to be trusted with a trip to Birmingham. Normally, Alan Webb would have been a banker bet for a lift, but Alan did not want to go.

Vic Cranfield was next on the list but it transpired he was travelling up the night before and I was unable to do that. Mickey Kavanagh might help – but no, he was staying over the night after.

By Saturday morning it was clear that I wouldn't get there and I really had the hump. Dare I risk my car?

Eventually, I decided not and after prowling around the house like a scalded cat, I eventually decided, as did the assembled company, that I'd be better off out of it rather than in it, given my mood…

I loaded the gear in the car and set off, not really knowing where I was going even. Halfway there I stopped, altered direction and headed for a big, old gravel pit where I hadn't fished for some time, instead of the lake I had

*A personal best common – and all because
I'd not learnt not to procrastinate!*

31

started out for. It was one of those where Alan Webb and I had located carp a few times in the past couple of years and caught some private lunkers but, as usual, word was out and others were at it.

However, on the day of the Carp Society Conference it might just be quiet and I was going to take a chance.

On arrival, I went for a walk round. It was windy and, quite frankly, I didn't see a thing until I arrived at a bay where I'd located fish in the past. I stood longingly looking across the bay, remembering how idyllic it looked in summer compared to how it looked now, when over in the corner I noticed a flattening of the waves caused by fish swirling.

In years gone by, I would have attributed that movement to a pike, but as I was after carp, then the movement had to be a carp.

By the time I had returned from the car with the gear, had baited and cast and settled in, it was about 10.30 a.m. I'd still rather have been at the C.S. Conference, but the 27½lb mirror which gave me activity at about 12 o'clock midday gave me cause to wonder and by 1.30 p.m., as I slipped the net under a 30lb+ common carp, I actually felt really pleased that my old Escort was as unreliable as it was…

Obtaining photographs was difficult, but we got them in the end and it was indeed a happy man who returned home that evening; a personal best common – and all because I'd not learned not to 'procrastinate'.

Whoever said luck doesn't play a part in fishing – summer or winter…

THE MIDAS TOUCH

Bob Morris

Have you ever had the feeling that you could do no wrong? This unusual state of mind affected me during the winter of 80/81 and I can honestly say that it had never happened before – and most certainly has not occurred since.

Although I have certainly had my share of success over the years, and I have to admit to the odd flukey catch from time to time, I have never regarded myself as a lucky angler, unlike some people that I could mention. In fact, looking back over my fishing years, and also through some of my old diaries, it seems that most of the good catches, big fish and consistent results that I have had, can easily be related to the time and effort put in by myself and various fishing colleagues.

I suppose the stage had been set for this event earlier that season, when Cliff Webb and I had baited up and started what turned out to be a very good run of action at the lake in question – the Dartford club water at Sutton at Hone. We had been catching fish very consistently during the midsummer spell on one of our favourite baits, known as the P6. It was not just the bait that was working well for us this year on the short baiting up programme we had undertaken; we also had another string to our bow, as it were, in the form of the magnetic bobbins which, I believe, Cliff had devised – with a little help from yours truly.

The method consisted of our old washing up bottle tops with a drawing pin inserted into the bottom. In Cliff's version, the bobbin was then placed on top of a small magnet that was pinned to the ground by means of a bivvy peg.

I later modified my set up so that I had a flat magnet clipped to the front rest below the rod bar, and the two bobbins sitting side by side on the small platform that this created. I well recall one bemused angler commenting "'ere mate, how come your dollies are balancing on that little plate there?"

The method worked like magic. The end tackle consisted of a two ounce running bomb (considered large at the time), a large hook – usually a size 1 or 1/0 Au Lion D'or, with a small, rock hard, pea sized bait pushed right round the bend and mounted on the eye of the hook, leaving the point and gape completely exposed. Later, we moved on to the 2/0 Aberdeen long shanks with two or three baits up the shank. The rods were set up at waist height, for convenience more than anything, as striking was not normally necessary – to put it mildly. The line was then tightened up as far as it would go without moving the lead or causing the reel to turn. Bottle tops were then placed on the magnets and it was all systems go.

The takes were somewhat spectacular, to say the least, and it is perhaps

A 22-pounder from Yateley, during the winter of 80/81.

just as well that at that stage we were still using fairly robust glass rods, as the crack of the bobbin hitting the rod could be heard about twenty yards away. This was, of course, another form of bolt rig, with the resistance being provided by the overall effect of the tight line, as opposed to the weight of the bomb, as used in some of the later bolt rigs.

The hook link was short, 6-8" or even less, and we became convinced that once the carp had picked up the bait and often dislodged the bomb, it would find it almost impossible to eject the bare hook, as a sort of catapult action would occur, due to the stretch of the line. In fact, we called the system the 'Mechanical Bolt Rig'!

I also noticed that it seemed to work better on a gravel or stony bottom; it was possible to tighten the line more when the bomb was lodged between two stones. The idea of using resistance to make the fish run was not new. In fact, we had used another form of the same set up for quite some time, with various clips to pull the line tight. We were aware of the hair rig at this stage but had it down more as a confidence inducing device. We did later use the same set up in conjunction with the hair and did have some very good results. I remember, on one occasion, watching Cliff who used, occasionally, to take the tight line theory to its limit, standing next to his rod with the reel check on, the line as tight as a bow string and clearing the water for about thirty yards, waiting for the butt ring to collide with the buzzer as a form of indication – which it loudly did some minutes later – all in the name of experiment of course. Anyway, I think that it is fair to say that a combination of a going bait and a different method of presentation were definitely doing the business for us that summer.

We had started the season at Darenth, then moved to Sutton for the midsummer spell, doing pretty well and taking a number of fish from each water, including some good ones up to twenty six pounds. However, as we had promised ourselves a go at a few bigger specimens, we decided that it was time to move on.

Our next stop was Longfield, the Leisure Sport water at Staines, which we knew to hold some very good fish. Although we were confident in the bait we were using, the Longfield fish had not seen any and we arrived for our first two day session not expecting very much to happen.

Nothing did happen the first night and day, but we did see a few good carp and get a bit of bait in. The magnetic bolt rig was not a good system to try at Longfield because of the thick weed that seemed to cover most of the lake. It was a bad situation for bait presentation as the water was an average of eighteen feet deep and the long strands of weed reached the water surface all over the place. For this reason I now made what I consider to have been a gross error and decided not to use the hair rig for fear of foul hooking the weed.

On the second night, Cliff had an abortive take that stopped just as he got to the rod. We had a number of these dropped takes, probably because of the line in the weeds and, on reflection, I think that had we used the hair rig we would have done much better than we did.

On our next session I had a good take at 11.00 p.m. the first night and connected with a powerful fish that soon came adrift in the weed in the middle of the lake. I had no idea how big the fish was when I reeled back to find that my trace had broken just below the swivel, but at least I could console myself with the knowledge that the carp were on to the bait.

The following week, after a couple of missed or dropped takes between us, I hooked and landed what was to be my only fish from the water, a superb leather of twenty four pounds.

Another angler then proceeded to catch a superb fish of thirty six pounds on his first visit to the water. Wasn't I pleased to learn later that it still had my hook in its mouth.

"Oh cruel world".

We fished on at Staines for a month or so but only put two fish on the bank, despite about fifteen chances.

A couple more incidents, that I now recall with a smile, from that spell at Longfield. On the last trip that I made there, I was on my own and had done two days and nights without a chance and it was about 10.00 a.m. on a hazy morning and very warm. The carp had started to show on the surface; I fired out some floaters and was amazed to see some interest shown in them by a large fish, only about 15 yards out. I decided to climb up a nearby tree to get a better view and, not being the best of steeplejacks, this took me about five minutes. On reaching the crow's nest I could not see the big fish nor any of the floaters that I had put out. It then dawned on me that the carp must have scoffed the remaining morsels and then gone down somewhere in the vicinity of my left hand bait. The depth at that point was about 18 feet and, of course, no self respecting mirror would be feeding both on the top and on the bottom at this time of morning and in this heat?

The next thing I remember is lying at the bottom of the tree with what seemed like a broken leg, mild concussion and a profusion of nettle stings, with the sound of my Optonic howling and my Mitchell 410 impersonating an electric motor.

"Oh you bastard".

This state of affairs seemed to last for ever, but it was probably only about 15 seconds before I was hobbling to the rod. The take had stopped, leaving me hard in the weeds and not sure if the fish was there or not. It turned out that it wasn't and I packed up in disgust and decided to turn my attentions to Yateley.

We had also bumped into two other anglers from our area – Dennis and Colin – who we found out later had been having a result at Longfield that summer. After the business of losing the 36 pounder, I was talking to them one morning and mentioned that I thought that this fish was about the largest in the water. Dennis smiled and Colin, who had landed a 40+ carp the week before, was not about to disillusion me. Anyway, I moved on to Yateley.

I decided to fish the Match Lake at Yateley and found myself in competition with my old friend Chris, who was doing very well there, with the lake really singing on his bait. I baited the lake with a mix which we called the 'filth', for reasons which I will not go into, and soon found that I was getting a bit of action, taking some nice doubles, including twenties, up to twenty three pounds. I was using the hair rig this time and trying to convince Chris of its worth. Chris was unconvinced of its value and continued to get more action and land more fish than me.

Looking back on it, I suppose that there was no reason for the hair to give me a better result on that type of water. After all, it was not very heavily fished at that stage, the carp were not hook shy at all and Chris had the advantage of having put a lot more of his bait in. By the autumn, a certain amount of rivalry had developed and I had been persuaded (against my better judgement, of course) to enter into a race to see who could first get to twenty twenties. At this stage Chris was in the lead by 15 to 10 but I had the feeling that if I could just get a bit more of the old 'filth' in I would be in with a chance. I would also be interested to see how the lake responded to the two going baits, as the temperature dropped.

We decided to fish together on the Match Lake for the winter, using the same two baits and comparing results, as well as competing for the prize which, as I recall, was an evening out at a venue of your choice at the expense of the loser.

By Christmas I had had enough; no, more than that, I had the complete pox with it all. The lake, at least on the swims that we were fishing, had turned into a muddy bog and it was like being in the trenches – wading round in a horrible, freezing slurry. It is true that there were no dead horses but with the weather alternating between sub zero nights and monsoon conditions on some days, I felt that I was up to my neck in shit and shells and I wanted out.

I had managed several doubles and one twenty, but Chris was now looking firm favourite at 17 to my 11 and still getting more action than yours truly. The crunch came when, after a particularly obnoxious weekend blank session, I left Chris and Terry (who was fishing to our left), to get something from the motor. Upon my return, Chris was just netting one that Terry had landed on one of my rods.

"It is only a small one" said Terry, but God and I knew differently.

I will always remember that as we hoisted the scales to register 22lb, Terry almost apologised.

"Oh it isn't is it?"

The bet was still on even though I had decided to leave Yateley to Chris. He was keen enough to fish over the Xmas holiday but I must admit that at this stage I was convinced that he would definitely have it in the bag by the New Year and made noises to this effect.

We were wrong, however, for after having the week off for the festivities, I discovered that in spite of the mild spell, things had now gone a bit slow on the Match Lake and Chris had only managed one more twenty.

I was rather heartened by this news and decided to start the New Year off on the big lake at Darenth. I fished with Cliff again and it was interesting to note that although we started getting action fairly quickly, it did seem that on this water the hair rig was scoring heavily over any other method being used. Obviously, the Darenth fish were very hook shy due to the constant pressure that the water was receiving, even then. We caught a number of good fish but the only twenty fell to Cliff and I could not help thinking that Chris was probably sweating on his last one at this very moment.

The weather turned bitterly cold and the action slowed, but ironically, this was to be the turning point for my results that winter.

At this point Cliff decided to try an afternoon back at Sutton at Hone and phoned me that evening to report. It seemed that the lake had fished very slowly so far that winter and there were now only a couple of anglers regularly fishing it seriously and they had been getting a certain amount of success, using maggots. Cliff had gone straight back in with the old P6 and done the business, taking three fish, including a 23lb. This seemed like a golden opportunity to me and we arranged to fish the following day.

The conditions seemed to have settled into a steady pattern of calm, clear nights with a hard frost and sunny days with a light breeze during the afternoons. Hardly the right situation for regular results.

On our first session, Cliff went back into the same pitch as the previous day and I opted to go in the swim next along in the interest of sociability. Cliff was soon into a good fish which turned out to be a superbly conditioned 18lb mirror. While we were busy photographing it I heard my Optonic scream. I raced back, but it had stopped, leaving the bottle top hard against the rod. Looking out to where I had put my baits I cursed to see a group of tufted ducks in residence with at least two of them juggling with small, rock hard balls of P6.

Later that afternoon a light, northerly breeze had got up and I was having a cup of tea with Cliff, when the same thing occurred again. This time the reel handle was rotating in a fairly sedate manner. I looked at the flock of tufties and, sure enough, several of them were down. I looked at the reel, which had picked up a bit of speed, then back to the ducks – 1 up, 2 up, 3 up, slight pause during which the reel accelerated to warp factor 9, 4 up and, yes, I was into my first Sutton carp of the winter. Unfortunately, I lost it after about 5 minutes

Bob with a lovely 21¹/₂ pound mirror from Sutton, Winter 80/81.

when the hook pulled on me (felt like a twenty).

The following day I returned to the same spot and fished the afternoon. I started just after noon and packed up at 5.00 p.m. In that time I took three good fish – two 18 pounders and a 17.13, as well as having two other pulls.

It was now the 11th February and I remember packing up and driving home with a certain inexplicable feeling that things were going to go my way from now on. And so it transpired that, in spite of the continuing cold, bright conditions, I caught carp consistently through until the end of the season.

I was fortunate enough, during this spell, to be able to fish almost every afternoon which, of course, helped in so far as the regular baiting of the lake went. This is an important feature of winter carp fishing, in my opinion, but there seemed to be more to it than that as Cliff, who had started well, now seemed to be struggling to get takes even on identical bait and rigs. Cliff's carping was usually done on a one session a week basis – two nights and a day – but he soon decided to change to doing short afternoon stints as the action seemed concentrated about this time. Strangely though, he still found that he was playing second fiddle to yours truly.

As the lake was fishing well for us generally, we decided to invite Derek over for a few sessions with us, in the interest of sociability, although we knew that this would mean giving a signed statement from the pair of us guaranteeing him a couple of twenties on his first visit.

Derek came over and we all blanked for the day. He was gutted and threatened breach of contract but we persuaded him to return the following week for a last try before the summons was served on us.

This session was to be my best of the winter and certainly one of my all time favourites – albeit for fiendishly selfish reasons. We all started at 10.30 a.m. (an early start) on a grizzly Friday morning which had all the makings of another blank and a potential trip to the Old Bailey for Cliff and myself. Although I had continued to catch in the past week, including another 20+, the lake had been frozen over most mornings and not fishable until early afternoon – and the water temperature was dropping rapidly.

We set up in adjacent swims with both Cliff and Derek to my left. A cold north east wind was getting up and what looked like snow clouds were approaching. In spite of this, I felt very confident and after only ten minutes had a slow take, which I managed to miss.

At 11.15 I was away with a belter of 13lb 4oz that got the competitive banter going in the camp and as I just knew that I was on a winning streak I was able to take all the abuse that was thrown my way with a smile.

The snow started at 1.45 p.m. but I was not concerned. I was doing battle with a superb mirror of 21½lb that posed sweetly for the snarling cameras of my two colleagues. Apart from the action that I had had, all was quiet in the camp and I could not help noticing that flying leads and baits were starting to

Sutton-at-Hone in the winter of 80/81, on the day when Bob did all the damage – and Derek and Cliff Webb blanked.

encroach on my territory from both sides as Cliff had now moved to the swim to my right.

"Oh well".

Unintimidated by this, I smiled as I struck into my third fish of the day which had to be landed amid derisory taunts of despicable 'shitter' and worse, but to me, of course, it was the nicest little 12.3 mirror that you could ever wish to meet.

The snow had stopped by half past four. We were sitting having our tenth cup of tea of the day and discussing my old theory that those with crystal balls gaze into the future, but those of us with golden ones rarely bother, when lo and behold, a screamer developed on my left hand rod, which is now to the left of Derek's right hand bait (only joking Del). This carp fought extremely well and looked a fairly good one as it eventually rolled over the net. The weighing sling was now as stiff as a board and I had to dip it in the water to thaw it out before hoisting the carp onto the Avons in the half light. 20lb exactly. I swear it. Remarks about knicker elastic and on the down stroke were ignored as I set up the flash for a twilight shot.

Remarks about knicker elastic and on the down stroke were ignored as I set up the flash for a twilight shot. 20.00 exactly.

Cliff decided, as a last ditch stand, to move to the other side of the lake to fish the swim directly opposite me, where he remained fishless until the lake froze over at about 10.00 p.m.

By this stage Del and I were back home in front of the fire with a brandy in one hand. We had decided to give it our best at 7.30 when the ice had started to form in the margins and the thermometer confirmed that the water temperature had dropped to 37°F. As we packed up, I was subject to more abuse which was only silenced by my last bait out screaming to the tune of a 16.9oz common – a mixture of bliss and frost bite followed.

As I said, one of my most remarkable sessions, and made even more amusing by the astonishing blank that the other two suffered. As Will Shakespeare would say "Now was the winter of their discontent".

The lake was frozen over for a few days but as soon as it started to thaw a bit I was back in action, consistently catching carp during the afternoon stints. I won't say that I never blanked but I certainly averaged at least one fish per trip. Cliff caught a number of fish but it did seem that for that winter, I had definitely got 'the Midas Touch'.

The great day was Sunday 8th March. I had started to fish the other side of the lake and had taken two fish the previous day weighing 24.2 and 15lb. The diary reads: 'Fished the same swim as yesterday. Weather still the same (S/W wind and rain) but not quite so rough. 10.15 a.m. had a fast churner on left hand rod and landed a 23.10oz mirror. My 20th twenty pounder and best fish of the season. Whoopee'.

I fished on and took a further three, 14.5, 19.10 and 16.7, packing up at 6.00 p.m., a delighted carp angler in every sense.

24.02 – and the twentieth twenty is just a day away.

I ended the season on 22 twenties and although I think that my regular approach during the latter part of the winter was very much responsible for my success, I had to concede that Cliff's relatively poor results (although good by most standards) tended to indicate that luck played a certain part in it all. I think that sometimes when you have got a water going well on a bait you can say that a certain amount of action will be available, but how it will be shared out amongst the participants is open to negotiation. Many factors come into play in deciding who gets the lion's share, but I am sure that confidence plays its part here and there because there is no doubt that when you get that feeling that you can do no wrong, you almost certainly fish harder and more effectively as a result. But at the end of the day, at the negotiating table, Luck is the chairman and will always have the casting vote.

I had not heard from Chris since I started my run of success and assumed that he would easily have taken the prize, but to my amazement, I heard that he had had it rough at Yateley and had to stay until (I won't mention what time) on the 14th March to catch his twentieth 20+ fish. He was amazed to hear that I had beaten him with six days to spare.

I haven't heard from Chris for years and I am still waiting for an evening out at the restaurant of my choice, but I am not really bothered as I had so much fun during that winter of 80-81 when I gave him a damn good thrashing!

Mind you, his best fish were 41.5 and 32.4 but that, as they say, is another story.

Fred, Bob & Company

~

BAIT TALK

This chapter refers to a group of anglers for whom I have the ultimate respect. Although they do not all come together in the same way, I learned from them all and, as a consequence, they are all deserving of mention together.

The individuals concerned are, Fred Wilton, for his contribution to bait and approaches to baiting; he really did change the carp fishing scene, moving it further forward than it had been moved for years, and we all owe him a great deal; Bob Morris who, in his day, was the most successful of all carp fishers; Alan King and Robin Monday.

Getting to know Fred Wilton and Bob Morris was a real eye opener for me. Have you ever been in a situation when, just when you think you've got it sussed, along comes someone who makes you realise you haven't got a clue?

Up until the time I met Fred in 1971, apart from standard baits, I'd only experimented with a range of exotic baits as they came to be referred to in those distant days, i.e. cat food pastes, sausage meat mixes, fish meal pastes etc. The furthest I'd moved on was to the heady heights of dried shrimp meal and dried pellet paste mixed together. It was a real killer and then along came Fred and Bob. Five takes in an evening when I was struggling to get one –

something had to be wrong for me, or very right for them, but I didn't know what it was, nor was I the type to deliberately ask.

Like many others, I read with great interest Fred's article in the old orange issue of the British Carp Study Group magazine in 1972 and, within a short period, was enjoying fishing with Fred, Bob & Co., in a group situation.

Fred's theories around H.N.V. baits have been well voiced and well argued across the years and I certainly do not intend to enter into any argument here; I'm sure they feature in the bait book in this series anyway.

For me there is no doubt at all that the better the nutritive value of the bait, the greater the chances of success – particularly if the bait is well balanced and offered as a regular food source to carp, which can be particularly important in winter.

I can see little point in listing a range of bait recipes – personally I've always believed in building a success when it occurs and for this reason have varied my successful baits very little over the years. I have used a range of particles as well as the occasional ready mades, but still always return to H.N.V. baits. As a consequence, my baits are always based on a mixture of casein, lactalbumin, calcium casinate, good quality vitamin mineral compounds, a small quantity of sunflower oil and a good smell or label used in sensible quantities. I have used both essential oils and others as labels. I roll my baits into whatever size boilies I require, boil them for an appropriate time, sometimes in particle size and sometimes much larger.

For the purposes of advice about bait, I would say always go for the best quality you can, and this advice would be particularly true in winter because that's when it would seem a better quality bait can really give you the edge – where there's one take to be had you'll get it; if there's three fish out there to be caught between three anglers, chances are you'll get two of them and so on – providing all other things are equal.

A good quality bait needs to be sensibly applied during the winter months: if you fish through the autumn period, or the whole season, using this approach, the fish should then be well accustomed to it and feeding on it by the start of the colder weather. In the period until the real cold weather starts, the amount of bait introduced can be in fairly large numbers if the fish are feeding on it, but as the water really cools and the fish's metabolism slows, smaller quantities on a more regular basis seem to be the most effective. A good starting point is 20/30 baits in a given area three times a week and, when fishing, possibly a two or three bait stringer with about 10 loose fed baits around them if this is possible.

There are other times when conditions don't look too good when I'll settle for just the stringer or, on really cold sessions, if I'm sure I'm in the right area, I'll just fish with hook baits. With experience of regular winter fishing, you'll get a feeling about what to do on any given day – although it won't always work.

HNV devotee Derek poses with a winter mirror of 27¹/₂lb.

47

The other phenomena which has developed across more recent years, are those bloody coots which dive continually for your baits, or the seagulls which swoop and seize boilies from the air as you are trying to catapult them out. For this reason a stringer is always my first line of approach for ensuring baits are in the swim, providing this does not inhibit casting the range required. Secondly, a throwing stick attracts less birdy attention than a catapult for putting out free baits if required and really is an effective way of putting out free baits at range.

When the coots are around but not attempting to dive in the area I'm fishing, or if they do attempt to do so then spook quickly and leave the area, I get quite enthusiastic about the prospect of success, as this suggests fish are present and on the move.

You should never be surprised by oddities in baiting up during the winter. I can remember two occasions when fishing with Alan Webb during January and February when the cold weather was really with us. I'd fished the night and up to the following midday with no action. I had been fishing with stringers only and I'd decided to put out the 60/70 remaining baits in my box before leaving. I'd just finished the final one and was putting my catapult away when I had a screaming take and landed an 18 pounder.

The following week, at around 4.00 p.m. in the afternoon following another blank night and day, I went through exactly the same procedure and within minutes was netting a 17½ pounder.

The third weekend and, of course, I had it really sussed. There was masses of bait all out in readiness and, you've guessed it, not a bloody take for 48 hours! So it really is a matter of making your own judgement on the day when it comes to introducing bait in winter.

Finally, the other vexing question is how often you recast during winter sessions, and this will vary from water to water. You should find such decisions easier to make when you know the place better. Without a doubt, there have been a number of times across the years when I have literally bombed a carp into action by casting out and before the indicator has been on the line I've been away. This has sometimes occurred after hours of inactivity on a stationary bait in the same area. Such situations occur either because you've landed a bait right on the carp's nose or the bait falling rapidly through the water has attracted the carp's attention. On other occasions I have induced takes by picking up the rod, winding the bait three or four turns of the handle of the reel and then letting the bait fall to rest, repeating the process every hour or so.

On my easier waters I will generally look to move baits every 2/3 hours during winter day sessions. Generally I will only reposition baits at night if I've had a take. On the harder waters I'll leave the baits for longer periods providing I'm sure I've positioned them properly from the beginning.

Much of my winter fishing in more recent years has been done with neutral buoyancy hook baits – those rolled with small, high density balls of polystyrene inside before being boiled. These baits can generally be persuaded to sink very slowly with the help of the hook weight. If not, the addition of a small piece of tungsten putty will help it. Sometimes I use a combination of floating and sinking baits on the hair together (as illustrated).

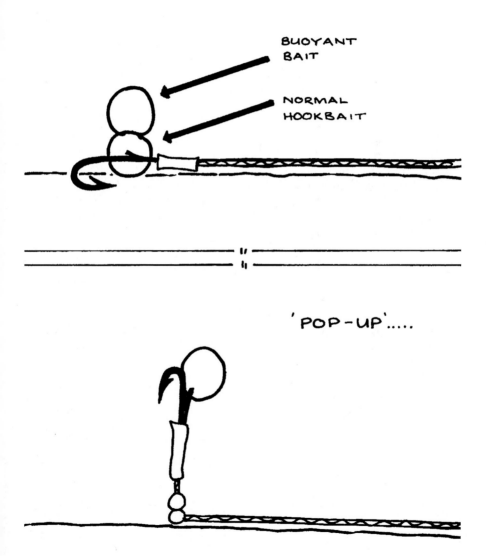

BUOYANT BAIT

NORMAL HOOKBAIT

'POP-UP'.....

Such baits are less likely to be lost among either the decaying leaves or weed which are a feature of much of my winter fishing.

There are many winter anglers who have taken a fairly successful summer bait and totally ruined it by increasing its flavour level for the winter to a totally prohibitive level, just because they thought they were improving the attractiveness of the bait. My advice would be to stick with the same level of attractor summer and winter alike.

On the subject of bait size, there was a time when one needed to change from summer to winter. Those were the days when we either used huge paste baits or when boilies were first around and we were making about 20 to a mix of bait for summer sessions and 60 or 70 for winter. Nowadays my baits are generally the same summer to winter. I generally roll between 180-250 baits to a mix, either made as round boilies if I need them for baiting at range, or alternatively as chopped up sausages for closer work.

I can remember long ago, when fishing with Tony Howells at both Shangri-la and Darenth in Kent, the huge sausage meat paste baits he elected to use and catch on in winter – and some of them were nearly tennis ball size.

WHEN?
PERIODS & TIMES

Traditionally, carp anglers have always viewed the period November 1st - March 14th as winter, and fish caught during this period tend to be referred to as winter carp. However, with global warming as it exists now and the very mild winters we seem to experience these days, generally the serious winter tends to be in the months of December, January and February.

Some of the best fishing I've ever experienced, summer or winter, has been during the months of November and March. By November many lakes are less crowded and the fish are in good condition, often at their highest weight and usually still prepared to feed strongly.

Again, in March, if it begins to warm up, I've had some pretty predictable fishing – almost knowing when a take would occur, based on the former day's activities.

Throughout the season, summer and winter alike, it is quite possible to chart feeding times etc., on some of the more heavily stocked waters. During winter months it is just as possible to do this even though feeding spells become much shorter and more spaced out. However, once these spells are identified, it is possible to home in on them, enabling shorter winter sessions to be fished with a fair degree of success, without some of the discomfort of the longer sessions in winter. All that said, if you're on a big water, or a very difficult one, then forget it and fish as much as you possibly can. You may, if you're lucky, identify periods if first you can locate the fish.

The setting sun in a clear winter's sky – conditions which can bring hectic cold weather activity.

Dave Campbell, a cold, frosty dawn, and a golden common. Mid-70's.

No matter what the time of winter, November through till March, one of the times really worth a try is the first day or night of declining temperature after a mild spell. Across the years I've had some pretty successful sessions over nights or days like this.

After a mild period, you arrive, set up – the sky clears and by 6.00 p.m. there's frost on the rods. Don't be surprised to get action and don't necessarily take too long to get the bait out again; it may be just the start of a frenzied period of activity, the type of which I've experienced regularly in such conditions.

Across the years there has been much debate about the best times to fish in winter. My initial offerings, in terms of writing, years ago about winter fishing advocated the hours of darkness. These writings were based on the experiences a number of other anglers and I had on waters such as Darenth, Horton Kirby, Bysingwood in Kent and Lake Meadows in Essex, and two lakes that I fished regularly in Hertfordshire, Essex.

On most of these waters no action would occur during the daylight hours in winter, but as soon as darkness came, it was almost like a light switch or

The rewards – Alan Webb playing a carp on a bright winter's day. The fish turned out to be a 31lb+ mirror, pictured opposite.

timer being set off. Sometimes there were twitches occurring on two rods at once and on many evenings, between 6.00 p.m. and midnight, I'd spend the entire evening teasing back twitching takes, striking, recasting, hooking or missing fish and not actually sitting down for more than about ten minutes of an entire session. Such sessions occurred particularly in the periods between 1971-78, while hooks were still buried in the bait.

Much has also been said about water temperatures, and the use of thermometers etc., to gauge the best times. Personally, I go fishing because I like being out and about and as long as I've got a bait in the water I like to believe I'm in with a chance of a fish. For this reason I never carry a thermometer, nor have I taken a water temperature for a good many years. However, this is a matter of personal preference and there are others who

Winter carpers don't give up easily. Waking up to a freeze up (above), and breaking out.

regularly check water temperatures.

During later years I would say I've probably caught an equal number of carp during daylight and darkness hours, and looking through my old diaries it is almost always possible to highlight feeding spells at particular times on particular fisheries.

During 1989-90 you could almost guarantee a take between 4.30-5.30p.m. on a particular water if you were in the right place.

During 1990-91 on the same water, the really good time has been 2.30p.m., with maybe another chase at 5.30 p.m.

On the two more difficult waters I fish these days, it can happen, or not happen, at any time, so I just have to stick with it.

A mate of mine, Alan Webb, swears that on hard waters he would always choose to fish between 10.30 a.m.-3.30 p.m., as the most likely times, though he never actually explains why. Suffice to say he succeeds at times.

Apart from months and times of the day, there are other factors to consider under the heading 'When'.

We should look at the type of weather conditions; whenever anyone talks or thinks about winter carp fishing, they always see a picture of them holding a carp against a snow scene background – regrettably you won't find one of those in this book. I have caught carp in the snow on several occasions but there has never been anyone around to take the photos so I've done them with the fish lying on the floor.

I also once shared a catch of several carp with Dave Campbell from a small Hertfordshire pit, fishing through a very small ice hole. Rather stupidly we put the fish back without photos – primarily because we just wanted to try to catch another one. Crazy eh?

However, the point of mentioning weather really is to point out that you will encounter a range of weather conditions in winter for which you will need to be prepared in some way. The range of weather conditions will take you from still, crystal clear, starry, frosty nights, lashing rain accompanied by gales, when you're hanging on to the brolly, bivvy and everything else for grim death; fog, banks frozen hard, banks so full with mud they're like treacle, snow, gale force winds, calm, sunny, pleasant afternoons. If you intend to fish seriously for carp throughout the winter, you will need to be well prepared for all of these conditions.

A Dave Campbell study of a typical winter's dawn.

GOOD ADVICE ~ KEEPING WARM

Fashions come and go in carp fishing these days – rather like Zsa Zsa Gabor's husbands – but there is now a good range of cold weather gear for the winter carp angler to choose from. This has not always been true in the past.

Winter carping mid-70's style. Tank suits and flying suits were the one-piecers of the period

Lake Meadows, Billericay, early 70's.

A modern set-up.

I recall my initial feeble efforts – thick jumpers, old army boots, blankets, etc., but I survived and caught fish nonetheless. Then there were tank suits, followed by flying suits, Dartex suits, woolly underlining suits etc., etc. The range of clothing is apparent from the photographs contained in this book.

I'll not go on too much about keeping warm, other than to say storm sides or a bivvy of some type will make winter nights more comfortable, and a groundsheet will make all the difference in keeping the gear dry and stopping damp from rising. A comfortable bed chair and a good quality sleeping bag, or if not, two lesser quality ones, one inside the other, will make for warmth during the hours of darkness if you intend to stay the full night. I also carry one of those small, silver reflective survival blankets, which folds up very small, weighs very little, but has proven to be a godsend on a couple of particularly cold nights.

A few of the small chemical bags which provide warmth for 12 hours by the mixing of two chemicals are also handy to carry, particularly if, like me, you sometimes get cold spots that you need one in, like in the small of your back, or one to each foot on really freezing nights.

Recently, at the National Angling Show, I saw some variations on these chemical bags, which were actually bags that were boiled in water and set off a reaction, but kept them hot for a long time. They look good, although I haven't had time to try them out.

Those items apart, essentially your own body garments are those which keep you warm and dry and here it becomes a matter of personal preference and affordability; there is lots of gear available for you to choose from; quilted undersuits, thermal pile teddy bear undersuits etc. Personally, I prefer not to wear one piece suits, having tried so many in the past. I find that they restrict my movements and generally make me feel uncomfortable, although I know many anglers swear by them.

Nowadays I wear, or carry, the following and find it more than suitable for most weather conditions: thermal underwear; long johns and vest – they don't have to be the super type that keep you warm going up Everest, just normal thermals which are a darn sight cheaper anyway and will do the job. I then wear comfortable, loose, jogging bottoms and sweat shirt type top and a really large, long, thick knit chunky jumper. When it gets colder I then cover these layers with a pair of padded ski trousers and a three quarter padded lightweight coat. This gives a similar warmth to walking round in a sleeping bag, but without the weight or discomfort. I also carry a recently acquired, longish, thickly padded Barbour coat, which comes out of the car boot for the wet sessions. I wear thermal moon boots (there is a range to choose from) for colder sessions and lighter weight Derri boots for milder sessions or those where I'm faced with a really long walk to swims. In the rucksack is a pair of thermal pile Hutchinson bivvy slippers for wearing in the sleeping bag, as well

NECESSITIES

Here's a reminder of some of the more essential requirements for winter carping. Keeping warm and dry is the number one priority. If you are cold or wet then your time at the water will be limited, cutting down on your chances of successful fishing.

Bobble hats are warmest, but they make my head itch so I wear a flat cap now. This is me on the Tip Lake in the early 70's.

Invest in a warm, weatherproof one-piece suit and thermal boots, like this set up marketed by Sundridge.

For overnight stays a warm bedchair/ sleeping bag set-up is a must. The bag and bedchair pictured are sold by Fox International.

Spirit stoves – like this Coleman – are far more efficient than gas in very cold conditions.

The original canvas bivvies are out of fashion now, but they are still the warmest.

as a pair of moccasins for occasional use on mild days or nights. I carry several pairs of thermal socks – mine were purchased from Sainsburys' Home Base and are brilliant; I change socks if I'm there for longish periods to keep my feet dry.

Always remember to dry out the linings of your thermal boots periodically, or put them in the washing machine and dryer, as dry linings in your moon boots will keep your feet warm longer.

Headgear is a matter of preference but nonetheless essential; I wear a flat cap, as woolly bobble hats make my head itch like mad. I also have a Damart thermal hood for really cold 'uns and a pair of Damart gloves which I don't usually wear, apart from when packing up the really cold gear etc.

All that said, I'm very impressed by the range of warm gear produced by Richard Skidmore of Stalker Products.

The other additional items which I also try to ensure carrying in winter are: a separate light source other than my normal fishing torch. This year I have used some very effective chemical light sources, lasting 12 hours, bright enough to read and bait up by and purchased from Bromages Tackle, Green Lanes, Essex. They work on the same principle as those light sources for floats. There's nothing worse than lying awake at 3.00 a.m. on a winter night, unable to get to sleep and trying to pass the time. I always have a book or magazine to read on such occasions. I also carry a small radio or cassette player, with an ear plug, to keep me company. Notice I said ear plug, rather than plugs – don't get too deep into a cassette and realise you've not heard a take.

The other smaller items I carry, especially in winter, are a small bottle of Glycerine to put on the rings to prevent them icing up; some lip seal as my lips crack badly in the cold; some cream to put on my face after a period of cold when it begins to skin (Christ, I'm falling to pieces!).

These things apart, I can truly recommend the Coleman's multi fuel cookers for a quick boiling up for a cuppa in winter. Anyone who's laboured with a gas cooker, even with propane gas, in winter will know what a long painful process it can be. I make tea even on short sessions – I find it helps break up the time. Food is, of course, a matter of preference – just make sure you always take your rubbish away with you.

Nowadays I always carry a camera with a tripod fitting as you can't always guarantee someone else being around to take photos in winter – over the years I've found this out to my cost several times.

Finally, never underestimate just how cold it can become in winter. There have been a few times over the years when I have made this mistake and I wouldn't recommend it to anyone…

CAMEOS
Tales of Three Winter Sessions

The screaming pain in my calf muscles made me wish that the clearing sky and the still night air that would inevitably render the ground like concrete by the morning, had done its job already.

As it was, I was faced with tramping through almost a mile of glutinous, sticky mud, which dragged on my Skeetex boots and had the effect of making my socks bunch uncomfortably under the bridge of my foot. The mountain of gear, including two sleeping bags, was beginning to really dredge on my strength.

It was a still December evening and Alan and I were making our way across the field to our chosen swim for a 24 hour session. The journey always started with plenty of friendly banter, but by now it was as much as we could both do to keep going without wasting valuable breath attempting to talk.

The expletives from behind let me know that Alan had done his usual and in packing his bag badly had deposited something on the path behind him as he walked and was having to pause to gather it up. I just didn't have the energy to stop and watch it, all I could do was struggle on, or not get there at all. Even my laughter was painful.

Finally arriving at the swim, I deposited all the gear behind me – literally where it fell – and turned to peer into the darkness to look for Alan. Although I couldn't see him, I could hear him cursing his ancestors as he came along the bank. I returned to look across the lake.

It was still, the sky was clear and it was going to be a cold and frosty night – the first one after a period of fairly mild weather. I love nights like this – I can cast baits into the same shadows as I've done a million times before and

WINTER
WARMERS

Above: A 1978 17¹/₂ pounder from Nazing.

A 19¹/₂ common taken on a nodding rod top across the pads.

know my free offerings are spot on. I can lie on the bedchair and watch the flashing lights of aircraft – this is a major flight path here. Have you ever wondered what you would do if, on such a night, two aircraft crashed into one another? Or, if they could look down from the darkness, what they would think?

"I ain't doing this any more Stritton! It's ****ing killing me!"

Alan had arrived; he has the same sort of love/hate relationship with carp fishing that I seem to have with most other aspects of my life. I could actually see steam coming from his body where he was sweating from the walk.

Lying back in the bivvy, with the baits out; the rods had frost on them now and I was listening to 'A Letter From America' on Radio 4. It was about 10.50 p.m.... Later I will sleep...

The banging against the back of the umbrella sounded like a herd of stampeding elephants. Alan was kicking it; he was playing a carp and wanted some help to net it. Before I knew it, I'd played a part in netting, weighing and returning the 16lb fish before I fully realised I was awake. I glanced at my watch; it was 1.45 a.m. It was clear as a bell.

I put the kettle on and made us tea; before I had a chance to drink it, three bleeps on my Optonic, followed by a screamer, saw me playing and landing an 18lb mirror.

By 4.00 a.m. we had landed five fish between us, up to 19½lb. Frankly, by that time it was so cold we'd had enough anyway. We fished on throughout the period until 8.00 p.m. the following evening with no more action...

It sometimes happens that way when the first sign of a real drop in temperature occurs after a mild winter spell.

It was a grey, dark, early afternoon in mid January. I'd been fishing since 11.00 p.m. the previous night with no action whatever. The wind was blowing from right to left and I was fishing in a slightly deeper area of the lake. Having spent a number of blank weekends, I thought I'd try elsewhere; for the past 5 or 6 hours I've been wondering if I'd done the wise thing.

I was fishing on my own and, for some reason, really wanted to catch a carp badly. At such times it's easy to dwell on the comforts of home – it's amazing the pictures your mind can conjure up. A log fire, a casserole in the oven, a good film on the T.V.: bloody stupid really when all you've got is central heating, a fridge full of Lean Cuisine and poxy 'Columbo' to watch.

It rained overnight. The puddle outside the bivvy actually appeared to get a chop in it like the lake. Some of it had run into the rucksack and other gear. The gas in the cooker was low and it took forever to boil the kettle for tea. I actually wanted to go home but I knew if I could make it until 3.00 p.m. I could tune into Capital Radio and listen to a local football match and hear all the up to date scores; that'd keep me going till darkness – there may be a chance of some action between 3.30-5.00 p.m.

I opened Angler's Mail and Times and reread the same reports and adverts I'd read four times already during the day. I wished I was in the mood for writing but there was no inspiration.

I decided to take down the bivvy and fish the remaining hours by the rods. It was a bloody mistake – the wind was far colder than I realised and I felt a bit naked after the protection of its cover, plus which it was now impossible to make a cuppa. I mistakenly decided to have a can of Tennants Supa left over from the pack of four, which had helped me sleep the night before. Because of the cold and the fact that I couldn't be bothered to cook earlier, it went straight to my head. It also encouraged me to open another, turn up the collar of my thick coat and knock it back. I was now slightly tired and turned my back to the wind, curled up and dozed.

I could hear the radio somewhere in the distance, then the Optonic let out a burst and stopped. I've had this before, no messing, I picked up the rod, wound like mad and eventually contacted the fish which had moved left and then towards me. The fight was not spectacular, in fact, the fish got on the surface quickly and I was worried about the hook hold. Eventually, it was near the net and I was feeling good; first fish for a while. This'll make Alan wish he'd not stayed at home – draw it towards the net…

…The lead flew past my right shoulder as the hookhold failed – all I could see were a pair of lips disappearing from wherever they came… Winter carp fishing can be bloody lonely and bloody cruel sometimes.

So much for the total reliability of Dartex suits! I wish I'd not left my backside hanging out of the bivvy door when putting the baits on during the storm. The rain had dripped off the umbrella and rolled down my back and found its way in through the elastic waistband; my back was decidedly wet and I was decidedly cold. The suit was now rolled in a ball and discarded in the back of the bivvy.

The rain had now stopped and I was sitting on the bed peering out into the darkness. 11.00 p.m. in January and I could not believe the change in weather conditions. Gone were the rain clouds; the sky was clear apart from the odd wisp across the moon. Every now and again there was a gusting wind beginning to blow, hitting the lake just beyond my baits. Some of my clothes were now damp and my back was cold and uncomfortable. I had no spare clothes; all I could think of to warm my back was to get my dirty old hand towel and use it as a barrier between my damp clothes and my back, before turning in for the night.

I suppose I should inject at this point that I was fishing a swim with which I was very familiar – a reasonably sized flat area, enough room for a brolly, storm sides and rods in comfort. The swim was well used by all and sundry in summer and was currently being well used by me this winter. I knew my way around it as well and had a tried and tested method to land fish when I needed to do so.

I was using three rods – two to cast to familiar marks at about 60 yards distance, the other fished along the margins to my left, precariously close to an overhanging tree. I lay in the bed listening to the growing strength of the gusting wind and slowly drifted into the land of silent, but uneasy, sleep.

When the take came, I was not in the least bit surprised, though somewhat disorientated. I managed to plant my feet into the moccasins, waiting in readiness by the side of the bed, stand, gather the rod and wind down into the fish. It was the margin rod and, to avoid the overhanging branches of the tree, the routine was always the same. Plunge the rod deep into the water and wind like mad for several turns, lessening the pressure after; this seemed to have the effect of making the fish swing out into the open water where they could be played fairly normally – netting was somewhat precarious on most occasions. The soil at the front of the swim had begun to erode badly and some water separated the swim from the board at its front.

The procedure was always the same when it came to netting – left foot on the board, net sunk in readiness, stand down, draw the rod back, lips towards the spreader rock; hey presto! There was no reason to suppose tonight would be different…

I stepped forward, aimed for the board – and missed. The unbalancing effect had my left leg leading the rest of my body as together we toppled into four foot of freezing cold margin and silt, rod, line and carp still in tow! My survival, and the eventual landing of the carp is worth a story in its own right, however, I could easily have died that night, if not by drowning, then easily by exposure and my survival from the cold was torturous.

First lesson learnt; always keep spare clothing in the boot of the car for every eventuality, and don't go swimming in lakes on January nights!

A dodgy swim and a January 22 pounder.

APPROACH & TACKLE

Very little changes for me in terms of approach between summer and winter. The most important aspect of all, as far as I'm concerned, is to think positively. Don't just go out and go through the motions of carp fishing – really go for it; give it your best shot and enjoy it. If you can't do that, then you may as well be at home.

Some people love winter fishing, others hate it – make your own decisions and stick with them.

It can be a lonely affair on occasions, which is why you need to be fairly self sufficient and at ease with your own thinking, in terms of confidence and enjoyment, otherwise it can just get the better of you, particularly during the long hours of darkness.

My tackle does not change at all in winter. I've heard anglers recommend lighter line etc., to reflect the lack of weed growth on some lakes. Personally, I carry on as usual.

Over the years I've used seemingly a million lead or end rigs; on my set-ups each one has been the best since sliced bread as they say… At present I'm using the Helicopter Rig which hasn't really changed at all from when I used it over ten years ago and we called it the 'Whirling Ted Smith Rig', the only slight modification is that in 1979/80 I used a small Drennan ring and today I use a Helicopter Bead!

Without getting too technical, all the following rigs are still in use and would catch fish on their day. I hope that the drawings overleaf will help you.

I also still float fish at times in winter, especially during the evening hours of darkness. Firstly, I find it a really exciting way of fishing and also, some winters, a really effective way of using a third rod for a short period and of helping to pass the time. I've caught a number of carp in this way over the years and I hope to continue to do so.

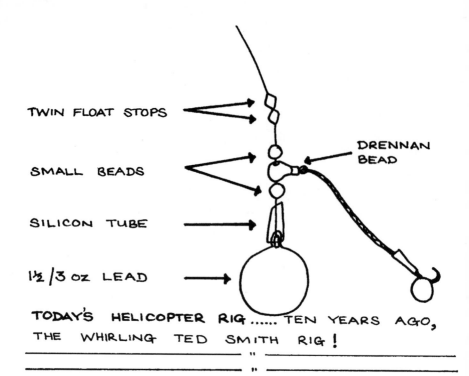

TWIN FLOAT STOPS

DRENNAN BEAD

SMALL BEADS

SILICON TUBE

1½/3 oz LEAD

TODAY'S HELICOPTER RIG ...... TEN YEARS AGO, THE WHIRLING TED SMITH RIG !

REMEMBER..... RUBBER TUBE MUST EXCEED LENGTH OF HOOK LINK.

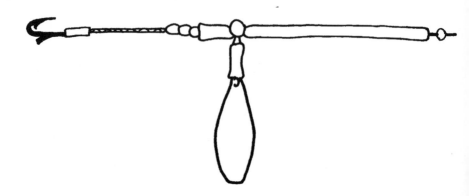

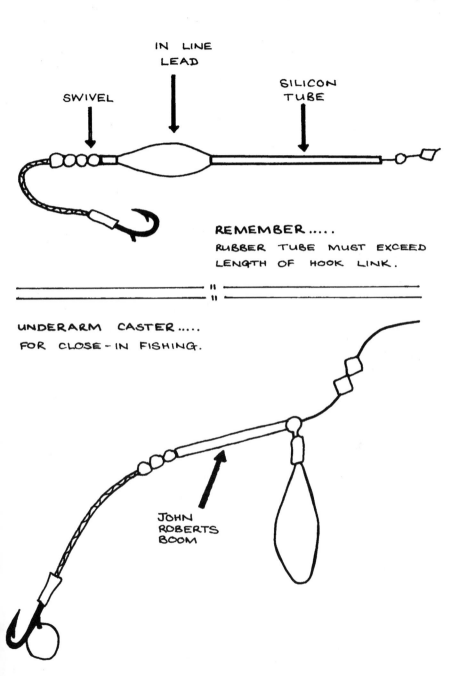

SWIVEL

IN LINE
LEAD

SILICON
TUBE

REMEMBER.....
RUBBER TUBE MUST EXCEED
LENGTH OF HOOK LINK.

UNDERARM CASTER.....
FOR CLOSE-IN FISHING.

JOHN
ROBERTS
BOOM

The floats I still use are those with a small battery in the body and a light emitting diode in the tip – starlight floats will obviously do the job just as well, but have a greater on going cost implication. Anyone who's watched a float rise and weave about in the water before lying flat and whizzing away, or just merely disappearing in a moment and bent into a carp hooked at really close range, couldn't fail to understand the excitement of it all.

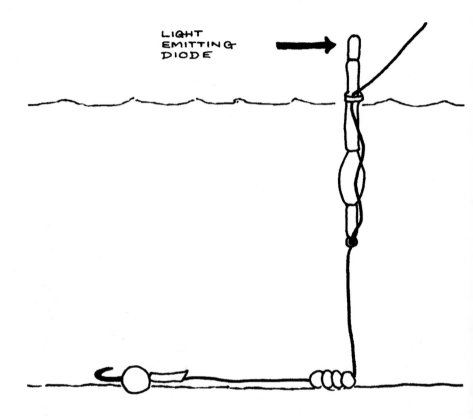

LIGHT
EMITTING
DIODE

THE
BOREDOM
OF IT ALL!

One of the things I've not touched upon too much in this book, but which, without any doubt, will be something which occurs to anyone who indulges in large amounts of winter carp fishing, is just how you go about coping with the boredom of longish winter sessions.

For many years I've always carried a small portable radio with an ear plug. It's amazing how interesting a phone-in programme can be if it's ten o' clock at night, you're the only one on your side of the lake and it's been dark for 6 hours. I wish I had a pound for every 'Letter From America' I've heard Alistair Cook read while I've been out fishing on a Friday or a Saturday night.

Another great time passer, if you've got a decent enough light source, is a good book or story. I once managed to read a huge educational tomb during a sleepless, actionless winter weekend on the Copse Lake at Yateley; not only did it help me to pass the uneventful hours, it also proved useful during the following week at work.

Another favourite time passer over the years has been to close down the front of the bivvy, put on the cooker and see how warm one could get inside. I've seen some truly spectacular events occur as a result of this one. Alan Webb, apart from being a really good mate of mine, has often kept me entertained during the winter sessions; Alan's full of predictions, e.g. "Tonight's the sort of night when you get action" – usually means, in reality, that sod all is about to happen. Or, "They'll probably be having it between dusk and midnight" often heralds a take at 5.00 a.m.

Needless to say, his comments to me on a Friday night arrival that his latest device for reading his new book would have me eating my heart out, had me waiting with bated breath.

Alan was clearly well motivated of late; after making do with his old canvas brolly with three broken spokes for God knows how long, the previous week he had turned up with a new 50 inch Wavelock brolly to match his bivvy.

He made comments about a candle in a jam jar technique which I often used to light my bivvy in winter, and when I went to speak to him later after he'd set up, I realised why he'd been crowing! There he was, laid back in the bivvy, like the Pope, surrounded by small, dumpy night candles, reading his book, a bottle of wine by his side and a hot water bottle ready for filling when he went to sleep!

"Eat your heart out, Stritton" he cried.

After the usual banter I beat my way back along the path, returning to wish him good night when I decided to turn in around 10.30 p.m.

The resplendent Pope was by now looking really pissed off; it transpired that he had not actually been getting sufficient light from his candles, so he had placed one in the spokes of his brolly. Apparently the first sign of something being wrong was a giant blob of green plastic landing on the page of the book he was reading. The top of his bivvy was on fire – and you could now view the night sky through the hole that was left! He got teased for ages after this with a chorus of Tony Howell's old song, 'I see the moon, the moon sees me', which greeted him every visit for months afterwards.

Putting up with the boredom is usually rewarded. These two 19lb+ commons were the biggest fish in the lake – and fell within an hour of each other on a December night of dropping temperatures.

GRUELLERS

I hope there will be no one who reads this book who, for one moment, thinks I have made light of some of the difficulties which can be encountered trying to catch carp in winter.

Even some of the most successful periods I have ever spent fishing for, and catching, carp in winter, have taken place against the background of far greater hardship and effort than I have ever endured in summer.

For example, during 1983/84, 1984/85 and 1986/87, when fishing successfully with Alan Webb, we were walking a distance of something like a mile to our swims for each session, often across squelching mud fields which dragged the Skeetex boots from your feet with every step and which used to cause my calf muscles and lungs to scream with pain by the time I reached the swim. I can remember numerous occasions after such a journey, looking at Alan and watching him literally 'steam' in the cold night air, only to hear him complain of cold within 30/40 minutes.

I can also remember numerous times across the years when, having fished waters hard throughout the winter period and endured long periods of inactivity and hoped for success, during the final few weeks of the season seeing the water totally change in character because a farmer had put down manure or chemicals on the fields and this, in turn, had affected the water adversely.

I have also experienced the extreme agony of watching a fellow angler who last fished at the end of the summer period of the previous year, return for a final fling in March before the season ended and catch in one session as many fish as I had caught during the entire winter period.

All these things, and more, make up winter carp fishing. As I said in earlier chapters, only do it if you really want to, not because others are at it; it can be a thankless pursuit if you don't actually enjoy it.

All that said, nothing can be more satisfying than even one winter carp from an entire winter season if it's the one you've been looking for, or a fish caught in complete solitude on a difficult, or unexpected water.

DYING EMBERS

HISTORY

To set some of the chapters in this book into some sort of historical context, and therefore for them to have meaning for some of today's new carp anglers, I perhaps need to point out that some of the early stories occurred during the pre-rig days when hooks were actually buried inside baits. Somewhat later, side hooking was occurring and finally, the hair rig in all its guises.

Rods have gone from cane to floppy glass fibre, steep taper glass for distance fishing, which bore greater resemblance to a snooker cue than a fishing rod, to modern, state of the art carbon fibre rods.

There has been a bait revolution. Carp in many waters have grown from 10lb to 30lb.

There is now a range of almost designer clothing and footwear, sleeping gear and bivvies for the modern angler.

Buzzers have gone from being totally unreliable antenna types to infallible wheel or magnetic types.

Attitudes have also changed – and not always for the better!

I hope this brief page sets some of my meanderings more clearly in focus.

GOOD ADVICE

Don't go unless you want to.

Know why you're there... what's driving you! What do you want from your fishing?

Carry a warm/very warm sleeping bag, possibly two.

An aluminium foil survival blanket takes no space but may be needed one day.

Always stay reasonably close to the rods.

Be self-sufficient; reading/radio.

Multi fuel cookers will ensure a quick cuppa.

Don't ignore float fishing.

Always look in areas overhung by bushes.

Scan the shallows as often as possible.

Fish at the first sign of a decline in temperature, prior to a freeze up.

Carry some of those shake and mix chemical warmth bags and light sources.

You don't need to be a fishing clone to keep warm in winter – a good puffa coat and ski pants bib and brace will keep you pretty warm; wear a hat of some type.

Carry a bottle of Lipseal for cracked lips in winter/cream for dry skin on the face and cracked hands.

A small bottle of Glycerine will prevent frozen rings though it ain't half yucky.

Be optimistic; get to know the lake's moods; fish longish sessions to begin with; isolate feeding times and then go for it.

Remember, winter fishing is about more than just sunny, snow bound banks; there is rain, gales, freezing cold and long, blank hours – much of it in darkness. Be prepared for it.

Always use as good a quality bait as possible.

Be alert – strike at single bleeps, nodding rods, the lot...

Be flexible – don't be frightened to follow hunches...

When all else fails you, go home. Remember, there's always another day.

Try to keep a regular trickle of bait going in if possible.

Finally, if things don't go right at first, don't quit!

A lake in Essex.

Sutton-at-Hone, a private club water.

PEDIGREE

Some of the lakes on which I've had success in winter during the last 20 years:

Two lakes at South Weald in Essex.

Two lakes at South Ockendon

A lake at Thurrock.

Lake Meadows in Billericay.

Three very private Essex waters.

Darenth Big and Tip Lake and Long Lake.

Horton Kirby.

Brooklands Lake.

Waveney Valley.

Blue Lake at Gravesend.

Bysingwood in Kent.

Two Hertfordshire lakes at Nazing.

A lake in Epping Forest.

Dartford Angling Club lakes at Sutton.

A Scottish loch.

A Yorkshire lake.

Wanstead Park Lake.

Eagle Ponds.

Walthamstow Reservoirs.

The Beggar's Hole at Tunbridge.

The Rookery Lake at Bromley.

A lake in the Colne Valley.

Bishops Stortford.

Shangri-la Lake in Essex.

A Lea Valley Pit complex.

A club lake in Cambridge.

Beggar's Hole at Tunbridge – mid 70s.

Winters can be pretty messy!

DECEMBER 1991 UP-DATE

I've just completed the print read of the book prior to publication. Tim wrote in his letter accompanying the script, "I think you may find yourself strongly tempted to alter all sorts of things, but we can only cope with corrections at this stage...". Wonder how he'd feel if I corrected the whole lot!

However, because there are a few additions, I am enclosing this final piece for inclusion in an attempt to bring the book up to date and 'right' at least one wrong. Whether this chapter will ever appear, only time will tell. It is written on 28th December, 1991.

Firstly, an update on my own winter fishing, which frankly cannot be claimed as brilliant of late.

November, 1991 began with a week in the Loire Valley, staying with Jon and Eileen Burrows and Paul. I fished a 267 acre lake in the valley. I thought the conditions would be good but the frosts came early for the region and to put the week at base level, I had an enjoyable but expensive blank. I won't be the first, or the last, person to do this on foreign soil I guess.

Back home, I couldn't believe how cold it was in mid to late November. My brief success on a shallow, 10 acre lake soon ended, but not before I'd netted a 25lb+ mirror and a couple of others. These fish were all taken whilst fishing over beds of 100+ boilies.

Since then, I have to confess to losing my way. Fishing one of my 'easier' waters, I've struggled a bit, managing four doubles and a few smaller fish but I haven't been able to identify any pattern to the feeding whatsoever, taking fish at 7.00 and 8.00 p.m. on one session, 2.00 a.m. on another and 7.00 a.m. and 11.00 a.m. on another. Today, I've just returned from an 18 hour blank (that's real winter carping for you!).

Tackle wise, I should mention just a few things. Firstly, hooks. Elsewhere in the book there is mention of the 'bent hook rig' and whilst this is a method I tried for some time, I would not wish the reader to believe that it is one I would recommend. Use of the rig during the winter of 1989/90, especially, when on an easier water where a number of fish were landed, convinced me of the damage it can cause to the mouths of fish both during the fight and the unhooking process. As a consequence, I ceased to use the rig and would not advocate its use at all. One cannot justify a single capture if it results in damage to the fish.

For some time after ceasing to use the bent hook, I played around with stiff tube on the hook, trying to create the same initial effect as the bent hook and then Jim Gibbinson published the 'Line Aligner' rig, which solved my problems completely. It is both very effective and a relatively easy rig to prepare as well. I use it in conjunction with both Drennan Star Points and boilie hooks and I am happy to recommend both.

Winter carping can be boring – as you might gather from this shot! This bivi-tent is very warm for cold weather sessions.

SILICON SLEEVE →

ANIRTAK BEAD →

HELICOPTER BEAD →

SILICON SLEEVE →

Right:
Derek's version of
the helicopter rig,
incorporating an
ANIRTAK
non-slip bead.

Winter reward.
A handsome 25lb+
mirror caught on
25th November
1991.

Comfort wise in winter, I have, in recent years, favoured a brolly with storm sides and a ground sheet, but I have now acquired none of those small dome tents which has an inner lining and a sewn in groundsheet. It is both incredibly comfortable and warm and will, I think, form my winter and 'long stay' summer home for some time to come, until something better comes along and makes my old cotton brolly from the late 60's look really inadequate.

The other tackle items worthy of mention are Terry Eustace Trilene line which I've used both for shock leader and main line this season and found it to be excellent. I've also been trying a range of Bruce and Walker rods, including the Hexagon range and, for the moment, these have replaced my trusty old Sportex blanks!

Another small item which I've been 'trying out' of late is the Anirtak stop bead which employs a twist wire to increase or decrease its grip on the line. I tried this initially because of difficulty which occurs with float stops slipping back up the line under the strain of casting. At first I was worried about the gripping device damaging line, but this appears not to be so. I always snip the wire to $^3/_4$ of its original length and slide a length of Drennan soft tube over it to avoid any possibility of tangles on the cast.

The loneliness of the long distance winter carp angler – a blank session in December 1991.

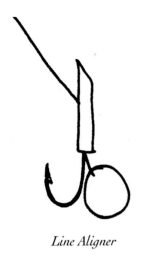

Line Aligner

Bait wise, I've not changed my opinion much, although nowadays I'm tending to fish much more with bottom baits rather than pop-ups or negative buoyancy ones. I still employ stringers in winter where casting range allows this.

There are now 'bait dips/bait soaks' which seem to be in vogue: I am sure the reader will be aware that I speak elsewhere in the book of not increasing flavour or attractor to prohibitive levels in winter. I cannot comment or argue the effectiveness of these soaks as I have not used them, but they must be of a different composition to the essential oils/flavour ranges I have used for bait attractors in the past.

Tim Paisley used one of these 'soaks' to some effect when we fished together earlier in the year (March 1991), when making a winter carp fishing video.

Finally, I remain as convinced as ever about my earlier comment in relation to 'group movement' of carp in winter and also the need to keep a regular supply of bait to help keep the fish active during the period November – March. I am sure my present season's failure to get to grips this winter is because of poor location and infrequent baiting.

THANKS AND DREAMS

This is the first (though hopefully will not be the last) book I have penned. I have always harboured a wish to write a book, but to use the words of many an eminent educationalist, a field with which I am fairly familiar, I am a somewhat reluctant writer, preferring to dream my dreams and fulfil my ambitions privately and away from others.

That said, I have always wanted to write for a number of people. For my children, Claire and Stephen, frequently deserted for my fishing; for my old Dad who introduced me to angling many, many years ago, when Essex rivers ran clean and clear and carp anglers were silent men with cane rods, potato baits and a far away look in their eyes.

There are also thanks to many anglers with whom I've spent time across the years, and particularly those with whom I've spent winter sessions and seasons: Jim Twitchett, Tony Howells, Greg Peck, Jeff Ducker, Fred Wilton, Bob Morris, Cliff Webb, Alan King, Robin Monday, Dave Campbell, Bob Chambers, Alan Webb, Mark Edwards, Bob Sloane, Brad Bradbrook, Brian Cannon, George Cansdale, Terry Seaborne, Roland Meldon, John the Fridge and Tottenham Bob, to mention but a few.

Thanks to Angling Publications and Tim Paisley in particular, for offering me the opportunity to write this book and then being prepared to publish it. To Barbara and Lynn who patiently typed the original script from my awful handwritten pages. And a final thanks to a special lady without whose support and encouragement the book would never have been written. Thanks.

A final word from me and then some quotes from others, more profound. Despite carp fishing for many years, my true pleasure only really emerged when I attempted to analyse why I actually go carp fishing and discover what I wanted from it. Nowadays, whatever else is going on around me, I am at peace with myself; when I visit carp lakes it is my form of escapism – I'm not wound up, angry, baying for someone's blood, or anything else. I'm there to relax, enjoy myself and the company. If I catch a fish then it's a bonus to me; if someone else catches one, then good luck to them – they must be doing something more effectively than me on the day.

Finally, for anyone who may have actually enjoyed this short offering, watch this space. A joint offering from Bob Morris and I, probably called 'A Carp For All Seasons'. Well that's it anyway…

Thanks… Goodnight… And here's to you, carp fisher, wherever you are…

I'll end with the immortal words of 'B.B.':

'The wonder of the world, the beauty and the power, the shape of things, their colours, lights and shades; these I saw. Look ye also while life lasts'.

And finally, as the man said, "Don't forget to smell the flowers on the way". That's if you can bloody well find any in winter!

When all else fails there's always the summer to look forward to!
Derek with two thirties caught within 2 hours of each other on 16th June 1991.
34lb 4oz and 30lb 8oz (held).

BRITISH
FANTASY
2013

The Best BRITISH FANTASY 2013

SERIES EDITOR
STEVE HAYNES

SALT

CROMER

PUBLISHED BY SALT PUBLISHING
12 Norwich Road, Cromer, Norfolk NR27 0AX

Selection and introduction © Steve Haynes, 2013
Individual contributions © the contributors, 2013

First published by Salt Publishing, 2013

Printed in Great Britain by Clays Ltd, St Ives plc

Typeset in Paperback 9/12

ISBN 978 1 907773 35 8 paperback

1 3 5 7 9 8 6 4 2

CONTENTS

INTRODUCTION

BRITISH FANTASY IS not what you think it is. Leaving aside the multiple classifications of Science Fiction, Fantasy and Horror, and their many sub-genres, what you see on the bookshelves of major bookstores will not be reflected in this book.

You will not find questing heroes in quasi-medieval realms here. Nor will you find children playing with magic wands, or adults riding dragons beneath the setting of twin suns. There are no burning spaceships launching submarine torpedoes or zombie hordes chewing their way through the local population. There are certainly no teenage vampires, or werewolves, responsibly refusing to mix bodily fluids and just saying no.

The creation of a novel is more of a collective act than many readers realise and sometimes what is commissioned, and ultimately published, can be influenced by how well an idea can be sold on a supermarket shelf. Writers of short fantasy stories, on the other hand, have a freedom encouraged by magazine editors and readers who are willing to take a chance on something very different.

Science Fiction, Fantasy and Horror have the short form deeply woven into their DNA. Just about every classic 'novel' of the 19th and 20th Century began as a short story concept, collection or a magazine serial. (Yes, I know there are exceptions to this, but even the epics of people like Tolkien were first shared in episodes among a small group of people and then fed into the construction of something much bigger.) So persistent is the short form as the basic building block of these genres that there is still an active culture and market for short stories. There are still enthusiastic readers who look forward to the next delivery of a magazine promising tales from writers they have not heard of and about subjects they are unfamiliar with.

I am going to refer to Science Fiction, Fantasy and Horror under the single banner of fantasy. I know this will anger many who closely guard the perceived boundaries of these genres, but I believe these divisions are illusory – that writers and readers flow across and around them, that they are marketing labels, and in short stories the walls are there to be broken down. This, in turn, gives me a freedom to gather a wide range of stories and writers under one banner (the work published or written in the latter part of 2011 and across 2012), and the contents of this collection reflect this eclectic approach.

In these pages you will find apocalyptic hangovers from unwise foreign adventures, political dystopias and a fear of the 'other' that leads to moral corruption. The most openly fantasy genre stories are rooted in a streetwise urban sensibility. You will find metamorphosis, psychosexual ghost stories in a very modern world, a little steampunk, folklore, phobias rising up from beneath the surface veneer of life and monsters walking amongst us. There are stories here that question that most horrible of modern phrases, 'the greater good,' and writers who take us beyond the boundaries of civilization. (I should warn you that there are some stories with children in and, in the tradition of our most ancient faerie tales, they are not pleasant endings.)

British fantasy writers are experimental and brave; they delve into disturbing subjects and mix one genre seamlessly with the next. Indeed, it could be said that British fantasy reflects the times we live in. I was surprised myself just how dark British fantasy is willing to go in the short form.

This collection has been gathered over a period of twelve months, from many different sources and the stories were originally written for a variety of purposes. They are purposely grouped into areas where two or more stories may complement each other. I have also tried to take the reader on a journey across the different realms that reflect the various streams of British fantasy.

These stories are written by people who are honing their craft and flexing their writing muscles. You will find writers who are familiar, who have been published in novel form, and you will find new names that will surprise you with their consummate skill.

Finally, I should point out that, in my experience, fantasy writers are light-hearted and friendly individuals; often they are enthusiastic fans who fell in love with their genres as children (just like you and me) and find immense satisfaction in reading, and watching, popular fantasy. But, like us all, they have their dark spaces, and their writing reflects the world around them as much as that within.

So, dear reader, if you're prepared to take on something different, if you're ready to look behind the curtain, if you feel brave enough, then enter the many worlds of British Fantasy. It's not what you think it is.

JON WALLACE

LIPS AND TEETH

Camp 15, Yodok, 16 December Juche Year 100

THE RAIN STOPS by morning, and a little sun breaks through the clouds, thank the Dear Leader. I get out of bed. I scratch at the lice. Then I pick up Jin-Song and step outside.

The yard is a small square of yellow and white mud, ten paces wide and twelve paces long. It's surrounded by a rotting dried mud wall, topped with rusty wire. In one place the wall has crumbled, leaving an opening. If I want, I can look out at the fields, all the way along the deep, narrow valley and up the mountains.

Sometimes there is a farmer with deep brown skin wading in the nearby paddy, carrying a tool that is not unlike Jin-Song. Sometimes I peer over at him and watch him work. I'm afraid of being caught, but Jin-Song is convinced that nobody watches me anymore.

In the corner of the yard is a pile of large rocks that it is my duty to break into smaller rocks. I start on the largest, most stubborn looking one, the one I didn't have the energy for yesterday. I lift Jin-Song over my head. He mutters:

'Here we go again.'

I lower him, drained by his tone. As pickaxes go his blade

is blunt, but his words are sharp. He thinks our incarceration is unjustified, our labour pointless. He also gets mad and spews treason about the Dear Leader, which I guess is why he's in here with me.

He's always telling me to escape, but I can't do it. It frustrates him, and he sometimes gives me the silent treatment. One time he didn't say a word to me for a year.

When he's not silent he talks my ear off about being special. He tries to make me think I deserve better than this. I tell him – if that were the case I wouldn't be here.

'You used to have balls,' he says.

'Let's just get on with the work.'

'This isn't work. This is punishment. You do know that this is a prison, right? You do know that?'

'I'm not a prisoner. I am being re-educated.'

Ha. He doesn't have an answer to that. It feels good to outwit him. He thinks he is so much smarter than me.

We start smashing the rocks, having talked enough for one morning. I only manage four swings before I am crumpled on my haunches, gasping for air. How old am I, anyway?

'You're 31,' says Jin-Song.

'No, no, that can't be right. I must be older.'

'Physically, yes. That's what a diet of gruel, rat and earthworm will do for you.'

I pant and stare at the rocks.

There is a seashell lying in the rubble. I pick it up and turn it over in my blackened fingers. I have not seen a shell like this in . . . how long have I been here?

I know the date precisely, but I can't remember when I was born, or how I came to be here, or how long I have been here. I know the days pass but I do not count them, ever. What would that achieve? Time here passes in ages. This is the age of acceptance. There was also an age of despair, and one of hope, or maybe anger, before that. I don't remember clearly. It's like that school textbook I once had – I can see the cover but can't recall the pages inside.

The shell is from an age that passed in days and even hours. An age where I sat on the beach and watched my father fishing.

'Nice shell,' says Jin-Song. 'I wonder how it got here?'

'It must be a gift from the Dear Leader.'

'Oh, for heavens sake. . .'

'You can't deny it. Only he could have provided it!'

I hold it in the palm of my hand. Briefly I'm seized by the urge to crush it to dust, but I hold back. If the Dear Leader meant me to have it I should not reject it. I drop it into my pocket and lift Jin-Song over my head, ready to get back to work.

'Here we go again,' he says.

CAMP 15, YODOK, 17 DECEMBER JUCHE YEAR 100

I cannot tell exactly what is happening because my yard is sealed off from the rest of the camp. Something about me is infectious and I am locked away, out of sight.

My cell has no windows. I never speak to the guards. I do not attend political education classes. Food is passed under my rotting, black, wooden door.

Still, I can hear a commotion nearby. I hear chanting, wailing and screaming.

I try to ignore it. I lie on my bunk and shiver, scratching at the lice, and turn the shell over in my fingers. It is perfectly intact, from fat end to curling point. I remember that it was rare to find them in such perfect shape on the beach.

I look into the shell and suddenly I remember the courtyard at university, the dead staring at me. I see the courtroom. I remember being unable to speak. I recall sitting in the back of the truck, driving up into the brown mountains, and soldiers laughing at me. I remember the blue room, and the pain of bamboo shoots pushed under my fingernails.

What is it that I did?

'I'm sick of telling you,' says Jin-Song. 'You'll just forget again.'

There is a noise. I sit up on my bunk and regard the door. Someone is knocking.

'Prisoner 11-17. Prisoner, are you in there?'

I fall off the bed I am so startled. I get up of my knees, dropping the shell into my pocket, and stagger to the door.

'Yes, sir,' I reply. 'Yes, Sir, I am here, thank-you, Sir.'

Jin-Song fumes at my groveling tone, but I must thank the guard. I haven't spoken to a person in so long. I want to embrace him. I want to tell him my name. Who am I anyway? My name is. . .my name is. . .

'Prisoner 11-17. You will join the other prisoners in the main recreation yard for our day of national mourning.'

'Mourning?'

There is a rusty shriek. The door is opened. A young Major stares at me. Two privates stand behind him.

'You will shave, prisoner. You will shave and dress.'

'Yes, I will shave and dress. Thank-you, Sir.'

The guards push me out of the cell, behind the Major, out into the courtyard and . . .

People! Hundreds, maybe thousands of other prisoners. They are lined up in neat rows, all on their knees, all wailing in horror. The noise is incredible. An old man chews on his hat, biting off pieces and spitting them out. Women shriek and pull their hair. I want to call out to them but I do not know what to say. What has happened?

I am led through the crowd, into another hut. I flinch when they push me into a chair, thinking of the blue room, but then a Corporal with a moustache begins to shave me. He is weeping too and his hands tremble. He starts with scissors, then moves on to electric trimmers. I sit and stare into the small mirror. I watch my face appear from behind the beard. I remember this face and I smile.

The Corporal stops his work. He slaps me hard across the face.

'You might be simple, but you do not smile today. Do you hear me?'

He pulls my hair, wrenching my head back, tears pouring down his cheeks.

'Do you hear me?'

'Yes, Sir.'

He gathers himself, wipes away his tears, and finishes his work.

I am led back out into the wailing yard. Thousands of bald, half-starved figures kneel and genuflect in the yellow and white mud, boxed in by the black dormitory huts. A poster of the Dear Leader hangs from a watchtower, smiling at their grief. The soldiers drop me to my knees at the edge of the crowd.

'Prisoner 11-17. You will mourn. You will return to your cell in three hours.'

'Please Sir,' I ask. 'What has happened?'

'The Dear Leader has ascended to the heavens.' He marches away. The two young guards take their place in the mourners, then begin crying and wailing themselves. Only the Major doesn't cry. He watches me, frowning.

I am not sure how best to mourn, so I watch my neighbour, an old man with hairy ears. He is banging his head onto a rock. I copy him, crashing my head as hard as I can onto a jagged white stone. Still no tears come.

I realise now, listening to this noise, that it is true. The Dear Leader is dead. Yet I feel nothing but the lice crawling over me.

I hold my eyes open until they sting. A few precious, merciful tears roll down my cheeks.

In a few hours the guards toss me back into my cell.

Jin-Song is propped against my cot. I drop next to him and bring the shell out of my pocket. It is still in one piece.

A terrible sadness overwhelms me and I begin to sob uncontrollably. Grief like I have never known shakes and twists me. I get to my feet, go to the rotting black door and thump on it as hard as I can.

'Let me out! Let me out! I'm ready to mourn now!'

Nobody comes. I sit on the bed. I howl and sniff and scratch at the lice, until eventually I am quiet again.

'Do you feel better?' asks Jin-Song.

'Yes, thank-you.'

'Did you notice something?' he asks me.

'What?'

'They didn't gag you. You are supposed to be gagged at all times, you know. I wonder if they've forgotten?'

CAMP 15, YODOK, 18 DECEMBER JUCHE YEAR 100

Whatever Jin-Song thinks they've forgotten, they've remembered. The two guards are back, wearing earmuffs. They look ridiculous, and they seem to know it. They throw me onto my back, and push a rag into my mouth.

I am dragged out into the main yard again, staggering barefoot through the mud. The prisoners are all there again, wailing and beating themselves. If only they had seen me last night. I expect to join them, but instead I am dragged past them, through the rows of stinking black huts, through a gate that leads to the guards' quarters.

Inside there are two neat concrete accommodation blocks with tile roofs. A small hut sits between them. I am pulled up the steps and shown inside.

The Major sits behind a desk, his wide brimmed hat resting on the table before him. He nods to the two guards. They drop me in a chair, salute, and leave. It is wonderfully warm in here. The Major has a heater which sweeps the room, warming my frozen nose. Thank the Dear Leader. Do I still say that? I suppose so. I wish someone would tell me who to thank now.

The Major doesn't look up from his file. He picks up a cup of tea, slurps it noisily and gasps.

'We have a snake among us.'

He looks up and smiles.

'Do you remember how you came to be here, 11-17?'

I shake my head. Jin-Song says people died because of something I did. I was trying to lead people somewhere, trying to change something. . . but what? The Major slurps his tea again and nods.

'You do not recall what it was that you were arrested for? It was quite a unique case. I have been reviewing your file and I can honestly say that I do not know of another like it.'

I shake my head again.

'Do you remember any of your time at Camp 25?'

Was that the place with the blue room? It may have been. Nobody told me where I was at the time. They were too busy pushing bamboo under my fingernails.

The Major shakes his head.

'No. Judging by the treatments listed here I can't say I'm surprised.' He sits up, running his hand over his thin hair. 'If I remove your gag you will not speak unless spoken to. Is that understood?'

I nod. He stands, steps around the table, and unties the gag. It is a relief to have the taste out of my mouth. He takes his seat and pushes a cup of tea towards me.

'Go on,' he says. I reach forward and drink.

'Thank-you, Sir.'

He smiles again.

7

'I was going to have you shot yesterday, do you know that?'

'No, Sir.'

He holds his belly like an expectant mother.

'Your quarters over there take up a lot of space. I have only joined the camp this month and I couldn't understand why you deserved such space all to yourself. A good thing I read your file. You have unique talents 11-17, which may be of use in the quest to complete our revolution. Do you understand?'

'I understand, Sir.'

If I can help I will.

'Now before we can go any further I need to know exactly how badly they damaged you at Camp 25. From what I read they made a complete mess of you. I quote from your chief interrogator's report: 'Subject's political re-education has compromised ability for independent action of the kind required by intelligence services.'

The Major drops the file, lights a cigarette, inhales deeply. He taps ash onto the floor. 'That's the curse of our countrymen, I think. Trying to achieve too much too quickly. Trying to leap too far forward.

'Well, even if you can't be sent abroad you may yet be of real service. You're clearly deficient mentally but what I need to know is . . . does your voice still have the same power? Can you still persuade people to do your bidding, 11-17?'

I turn the shell over in my hand. The question makes a kind of sense to me. It is also completely meaningless. The Major claps his hands.

'OK. Time for a simple test. I am going to call in one of the guards. When he comes in I want you to tell him to shoot himself. Do you understand?'

I chew my lip, uncertain.

'Look, 11-17. Let me spell this out for you. If you can't do this there's no reason for your accommodation here to go on.

8

You've survived until now by slipping through the cracks, but that's over now. If you can't do this I will have to shoot you and demolish your little hut. Do you understand, 11-17? You need to give this everything you've got.'

'I will, Sir.' The Major stands, steps behind me, opens the door. He calls in one of the guards, who walks in and stands at attention. He's lost his earmuffs.

The Major sits on the edge of his desk and narrows his eyes at me.

'Well?'

I stare at the guard and say nothing. I don't want to hurt him.

The Major prods his cigarette out on the desk. I think I have made him feel foolish. I wonder what Jin-Song would advise in this situation? Probably something like:

'Do what he says, you idiot!'

I look up at the guard.

'Hey,' I say. He glances at me. 'Shoot yourself.'

The guard picks up his rifle, jams it in his mouth, and pulls the trigger. The back of his head blows out across the office.

The Major steps carefully through the mess and kicks the solider with his boot.

'Well done, 11-17,' he says. 'Most impressive. Now put that rag back in your mouth.'

I replace the rag.

'You have done well,' he says, securing the gag. 'You have done very well. We will work closely together you and I. We will be as close as lips and teeth.'

He grins, as if he finds this very amusing.

CAMP 15, YODOK, 21 DECEMBER JUCHE YEAR 100

We are breaking up the rocks in the yard. Jin-Song is very excited by developments.

'This is excellent. This could get us out of here. We might never have to smash another rock again.'

'I don't see why?'

'I've been telling you this stuff for years. Your words have power over people. They do whatever you tell them to. Why do you think I've been begging you to speak to that farmer? You could have told him to break you out anytime and he'd have done it!'

'Nonsense.'

I bring him down with a crash onto a stubborn rock. He bounces off without effect.

'It's not nonsense. Don't you remember what you did at University? You had 1000 students ready to burn down the Supreme People's Assembly.'

I laugh.

'It's true. You know it's true, you cretin! They had to shoot that entire university to stop you!'

I close my eyes and smash him onto the rocks harder than ever.

'I would never threaten the Dear Leader.'

'OK, let's not get tied up in that again. You'll only forget. The important thing is that this Major obviously wants to use your power for his own ends, which almost certainly means leaving the camp. He'll have to take your gag off at some point, and that's when you'll strike! You tell him to drive you to the Chinese border. He'll do it, believe me. Everyone does what you say.'

'I want to stay here.'

'I know, I know. That's why you're going to need to take me with you.'

'You? Why would I take you?'

'Because I'm the only one you can't persuade.'

23 DECEMBER, JUCHE YEAR 100

When we drive out the gates I can barely contain my excitement, but Jin-Song keeps me calm. The Major laughed when I asked to bring my pickaxe. Whatever makes you happy, he said.

We drive along empty roads, passing people on foot. I'm not sure if they're prisoners or normal people.

The Major is driving us in an army truck. The heater is broken and we can see our breath. We go on and on for hours, driving through the night, until the Sun rises. I stare out the window, shivering, scratching at lice, wanting to laugh or sing or cry out.

The Major doesn't say anything for the entire journey, apart from:

'Damn cold.'

Then we meet a track and begin to climb up into the brown mountains. Something about the road is familiar. It makes me want to vomit. The Major lights a cigarette.

'As you know 11-17, The Dear Leader ascended to the heavens this last week. What you don't know is that our imperialist enemies have taken the opportunity to intrigue against us, to plot counter revolutionary activities. They have corrupted some of our weak-spirited comrades. They plot against the revolution and we have to stop them, do you understand? These are uncertain times, and uncertainty breeds trouble. We must be decisive. We must snuff out the flame of counter-revolution immediately. The eternal president himself has charged us with this mission, so we cannot let him down. Do you understand?'

I nod. Jin-Song scoffs. The Major points at me.

'You yourself plotted against the revolution at one time. But The Eternal Leader gave you the opportunity for re-education, and now he is giving you the chance to complete your redemption. Do not disappoint him.'

He leans in closer.

'Now listen, 11-17. In a minute we are going to reach some gates. You are going to get out of the truck and speak to the guards. You're going to tell them to shoot themselves, just like you did with the man in camp. Understand?'

'This is it!' says Jin-Song. 'Now's your chance. When he removes the gag tell him to drive us to the border.'

The Major removes orange plugs from a plastic case and presses them into his ears. Only then does he remove my gag. Jin-Song is angry.

'Sneaky bastard. He knows what you can do.'

We approach the gate. A large 25 is printed on a metal sign above it. Either side are two watchtowers. Behind I can see a driveway, leading up to a huge concrete cube.

CAMP 25, CHONJIN, 23 DECEMBER JUCHE YEAR 100

The guards start shouting at us as we slow down. The Major pulls up, and they surround the truck. The Major rolls down his window and has a gun pressed into this ear. They ask him what he is doing here, demanding papers. I've never seen one soldier threaten another before. The Major punches my arm.

'Do it, prisoner, now!'

'Let the bastard die!' says Jin-Song.

I jump out of the truck. The guards prime their weapons and surround me, dragging me towards the gate. I see another two pull the Major out of the cabin.

I scream out the words.

The guards turn their guns on themselves and tumble in a

hail of gunfire. The Major gets to his feet, nursing a cut on his head. I go to help him up. He strikes me hard across the face.

'What the hell were you waiting for?'

'Hit him back!' yells Jin-Song from the truck. 'There's just the two of you. Pick up a gun and shoot him!'

I can't do that. Finally I am part of the revolution. Finally, somebody is telling me what I must do.

We pass through the gate and drive towards the cube. Even in the gloom I recognise it. Somewhere in there is the blue room. Nothing stirs. Did nobody hear the shooting?

We drive around to the back, and I am startled to see a small, pristine house, with a lawn. There are a few lights on inside. We park and walk to the rear. The grass is soft and strokes my bare feet. We walk up a flight of stone steps to a quiet porch. The Major presses a button in the wall. There's the distant sound of a bell.

A maid answers the door. The Major grabs her, puts his hand over her mouth, and looks at me.

'Tell her to show us where her master is.'

I do as I am told. So does she. She leads us down a corridor. Paintings of white people hang on the walls. There are no images of the Dear Leader or our revered Eternal President. The carpet is even softer and deeper than the grass.

The maid shows us into a large room. A fire burns in a hearth. An old man in a dressing gown sits in a leather armchair, reading a book. He hasn't noticed us. The Major pulls his gun and shoots the maid in the back of the head.

The old man turns. He looks at me, then at the maid. The Major grins.

'You backed the wrong horse.'

The old man almost smiles. He lowers his book and removes his glasses.

'That suggests we have a race. All I see is one half mad

13

donkey running backwards. And you're asking everyone to be excited.'

The Major shakes his head.

'Why did you do it? Why try to disrupt the succession?'

The old man considers.

'Guilt,' he says.

The Major shrugs.

'OK, let's get to the point. You're going to tell me who else is with you.'

The man snorts.

'Never. There's nothing you can do to compel me, Major. I know too much about pain to be compelled to talk. You know that.'

'Well to be precise,' says the Major, 'you're going to tell him.'

The Major points at me. The old man peers almost through me. I might recognise him. I think I know him. I tell him to give us the names of who else is involved (in what?). Instantly he reels off a list of names, tears pouring down his cheeks. I wonder what else he would do if I told him to. I remember wondering the same thing as my fellow students stood in the courtyard, cheering me, ready to follow me. I remember the feeling of power.

When he is done the Major claps his hands.

'OK. Ask him where his family is hiding.'

Camp 25, Chonjin, 24 December Juche Year 100

The Major stands on the porch with me, smoking a cigarette. He even takes out his earplugs. I think about telling him to drive me to the border, as Jin-Song suggested, but I know I won't do it. He seems to savour this moment.

'You did well,' he says. 'You will live, 11-17.'

'Will I be freed?' The voice doesn't sound like mine.

'No. I need you to stay where you are. You are a useful tool. I may need to call on you again.'

'Yes Sir, thank-you, Sir.'

'You should be proud,' he says.

Cigarette finished, he replaces his earplugs. 'Come on, time to get you home.'

I trail after him, looking forward to getting back. In the camp I will forget what I've seen.

CAMP 15, YODOK, 23 JANUARY JUCHE YEAR 101

'Proud of yourself?' asks Jin-Song.

It's the first thing he's said to me in a month. He wanted me to kill the Major on the way back from the mission, or jump out of the truck and run away. I ignored him and he is furious with me.

The Major locked us up. I know I will never see him again. Jin-Song said he probably took the old man's position in the new government. He said that is how things work. I told him I didn't believe him and he started with the silent treatment. Now he's talking again. I'm surprised.

'Have you forgiven me?'

'Of what? Murder?'

'I didn't kill them.'

'No, no you just watched. Much better. I suppose I shouldn't criticise. It was revenge on your part, after all.'

'What? No it wasn't!'

'Yes it was. It's just your dodgy memory doesn't know it. I can understand you wanting to see the old swine suffer after what he did to you. Trouble is that he was one of the few people in this country who could have made a change. He was a brutal enough bastard to see it through. Probably had some kind of coup set up. It would probably have failed but you never know. He might have changed things more than you ever managed. And you had to go and kill him.'

I am enraged. I have finally done something of value and still he finds fault. I grip his handle until my knuckles turn white. Heaving with all my might I throw him over the wall.

I pace around in the yellow mud. I pull the shell out of my pocket and find that it is damaged, a hole smashed in the fat end.

I stare through it and see the face of an old man, smiling in the blue room. I drop into the mud on my knees and ask the Dear Leader for guidance. Then I remember he's dead.

'Excuse me,' says a voice.

The farmer stands at the broken section of wall, smiling, holding Jin-Song.

'Would you like this back?'

I wave him away.

'No. No. I don't want it.'

'Oh.' The farmer frowns. 'Can I help at all?'

I wipe my eyes and look at him.

'Well . . . perhaps you can.'

Jin-Song sighs, swinging in the farmer's grip.

'Here we go again.'

LAVIE TIDHAR

THE LAST OSAMA

I WAS RIDING through the lowlands, the horse's hooves scattering dry dust into the air. An inflamed red sun hovered on the horizon like a damaged eye, leaking tears of yellow and blue and tendrils of puss-like white clouds. A group of men in the distance were hanging Osama. I stopped my horse on the crest of the hill and looked down. They were too busy, drunk with power and excitement, to notice me.

That was a mistake.

There were around seven of them. They were dressed in torn green clothes, like uniforms. The Osama was between them. They had formed a circle around it. One of them had a rope. He threw the rope over a branch. There was a tree there, it was the only tree for miles. The second time they threw the rope it caught. The Osama was struggling against them – a young specimen, shiny black beard, strength in those wiry arms. They held him down, eventually. Got the noose around his neck. They were too busy to look up, and anyway the sun was setting. I couldn't hear them, I was too far. I wondered what they were saying, and what language they spoke. They were ill kempt, their beards grew wild. I imagined the stench of their unshaved bodies. I readied myself. They strung the Osama up and pulled –

17

I had it in my sight. I took a deep breath and let it out slowly, focusing, my finger tightening on the trigger until, with a soft exhalation, I pressed it. The gun fired. The sound of the gunshot was loud in my ears. It travelled fast, but not faster than the bullet.

It hit the rope and cut it. The Osama fell down to the ground. I needed it alive. The men reacted almost comically. They looked around them with bewildered expressions of surprise. I got back on the horse and cantered towards them, the gun at an angle. I didn't hurry. I didn't need to.

They saw me approach. They had no guns or they would have used them already. They just stood there, seven burly, belligerent, tired men, the fight suddenly knocked out of them. They stood almost motionless, the Osama on the ground between them, and they watched me approach.

When I came close I stopped. The men looked at me. None of them made a move. One, the closest to me, regarded me thoughtfully for one long moment then spat on the ground, a long string of juice hitting the earth wetly.

'Move,' I said.

None of them did. I showed them my gun. It was usually my winning argument. 'Sorry, boys,' I said. 'He's mine.'

Their faces changed. Resentment. Disappointment. I couldn't read their faces, they had been feral for too long. I didn't know if they understood my words. I didn't want to kill them. I hadn't been paid to.

'He's mine,' I said again. I touched the butt of the gun for emphasis. Still they wouldn't move. The Osama was motionless on the ground, but I could see it was still breathing.

The man closest to me spoke. 'One,' he said. I could tell the words came at an effort. 'One ... man.' He looked at his fellows, pointed, as if articulating a difficult proposition. 'Si ... seven,' he said. He sounded proud. 'Seven men,' he said.

I nodded. Then I showed him my gun again. 'One gun,' I said. I nodded at him and his fellows. 'No gun,' I said.

I could see their minds working, it was that slow. Something like a silent communication passed between them.

'One . . . Osama,' the man said at last, speaking for the group. He pointed, vaguely, in the distance, at an easterly direction. 'Many . . . Osama,' he said, hopefully.

I shrugged. I was only being paid for this one. 'Mine,' I said, simply. The man's shoulders slumped.

'Here,' I said. I opened my saddlebag. They looked up at me but made no move. I pulled out a packet. I opened it up slowly, showing them. Half a loaf of bread, a lump of hard yellow cheese.

'Food,' the man closest to me said. The others echoed him, one after the other, that single word going around in a circle. 'Food. . .' The sun was setting fast. The Osama was breathing quietly on the ground.

I closed the packet and threw it to them. The man closest to me caught it. 'Food,' he said.

'Go,' I said.

He nodded. I nodded too. My head inched at the lying Osama. 'Mine,' I said.

'Yours,' the man closest to me said. I waited. The man shrugged, then spat on the ground again. Then he and his men dispersed, ebbing away from the lying Osama, walking slowly, heading to the setting sun. I waited until they disappeared. I got off my horse and approached the Osama. The gun was pointing at it. It opened bright eyes and looked at me. I couldn't tell what was in his eyes. Hate or bemusement or resignation. Eyes too alien to read. 'Turn on your stomach,' I said. He didn't move. 'Do it!' I kicked him. He rolled over. I grabbed his hands and pulled them behind his back and tied them with the rope that was lying there. The noose was still on the Osama's neck. I tied his legs together. I stuck a piece of cloth in its mouth. Trussed up, I lifted him up. He was light, they were all so light. I put him on the horse, behind the saddle. I climbed on. The horse neighed. I patted it.

We rode on, into the night, me and the horse and the Osama.

The town was called Ninawa. It wasn't much of a town. The buildings lay half-formed, the life had been shelled out of them. An Osama was hanging from a tree as I approached the town. Buildings were burnt and shelled and broken but amidst them some rebuilding effort had taken place, and a major artery had been cleared through the rubble where wooden houses rose over the old broken concrete. There was an inn and a hand-painted sign showing a man being swallowed by a whale. I rode into town. On wooden porches men watched me uneasily. From the windows of the brothel I could see the curtains twitch. I rode on. I came to the sheriff's place. A single star on the door, and a crude crescent moon beside it. The sheriff came out to greet me. He was a fat man, in a torn military uniform that had once been clean. He spat when he saw me. Chewing tobacco. His teeth were stained.

'This the one?' he said.

I nodded. He didn't look that interested but he came over. He lifted the Osama's shirt and checked and found the mark and nodded, and spat again. I got off the horse and pulled down the Osama and left him in the dirt in front of the sheriff's place. The Osama looked up at me, silently. The sheriff went back into his office and returned with a small leather bag and threw it at me. I heard coins jingle. I caught the bag and put it away. The sheriff opened his mouth to say something then seemed to change his mind. He nodded. I nodded back. I got back on the horse and rode to the inn and tethered the horse there. I went inside and ordered a drink.

The proof copy of <u>Osama</u> arrived yesterday morning. I held it in my hands and opened the pages wide and put them against my face, and smelled the pages. They smelled like paper. I wrote the earlier part of this story in Jaffa, but I am now in a place just outside London, in Surrey, and there's a fox on the low rooftop of the garden shed, just standing there, watching. The air is much cooler here, the relentless heat of Jaffa dissipating like it never was. I was here when King's Cross went, E——— would have been travelling to work that day but had been out of the city for an interview. My friend S———, also a writer, had come to London that day too, for a conference. He said his plane kept circling in the air, and they weren't told why. When they landed the captain said it was a stormy day out there, and passengers were advised to use umbrellas.

There were three of them and they'd been waiting for me. The bar had a long wooden counter and it was dark inside and it smelled of spilled beer and stale smoke and stale sweat. There was a flag on the wall with too many stars on it. The walls were stone and it was cool inside. There were low wooden tables but only one man sitting down, his back to the wall, his face in the dark. I sat down at the bar and ordered my drink. The man behind the counter had one eye and his hair grew long over the one that was missing. He brought me a beer in a none-too-clean glass. I passed over a couple of coins and he disappeared back into the shadows without comment.

I took a sip from my beer. Then another. I didn't move when a man sat down beside me. Did not look sideways. Took another sip. Waited. Felt his attention on me. I was calculating my next move – swinging the beer glass into his face, breaking it, rising, kicking the stool from under him, pulling out my gun. I took another sip. The bartender didn't come back. The man beside me on the bar said, 'We wondered if you had a minute.'

I turned my head at that. His hair was cut short, he was

greying at the temples. He wore a uniform and his shirt had been recently ironed. There was sweat on his brow. The bar was very quiet. I heard footsteps and a second man appeared, walking towards us. He was zipping up his pants as he walked.

'This him?' he said, nodding at me.

'We just want to have a chat,' the man sat down beside me said, patiently, ignoring the other one. He had a softer accent, I realised. And there was a crown and crossed swords on his badge. 'A friendly chat, Mr. Longshott.'

'This the guy?' the man standing up wiped his hands on his trousers. Looked me up and down. His nails were dirty. 'You an Osama sniffer? You catching Os, cowboy? Shit -' he made that last word drawl. 'Fucking *cowboys*,' he said.

'A chat, Mr. Longshott,' said the one with the soft accent, softly. 'We have a job we think you're the man for.'

I took a sip from my beer. It wasn't a very good beer. I stood, pushing the stool away. The man standing up jumped, just a little. The man sitting down never moved.

I looked at them both. Then I turned around and looked at the third man, the one in the shadows, the one with his back to the wall, sitting on his own at the one occupied table. I nodded, once. He nodded back. I walked over, not hurrying, and the two other men followed me like shadows.

I stopped before the table. The man sitting down pushed a chair towards me with his foot. It scraped loudly against the stone floor. When he moved, leaning towards me, his face came out of shadow and into the light. He had a long face and thick grey hair and he smiled easily and without humour. I knew his face almost as well as I knew Osama's, or my own. Once his face had been everywhere. Recently, not so much. His teeth were white. He said, 'Mr. Longshott.'

I nodded again. 'General.'

'Please. Sit down.'

I sat down. I put my beer mug on the table. The other two men remained standing.

'I'm listening,' I said.

'One of our Osamas is missing,' the old general said.

In any of the great Vietnam War movies – Apocalypse Now; Platoon; Full Metal Jacket – the Vietnamese never speak. This is not their story. It is the story of a war and the soldiers who fight it, against a nameless, voiceless, faceless enemy, an alien enemy. The Vietnamese in those movies are the alien Bugs of Starship Troopers. They are without humanity, Charlie-devils in the jungle-hell.

I wrote Osama in Laos. In Vientiane, across the Mekong from Thailand. 'Why Vientiane?' Joe asks, at the end of the novel. Because it is the middle of nowhere, and everywhere, I could have told him. The setting of another war. It was safe, in Laos, to recall the other incidents, Nairobi and London and Ras-el-Shaitan. To contemplate the war from the other side. US forces have dropped over two million bombs over Laos in the Vietnam War. Kids would go looking for scrap metal and come back without a leg, or an arm.

In Vietnam, they call that war the American War.

I once had a drink on the Mekong with a UN volunteer who specialised in making artificial limbs. His previous posting had been to Afghanistan.

'I'm still listening,' I said. The general leaned forward, across the table, his face half-masked by shadows. The man with the soft accent came forward then. He was holding a file in his hands. It was made of rough brown paper. I saw my name written across it in bold black letters, handwritten. *Mike Long-shott.*

'Longshott, Mike,' he said, that same soft, almost apologetic voice. The other one, the one with the dirty nails and the bad manners, snorted. 'Fucking *cowboys*,' he said, to no one in particular.

'Served with decoration in the second war and again in the third one. Discharged in -' he named a date that meant nothing. 'Current occupation, various, but predominantly bounty hunting. Osama captures: fifty-seven.'

The man with the dirty nails whistled, sardonically.

'Osama kills,' the man with the soft accent continued, ignoring him, 'unknown.' He coughed, apologetically I thought. 'But presumed high. Mr. Longshott, you have an impressive record.'

I took a sip of beer. Waited him out. No one seemed inclined to talk. I took another sip. The room was very quiet. There was no sign of the bartender. I sighed and put my beer back on the table. 'I wasn't a member of the original team,' I said. 'I wasn't in Abbottabad. I wasn't a part of Neptune Spear.'

I felt I was talking too much. I was the only one talking. I saw them exchange glances. I wondered what else my file said. Abbottabad was a long way away, beyond the mountains, and in another time. The compound, helicopters approaching, men dropping, machine guns firing, we stormed up the stairs and there he was, at the top, looking down. He went back into his bedroom and that was deemed a hostile action. When we burst in he was standing behind two veiled women who were trying to protect him. We pushed them aside. Then we shot him, kill shots in the head and chest.

'Mr. Longshott.' It was the general, speaking. 'We need a man to go up-river and catch us a son of a bitch.'

'What do you need me for?' I said. 'You have -' I gestured with my hand, not completing the words. *The remnants of an army*, I thought but didn't say.

He said, 'We believe this is not just any Osama.'

I remembered the Abbottabad Compound, the gunshots

going into his soft body, and the explosion. Like a cloud of insects, rising . . . I felt a tightness in my chest. The old general nodded. 'Play him the tape,' he said.

The man with the soft accent put a device down on the table. He pressed a button and a voice came out of it, disembodied. I felt a shiver run through me when I heard his voice. I had forgotten it, or hoped I had.

'We fight because we are free men who don't sleep under oppression.'

There was a scratchy quality to the recording. His voice never wavered. 'No one except a dumb thief plays with the security of others and then makes himself believe he will be secure –'

The man with the soft accent pressed a button and there was a sped-up sound and then he pressed a button again and Osama's voice resolved again, somewhere else in the speech, some terrible recollection, and he said, 'Blood and severed limbs, women and children sprawled everywhere. Houses destroyed along with their occupants and high rises demolished over their residents, rockets raining down –' the man with the soft accent pressed another button and the silence returned.

'You will travel up the Euphrates,' the old general said. 'You will locate the Osama and you will destroy it. All of it.'

'Blood and severed limbs, women and children sprawled everywhere. Houses destroyed along with their occupants and high rises demolished over their residents, rockets raining down.' He wasn't talking about Al-Qaeda, he was talking about an American-aided Israeli invasion of Lebanon, one that he witnessed. My dad fought in that war, that invasion.

It is so quiet here, in the room overlooking the garden, with the sun out, and the radio playing in the background. Here in an England whose people cheerfully divided up the Middle East and went to war in Afghanistan and Iraq and who genuinely had no idea as to why they were being attacked. Outside women in burqas walk their children to school and their white neighbours complain in low voices about immigrants, and those Muslims, and how can they treat their women this way and they should go back to where they came from – to the places we bomb. The places we continue to bomb.

Osama comes out in two months. And I am hoping to finally put an end to it, this occupation of my life, this invasion of my mind. I remember Nairobi, the Hilltop Hotel on Ngiriama Road, the narrow bed we lay on, the terrorists a floor below. I remember the shell of the American embassy, the ring of soldiers surrounding it, uselessly, now. I could not not write Osama. Not with the ghosts, and their whispers in my ears.

A day's ride out of Ninawa and I was alone, alone under the stars. The river came into view. It was not the same river. The river was life. You say Euphrates, but it was not Euphrates, not exactly, not since the world changed, not since they picked it up like a toy and shook it, shook it hard until it fell sideways and into pieces and when it was formed again it was different. There were high mountains in the distance, and beyond those mountains there was nothing any more, not since the Compound, not since the spores. 'You'll be going into the wild lands,' the man with the dirty fingernails told me. We were outside. My meeting with the old general had been concluded. 'The lands where the wild Osamas are.' He laughed without humour, hawked on the ground. 'Bring us the head of Prince Osama,' he said. He looked at me and shook his head. 'Fucking cowboys,' he said, compassionately.

I left him there and felt his eyes on my back as I rode out of town. As I left I saw them hauling the Osama I'd caught up on the gallows.

I made a fire by the bank of the river and watched the stars. The Euphrates was dirty brown and the water running fast. The wild lands, the man with the dirty fingernails said. But everywhere was the wild lands now. I slept and in my dreams I was back up those stairs, and bursting through the closed door of his bedroom, pushing aside the veiled women, and then I was pressing the trigger, once, twice, three times, bullets hitting soft flesh, chest and then head, and then the explosion. They were still running the war in the world, the world was war, and the old Euphrates travelled in and out of space and time, it travelled through Uruk and Avagana, it was everywhere and nowhere and he was at the end of it, they told me but it couldn't be right. Osama Prime.

When I woke up it was early morning. I saddled up and rode again, the sun low on the horizon, climbing, like a beetle, climbing.

As I travelled the landscape changed. Low hills, occasional settlements. I skirted the villages. There were men in the world and the things that had once been men, and there were Osamas. Several times I saw fresh tracks. Wild Osamas. I kept thinking of his voice on that tape. 'You were a soldier,' the man with the soft accent told me, before I left. 'But this is no job for a soldier.'

I followed the river. Seagulls cried overhead. Several times I smelled smoke, cooking fires. Twice I came across the bodies of men. They had been torn apart. I waited, but when the attack came it still caught me by surprise.

They came out of the water. Their skin was a grey-green, like a diver's suit. Their hands extended into flippers or claws or human fingers, depending. They rose out of the water and the water fell from them. They had once been human, perhaps they still considered themselves so. I shot the first one in

27

the gut and he dropped, flopping on the ground. Seal-men. The others were upon me then. They shed remnants of their humanity like skin. They clubbed me like seals. They bit into my skin, tore chunks of flesh from my arms and thighs. I shot another one and the shot went through his skull and I kicked out at another, uselessly: they were heavy and slippery on the ground there in the night under a crescent moon.

When the world changed and compressed and all there was was war, the moon, too, changed. It had stopped shape shifting. It was a war moon, a constant moon, a crescent moon. I tried to fight but they were too many and I felt myself growing weak. The irony of dying like this made a laugh like a cough work its way out of my bruised lungs. I fell under their weight. I was doing knife-work now, cutting through blubber, trying to reach vital organs, trying to take as many of them with me as I could before I went.

Then there was a terrible, high keening noise. It cut through the air and for a moment I thought it was the sound of my death, the sound of a heart, stopping. Then a tearing barking noise and the seal-people fell back. I turned, I was on my back, I wiped blood from my eyes, the weight on my chest had gone and I felt lighter. I blinked in the light of the moon. A wild Osama was standing above me.

It was an old Osama. An Osama having gone through all the life-stages of an Osama. His beard was white and his turban was dirty grey. His skin was wrinkled, his lips bloodless, but his eyes were still the Osama eyes, that clear, penetrating gaze. The seal-folk moved away from it. They growled but if they had language, they had forgotten it. The ancient Osama advanced on them, his feet bare on the ground. I turned my head, and saw.

Behind him, ringing me in a half-circle like a moon.

A pack of wild Osamas.

There were Osama brats, half-naked, with bare, hairless cheeks, and cheeky grins, and young Osamas, student-like and studious, and militant Osamas, post-desert, with that hungry look, and cave-Osamas with that hunted look about them. No wonder the seal-men turned back. They oozed into the water, cursing wordlessly, bereft of language. We were all bereft of language, those of us who were left, I thought. I felt a little shaky. The Osamas approached me, cautiously. I could see them sniffing the air. You had to be cautious, you were an Osama in the wild. There were trappers out there, villagers, military remnants, bounty hunters like myself. It was a hostile world to be in, for an Osama.

I didn't know what they'd do. I had seen them tear a man apart, before. Wordlessly, they stared at me. Then the old one, the leader, keened again. There was a sense of loss and pride in that sound, but something else, too, that I did not understand at the time. A sound like victory. Then they turned away, the whole base camp of them, and left, just like that.

I was left lying there, on the bank of the Euphrates, staring after the departing Osamas. After a while I sat up. My ribs hurt. I crawled to the water's edge and drank, though the water was filthy.

I plucked 'Mike Longshott' out of the moulding Hebrew pulp novels of the sixties and seventies. He was a composite being, a man who did not really exist. Longshott wrote soft-core pornography, tales of Nazi concentration camps where prisoners were abused, physically and sexually, by Aryan goddesses, sadistic nymphomaniacs of the Third Reich.

He was a pen name broke young writers hid behind for cash. He was a collective, burrowing into the sexual and social taboos of his era. He wrote crap, was paid crap, and his books, sold under the counter, went from hand to hand and bathroom to bathroom, their covers featuring naked flesh and whips, guard posts and POW slaves and a plethora of large improbable breasts. He never lived, he never breathed, his prose was eminently forgettable. He was a hack, a pulpster, a paperback writer. His name was Mike Longshott and he was going to be my hero.

I was on a boat, and my wounds have been bandaged. I was on a dhow, and the sail was pushing us, up or down river I couldn't tell. But I could smell the wildlands, the Osamalands, and I knew I was getting closer. I opened my eyes. A man was looking down on me. I blinked and then I knew why I felt so well, in the bandages, as if some medical professional from the days we still had those had taken care of me.

I looked up at the man and he looked down at me without expression. His mouth was a scar. Scratch that. His whole face was a map of scars. I sat up, despite the pain. They had fed me some sort of painkiller, I thought. Not the type that came in capsules, we didn't have those any more, pain had been allowed to flower a long time ago. Some sort of plant, making me thickheaded and woozy and strangely happy. The man was almost naked, and each and every inch of him was covered in scars. Some were old and scabbed over. Some were new and still bleeding.

I tried to speak. My mouth was raw, as if I'd swallowed razorblades. 'Where are you taking me?'

He looked at me. One of his eyes was missing. He drew a knife and calmly cut himself, above the left nipple, a long slow trail, the end of the point sharp, drawing a long line of blood on his wounded skin. He sucked in his breath, like a prayer. 'Ahhh...'

'Wherever you want to go,' another voice said. I turned my head. An older version of the same man sat in the front, watching the water. All but naked, deeply scarred. We were all deeply scarred, I thought, but some of us had taken it to a whole new level.

I sank back on my mattress, there on the deck, under the stars.

Scarrists, I thought.

I'd been picked up by Scarrists.

Mr. Scar was at the helm. He looked nineteen. Mr. Scar was handling the sail. He was the oldest one of them, a drawling accent and the remains of a tattered uniform still on his puckered skin.

Mr. Scar was the chief, he ran this boat.

Mr. Scar was the machine gunner, he was the one who never spoke.

I had time to recover, on the boat. You never got off the boat. The Scarrists had everything they needed right there. They had their knives and their bandages and their lotus flowers, and the thick paste they made out of them. The river was thick like oil. It was sluggish like blood. The deck of the boat was covered in old stains. When I stood up at the rails I saw the landscape shifting past the boat. The sun was always setting. It was red and pussing like a sore. The mountains looked crudely drawn in the distance. Sometimes I could smell smoke. Sometimes, in a great distance, I could hear their calls, the last song of the Osamas.

But with each passing mile they were growing closer. I could feel them coming closer.

I could feel his nearness, too. His, most of all.

Bin Laden, Osama.

Born March 10, 1957 in the old count, to his father's tenth wife. His mother divorced. He lived with her and her new husband and their four children. Inherited almost $30 million from the family's fortunes. At university, studied economics and business administration. He wrote poetry, and was a fan of Arsenal football club. Married in 1974, again in 1983, 1985, 1987 and 2000. Fathered 20 to 26 children. Fought against the Soviets in Afghanistan, then ran a campaign against the House of Saud. Established base in Sudan. Expelled following failed assassination of Egyptian president. In 1996 declared war on the United States. Returned to Afghanistan. Has been in hiding since September 11, 2001. Located and executed at the Abbottabad Compound, in Eastern Pakistan, ten years later in 2011.

I stared at his dossier. Old dates, old names for places we no longer had. They hurt, they felt like scars on the tongue.

We never caught him. Abbottabad had been the source, it was where it had started. The days on the river floated by. Mr. Scar ran the boat with silent command. They weren't bad, the Scarrists, they just had nowhere else to go. None of us had. The river ran and I remembered, I remembered Abbottabad.

I remembered running up those stairs, the orders had been clear enough, he'd have to work pretty damn hard to get out of there alive, he was at the top of the stairs, I pushed in, he retreated into the bedroom, the women trying to protect him, screaming, I pushed them, I put the bullets in him, in his chest and head.

A soft, popping sound . . .

Time seemed to slow. He exploded not in blood and bones and brain but like a pillow, bursting open. It was silent. Things that were not feathers came out of him. He disintegrated as I watched, helpless. The women turned their heads.

So pretty . . . they floated in the room, these things like feathers that were not feathers. Soft, almost weightless. So much of them. The windows had been open and they floated out, and I followed them with my eyes. One tickled my nose and I sneezed –

Time sped-up, but still it was so silent there, I heard someone break the silence with a 'What the *fuck*!' and I turned, I don't know why, I don't know why even today I don't know why I was the only one who wasn't affected, I didn't –

I turned and saw M———, he was an officer, I saw the first of the – they were not feathers, they were not, they were –

Spores, and I saw the first of the spores float through the air – so pretty! – and come to land, gently, so gently, like a whispered kiss, on M———'s forehead –

It seemed to *dissolve* –

It was absorbed into M———'s *skin*.

It went *inside* of him.

For a moment nothing happened. He opened his mouth, to speak, perhaps to say, 'What the *fuck*!' again, but his lips were changing and only a soft exhalation came out of his mouth and a rash began to grow on his face, on his skin, and it took me a long moment to realise it was a thick, black beard.

I woke up screaming in the night. Hands held me down. A sickle moon looked down on the boat. Never get off the boat, only I would have to, I had no place here, no place anywhere. 'Take it,' a voice whispered, close by, 'take it.' I stared at the knife. I took it from him. I ran it, gently, gently like a shiver, down my arm, and blood welled out.

'There . . .' the voice said. It was Mr. Scar, the old one. 'There . . .'

A peace came upon me. They bandaged me, and gave me poppy juice, and I slept, and woke up with a new, fresh scar.

There are memories smudged into the brain, as if a child, clumsy with finger paints, had left sticky finger marks and traces of Guasch crammed inside the cranium, into places it is impossible to erase them from. This is Nairobi for me, the American embassy a blackened shell of a building, the soldiers surrounding it. I remember the Hilltop Hotel where we stayed alongside those hidden Al-Qaeda operatives, the dimness of the rooms, the quiet. Outside dust motes hovered in the still air, shoe shiners sat in the shade waiting for custom, they were selling scratch cards from a booth and I bought several, we walked in the dark to an Indian restaurant where we were the only customers, a hush had settled over the city, the spirits of the dead wafted upon the waters.

The Sinai in 2004, E——— on the beach, the sun had set and it was dark, quiet, a fire was burning nearby, in the kitchen a young Bedouin was roasting a chicken, someone was smoking a joint, the smell of it rose in the air, the beating of the Red Sea against the sand –

BOOM!

Like a comic book explosion, exclamation marks rising from it like flying darts –

KABOOM! POW!

The car bomb exploded just further up the beach, in Ras-el-Shaitan, driven into a camp identical to the one E——— was staying at, reed shacks on the beach, stoned backpackers, mosquito nets and mosquitoes –

The screams rose into the night air, E——— did not know what to do, she watched the flames, we were apart, I couldn't phone, the news were jumbled, no one knew who had lived and who had died, a random person phoning, heard from someone who'd heard from someone who was there, E——— is all right, please phone C———, a stranger, and tell them their friend is alive, too –

The spirits of the dead coagulated, restless, amassing now, more and more of them, and E——— passing through King's Cross to work when the bombers struck, but she had been away that day, could not get back into the city, we spoke on the phone and watched the news on the television –

And E———'s friend L———, who worked with her in Laos, a fellow aid worker, they would not renew her visa so she went back to Afghanistan, she had loved it there, kidnapped and then a rescue attempt, US forces storming the camp where she was held, killing her with one of their own grenades –

KABLOOEY! BAM!

Cartoon war with a cartoon president reading a story about a goat, and a cartoon villain muttering threats into a camera, mutual ghost-gatherers, God-botherers, and we were fodder for their hate.

'We don't go any farther,' Mr. Scar told me. Ahead of us the river curved and I could see a village on the point, smoke rising. The sick moon, the sickle moon, hung above our heads like a scar carved into the sky.

'Why?' I said.

He shrugged. 'It's hairy out there,' he said. He pointed. 'That's Osama's point.'

'Osama don't surf!' I said, but he just shook his head at that, perhaps remembering a time we had cinemas and movies, a door into escape. One by one the doors had shut, and we who remained were trapped here, in this new Osamaworld.

'This war . . .' I began to say, but he stopped me, with a gentle smile, a smile like a scar, and a hand on my shoulder, and he said, 'The war is already over. It was over a long time ago.'

I watched the boat sail back. I was left alone on the bank. I had no horse. The seal-folk killed my horse and his blood ran red into the brown river. I walked. I followed the river, remembering.

The spores rose into the air that night. They hovered over

houses and rooftops and were blown far and wide by the winds.

I saw the men – I saw my friends – I saw them change. I saw the beards creep up along their naked chins, I saw their smooth-skinned arms fill with wrinkles, and saw their eyes change, saw the look in them become a penetrating gaze, their lips thinned, they spoke in tongues, they said:

'Security is an indispensable pillar of human life -'

'Free men do not forfeit their security -'

'Just as you lay waste to our nation. So shall we lay waste to yours -'

'Does the crocodile understand a conversation that doesn't include a weapon?'

And so on. I saw them reach for weapons. I saw them look at me. They shot down the helicopters and the men, dying, were transformed when the spores hit them.

I ran. Somehow I was not affected. I was not Osamaed. I ran and they followed, the first of the wild hunt, the Osama-spawn, they hunted me and each one I killed exploded in a soft cloud of spores that rose and rose and then fell, softly, drifting in through open windows, settling on the faces of sleeping women and men, transforming them.

They hunted me through the long night and the world contracted and changed, we lost the war that day, we were lost that day, and I lost them in the mountains and hid in the deep black caves.

I walked through the night. Nothing troubled me. The world was a quieter world nowadays. The remnants of men and their army still congregated together in what was left of the cities, places like Ninawa and Caubul and Nuyok, and hunted and kept away the wild Osamas. But out here, in the wildlands, men were few and far between. I walked and the river followed me, until I came to the place.

They called it, simply, the base. Al-Qaeda: the base. There were low buildings and a fence, trees growing there. The river flowed nearby and it was in the shadow of the mountains. Osamas of varying shapes and sizes watched me mutely. I saw a human corpse dangling from a rope and a sign on its chest in childish white letters that said Sorry.

My bare feet sank in the mud. My beard had grown in my days on the boat. The silent Osamas watched me. A raven screeched high above.

I walked through the valley of the shadow of death and I felt no fear and the stars were bright overhead. I came to a hill and I walked up it and I reached him. He was sitting on a folding chair, watching me. He was very old. A jester at his feet, a man who was not Osamaed, in the remnants of a military uniform, with no insignia. He smiled a manic grin and chattered at me. 'The poppy fields are beautiful, red like the blood of martyrs.'

He had a high trembling voice. He said, 'God lives in the clouds like smoke, he has a long grey beard.'

The man sitting on the folding chair turned his gaze on him and the jester scampered down the hill.

The man turned his gaze on me. His eyes were rheumy but still somehow sharp. Almost, I fancied that he smiled.

'You have come to kill me,' he stated.

'I have come to . . .' my voice sounded different in my ears. The man in the folding chair had a long beard turned white with age. 'You have tried before and you have tried many times,' he said, not unkindly, 'but do you not see? Killing the man is not enough. A man is more than flesh and gristle and bone and blood. Kill the man and all you do is preserve the image of the man. His icon. Kill a man and a thousand spores of faith and belief, a thousand spores of idea erupt into the world. Look,' he said. He reached his hand towards me. I took it in mine. Our hands were the same. I raised my free hand to my beard and he did likewise, to his. 'We are not so unlike, you and I.'

I was running up the stairs and he was at the top. He had backed into his bedroom. I burst through the door and the women were screaming, they were trying to shield him with their bodies. I pushed them away. The gun was in my hand and I used it, firing bullets at point-blank range into his chest and then his head, confirmation kill, eliminating with extreme prejudice.

I fired into silence and a cloud of spores rose into the air, like ideas that wouldn't die, and the world was quieted, with a sound like the hiss of escaping air.

Osama and Osama and Osama, amen.

JOSEPH D'LACEY

ARMAGEDDON FISH PIE

Everyone was so down hearted.

You could actually see people walking down the street and crying unashamedly. And this is England we're talking about – a country in which emotional displays, particularly public ones, were taken as a sign of mental illness as recently as the nineteen eighties.

Gone were the times when you could lose your entire family in a freak industrial accident on the same day as filing for bankruptcy and coming down with a nasty case of cancer and a 'nice cup of tea' was enough to put a smile back on your face. I mean long gone.

It would have been bad enough popping round to a mate's house only to find him weeping into his can of Carling (which, incidentally, I did – otherwise I wouldn't mention it. He was so upset that he couldn't watch the West Ham match, which was the point of the whole evening.) but to actually see Joe and Jane Public lamenting outside Woolies on an otherwise unspoiled Tuesday afternoon struck me as pathetic.

I wanted to walk right up to these people and ask them what the hell they thought they were doing lowering the tone of our proud British society. And where, I felt like demanding, was the stiff upper lip that had brought us through so many other trying times? Of course, I didn't do it. Being British, I'm too bloody polite.

It was worse on TV. I had to stop watching it after a while. The Americans were the ones that finally did it for me. I promised myself no more News after seeing how they were dealing with it. They weren't just crying spontaneously and publicly, they were getting together in parks and city squares to have a good old sob in huge pitiful groups. Hordes of overfed, under-nourished 'Free' and 'Brave' citizens wailing and gnashing on international television. Didn't they have any shame at all? God; and the hugging and the conciliatory, defeatist pats on the back and the 'I forgive yous' and the 'I love yous'. It made me sick.

Everywhere else was the same, near enough. Miserable bastards all over the world. It was biblical. It was sad. And even though we were British, we were no better at coping than anyone else.

My mum died a few weeks ago. No, it's all right; I don't want your sympathy. And I'm not telling you in order to have a chance to gush like everyone else. I just want all the circumstances to be clear.

It was sudden, a heart attack. No one knew she had a dodgy ticker. They found her in the kitchen. Not surprising really; that was where she spent a good part of each day. She was a great cook, my mum. Made all your traditional English dishes and none of this foreign nonsense you see all over the TV and the colour supplements.

She had no need to cook really. Dad's been gone ten years and I left home thirty years ago. But cook she did. She'd give the stuff away for the church to sell at the 'bring and buys' and the fundraisers and she'd pop meals in to elderly types who lived alone. She wasn't with 'meals on wheels' or anything;

she did it because she liked to look after people. I suppose she didn't see herself as an elderly type that lived alone but that was what she was.

Whenever I went to visit I'd leave with armfuls of stuff for the freezer; you know, cakes and hot pots and pies and soups. My favourite was always her fish pie. So simple and yet absolutely delicious. Just thinking about it takes me back to the days when I'd come in from school on Fridays and smell the richness that had suffused the whole house.

Ah, fish pie – the ultimate comfort food. God, it's good.

She'd just finished making one on the day she died. I didn't want it to go to waste, so it's in my freezer now waiting for a special occasion: a Friday, a most particular Friday.

Yes, I did feel a little odd about taking the pie – after all, it might not have been meant for me – but I didn't attach any kind of morbid superstition to the fact that it was last thing she did before she passed away, I just thought carefully about whether she'd have wanted me to take it or not. And, of course, I knew she would have.

They say fish is 'brain food', don't they? I've never really known why, but I have heard that your brain can be responsible for burning thousands of calories in a single day. Imagine that. Just thinking hard can use up all that energy. When I look around these days, I find it hard to believe that any of the moping masses are burning up many calories above the neck. They're too busy living in fear.

A large number of people, the number is in the thousands, have committed suicide over the last few weeks I was shocked to discover. Things get a bit tough and they just give up. Lovers taking pills together, teenagers hanging themselves in their bedrooms. A number of fathers have murdered their families while they slept and then shot themselves. They weren't bloody thinking, were they? Not enough fish pie as youngsters, I suppose.

41

Fair enough, I shouldn't joke about it – there's nothing funny about people killing each other but I'm not laughing at them. Not really. It just seems better to be laughing than pursuing the alternative. No. You won't catch me losing control like that; you won't catch me not thinking.

You probably think I'm a bit cynical, a bit critical of others. Well don't worry. I see the good things too, and I can admit I've got my own faults. My problem is I'm honest. I always have been – that's another wonderful thing my mum gave to me; the courage to be honest no matter what the cost. I've never regretted honesty, not for a single moment of my life.

So, the upside then. People are making up over the things they haven't been able to forgive each other for in the past. The lady across the street in Number 46 has let her husband move back in. Apparently he'd had an affair and it was more than she could stand. He said he'd made a mistake, that he loved her and that it would never happen again, so she invited him back. I did think that was a bit of a joke; I mean if he decided to be unfaithful again he'd have to be a hell of a fast worker. Anyway, good for them, I say. I've never seen them as happy and that's really what's important isn't it? To spend each day happily if you can.

On a global scale a lot of conflicts have been spontaneously resolved. It's not the politicians that have done it; they'd keep us at each other's throats right up to the final minute if they could. But soldiers everywhere have lain down their weapons and gone home to their families. No one has the power to stop them. After all, they are the power, aren't they? They've just walked away.

In some places there's been looting, but it's half hearted. There's not much that people can do with the stuff they've nicked. There isn't enough time. So things haven't been as bad as predicted.

And I haven't been to work since I first heard what was going to happen. They called here every day to start with, trying to threaten me with the sack and all that rubbish. I even had the boss on the phone saying he'd cancel my pension for breaching my employment contract. That was the best laugh I'd had in years. Laughed out loud right into his lughole. I didn't bother trying to explain the foolishness of his arguments to him, I just told him to do whatever he felt was best. And I meant it too. I knew he'd realise eventually that everything had changed even if he wasn't prepared to admit it to himself right at that moment. It was his business, the great project of his life; I don't think he could quite believe that he was about to lose it all. I hope he has by now.

The point is that I've had plenty of time to think and I've really enjoyed not working. It's been the best holiday of my life knowing that there really is absolutely no point whatsoever in going to work. I might be cynical but I've never been so cynical as to actually enjoy spending most of my waking hours doing the bidding of someone I neither respect nor like, for a wage that was always inadequate.

I've taken a lot of nice long walks down by the canal. You can see the back end of the city from the canal, the side it rarely shows except to rail passengers and the odd vagrant. It's the place that seems most real to me, and the most peaceful. It's been warm out there and I've spent a lot of time in my shorts and shirtsleeves sitting on a broken bit of wall and banging my heels against the bricks like a bored kid. But I haven't been bored – I've been thinking.

I've thought about how I've spent my life. Packing in work made me see things differently and the work that I'd been doing, which was no more than greasing the wheels of the huge money machine the world has become, appeared immediately pointless once I realised that the wheels wouldn't be turning for much longer.

I haven't any regrets about my life; what I mean is, I'm not taking up sky diving or bomb disposal just because I suddenly have nothing else to lose. It's not like that. I just wonder what else I might have done with my life had I known in advance that all this was going to happen. I wonder what the difference would have been for me or for the world if I had decided instead to be a dustman or an artist or a spy.

I keep coming back to the idea that, if things hadn't come to this, the most important thing would have been for me to be happy. Not in a way that meant I could just as easily be unhappy but in a way that meant I was content with my life regardless of circumstance. It points to the fact that I probably wouldn't have changed a single thing. Perhaps the fact that I'm spending the last days of my life dawdling by a canal instead of going to work just means that I'm lazy but I don't really believe that. Yes, it's a little bit daunting and yes, it seems a little bit sad, but in the face of it all I find that I am content with how things are. I don't feel the need to try and change or make up for anything. Maybe it will all hit me in some new way near the end and I'll start panicking, but honestly, I just can't see that happening.

Wednesday today. Less than two days to go and although I feel fine in myself I found I haven't been able to eat a single morsel for the last three days. I manage the odd cup of tea now and again, but that's it. It feels strange not to eat anything at all; it's literally breaking the habit of a lifetime but I feel lighter and more awake and my mind is clearer than ever. All the colours around me seem brighter and more vivid as if objects have been lit up from the inside. People would probably argue that I'm hallucinating, but people can say what they like.

I can feel myself starting to sit back from it all. In many places people are really starting to panic badly. I haven't switched on the TV but I hear rumours about angry mobs and crowded churches. There's a kind of mass response taking place but from what I can tell it's a desperate one, a meaningless one. For my own part I feel drawn back from other people. Not in an unfriendly way, but as if I've stopped being concerned about them. It seems that, more than anything; this is a time for me.

There was a loud knock at the door this morning and I went to answer it in my own leisurely time. There on the front step was a young couple probably no older than twenty or so and the girl was carrying an infant that could only have been a few weeks old. Their expressions were tense and desperate, but overlaid was a kind of expectant fervour and I knew what was coming. In the old days I might have turned them away immediately, especially for using their child as an enticement but, despite my new detachment, I found I had time for people now, time for everything. I waited for them to speak.

'If ye repent, if ye plead for forgiveness and accept Jesus into thine heart ye shall be saved.'

I couldn't help the smallest of smiles. 'So he can put a stop to all this, can he?' I gestured skyward.

'This is his doing, now is come the day of judgement when all souls are sent either to heaven or eternal damnation.'

I looked from the two fevered faces of the parents to the face of the child. I looked into its new eyes and it looked back into mine, hardly blinking at all. We shared a moment of simplicity. I knew that everything was fine.

'I'm sorry,' I said looking back at the young parents, 'I don't think there's anything I can help you with.'

'No, mate,' said the young man, suddenly aggressive and having lost all trace of his New Testament syntax, 'we've come to help you. Repent now, ask for forgiveness and you will be saved.'

It was very obvious that we weren't going to make any more

progress so I just said, 'Come back another day,' and closed the door very gently.

'But there are no more days. You're out of time.'

I heard them shout at me for a few more seconds and then heard a hissing sound followed by their departing footsteps.

When I checked outside the door I saw that they'd painted a red, downward pointing arrow on it. They'd done it using an aerosol and it looked disrespectfully urban and scruffy. I looked around at the other doors on my street and saw that almost all of them had white cruciform graffiti signalling their acceptance of Jesus into their hearts. Why couldn't they have done it when there was time to make it worthwhile, I wondered?

I shut the door just as gently the second time and went to sit in the garden for a while. It certainly was turning out to be the most glorious summer I could remember.

They didn't need to put a sign on my door. Unless, of course, they were thinking about coming back and handing out some punishment themselves because God was too busy. I knew that if there was a God, he could see inside my heart and he would know whether I was truly a sinner or not, if indeed, such criteria mattered to him. I also knew that he wouldn't take it personally whether I believed in him or not.

I did think about food from time to time, but it really did seem wrong to be eating and anyway, I had no appetite so I just let it slide. To be honest, I was enjoying the feeling that not eating gave me. The only thing that interested me was the fish pie in my freezer. Thinking about that perfect little beauty made my stomach grumble. It took a discipline I didn't know I had to ignore those thoughts and put my mind on something else.

By Thursday evening I really needed a distraction so I finally gave in and turned on the TV for the first time in over a week. I felt so removed from everything by that stage, so objective, that I didn't think it would bother me to watch the last few gestures and goodbyes from my doomed world.

After my own absence from work, I didn't really expect to find much on the TV so it was with a good deal of surprise that I discovered the 10 o'clock news still broadcasting almost as if nothing had changed. It reminded me of the string quartets that had continued to play music on the decks of the Titanic as it sank so surely beneath the black cold waves of the Atlantic. The difference was that you couldn't consider the news that was being shown to be any kind of entertainment.

Almost everyone on the planet seemed to feel cornered by their destiny. They were not at peace and it seemed strange to me that given the choice of dying calmly and quietly or in a state of total hysteria that most chose the latter condition.

In the streets, dogmatically opposed mobs from various religions battled it out with shotguns, kitchen knives and finally hand to hand. The need to own God had only intensified in the final days. Suicides had increased and instead of people meeting in large groups to hug and dance and cry, now they were meeting to die en masse. The bodies lined the pavements and the roads in every country – there was no one who could be bothered to go and clear them away. There was no time left for burial and ritual. All that was left? Insanity.

Even the news presenter, a man whose face I had watched every night for years, looked strained to the point of snapping. Maybe it was just the fact that there was no one working in the make up department of the TV station any more. It didn't seem to matter; the man's face was a portrait of woe. When he came to say goodnight, it seemed he did so with disbelief. The hint of a mad smile twitched in the muscles of his face. His job, also, was finished forever.

I switched the TV off for the last time and it set me to thinking once again. What was really happening here? I mean, just

47

how bad a thing was it that after one thirty the following after-noon there would be no more world. I thought about it hard.

It struck me that, as human beings, the only conscious-ness we experience throughout our entire lives is our own. It is impossible to do otherwise. Even if such a thing as rein-carnation were a real factor in existence, we would still only experience one awareness at a time and that awareness would last from the moment we were born to the moment we died. Either it would be followed by some thing good, like heaven or another life, or it would be followed by the end of personal consciousness forever.

I realised at that point that no matter how many beings were snuffed out the next day (and that would be all people and all plants and animals), none of their consciousnesses would join up to die together. There would merely be billions of single consciousnesses winking out at exactly the same moment. In a way, that meant that only one being was dying, and that only one being had ever lived. I took comfort from that thought. Maybe that was what I'd believed right from the start. Maybe that was why the whole issue had never really bothered me. It appeared that most people thought the most terrible tragedy was occurring, that the whole world and all of humanity was being wiped out. That this was a huge crime. That this was somehow wrong.

I understood right there that the only thing those people were actually experiencing was the voice of their incredibly tenacious and petulant egos saying 'it isn't fair, it isn't pos-sible, it can't be happening.'

But, of course, it was.

You would think I might have stayed up a little later than usual on the last night of my life, but I was tired and felt I needed an early night. Besides, the next day was going to be a big one. I went past the kitchen on the way to bed and took the fish pie out of the freezer. I wanted to make sure it had completely defrosted by the time I would need it, around lunch time the following day – the final Friday in history.

I've even managed to have a bit of a lie in this morning, but I finally got up because I couldn't get the thought of mum's pie out of my head. I stood staring at it whilst still wearing my pyjamas and slippers and worried for a few moments that it didn't seem up to much. It was pale and soggy looking, there was no soul in it.

I realised before long that it only looked that way because it hadn't been cooked yet. While I washed and dressed I turned on the cooker to preheat and put the pie into the fridge. I couldn't bear the thought that it might spoil in the heat. Now that would have been a tragedy – I didn't want to die on an empty stomach.

I ironed a shirt and put on my best suit. I gave my shoes a polish too because they were looking scruffy and would have brought the whole effect down a notch or two. For the first time ever, after shaving with the grain of my facial hair, I shaved a second time against the grain and my face felt as smooth as polished oak. I hadn't had a thing to eat for five days and I felt as clear-headed and optimistic as I could remember. I checked my watch. The preparations were taking up time; it was already midday.

Back in the kitchen, I took the pie out of the fridge and without allowing myself to obsess over its pallor and apparent lifelessness, popped it into the oven. I liked the potato on the top to be almost burned with crispness so I had set the oven between medium and high. I decided an hour would probably do it. That would just leave time for one last stroll down to the canal before the big moment.

The streets were so silent it seemed like everyone might already be dead. Here and there however, I did notice signs of life. A flickering curtain, a baby being hushed, a door closing quietly. The lull was one of tense anticipation but I didn't let myself tune into it. I didn't want to spoil what was turning out to be the most gorgeous day of the summer so far. The sky over the city was a magnificent pure cobalt, as if all the fumes that had ever clouded it had been vacuumed away and the surface of the sky itself had then been polished.

I could smell the flowers that grew along the towpath long before I reached it. They were weeds really, but it didn't seem to matter. It was too warm for a suit. The midday sun beamed its benevolent, life bringing light so strongly that after a few minutes I could feel it burning the top of my head where my hair has thinned recently. I took my jacket off and slung it over my shoulder as I headed down to the broken wall where I had sat so many times.

It didn't seem a problem that I would get my suit trousers dirty, the important thing was that I had made the effort to wear the right sort of clothes for a special day. The strange thing was that I didn't see a single bird or animal. Not a fish jumping in the canal. Not even a fly or wasp about its business. The flaming blue day was empty it seemed, except for me. So, by the stillness of the canal with its green smells and its secret views, I sat and spun on the edge of the world without even knowing that I was moving.

Well.

All those moping bloody faces. All those unhappy souls destroying themselves like that. How could they have found life so disheartening? How could they give up so, so easily? Perhaps they didn't feel they had anything more to look forward to. If they felt that, then they were wrong.

I'm looking at the most gorgeous thing currently on the planet. It is not the face of my beloved, as I don't have one. It is not a religious icon that will give me hidden strength and succour. It is not an object that changes the meaning of anything or gives my existence any more purpose than I ever thought it had. It is a fish pie.

It is the best-looking fish pie I have ever seen. This may well be because I haven't eaten a scrap of food for almost a week but I'm not too concerned about why the pie is beautiful. I just know that it is, more certainly than I've ever known anything. It is crispy on the top and seems to have risen slightly as if imbued with inner power. The crispiness is just right. I know because I have been unable to stop myself from tearing a bit of potato off and testing it. I have a feeling that I may eat the entire pie if there is time. It is fluffy in a heavy, wholesome sort of way. It is proud without being arrogant – a noble pie, therefore.

It smells of after football hunger pangs when food is so completely deserved and desired. It smells of the security of my mother's care. It smells of goodness, but most of all it smells of creamy, baked fish and the whole house is warm and moist with its scent. I pour myself a beer. It's a special occasion, after all.

Out on the tiny back porch I sit at a card table with my beer and my plate and my scorching hot pie on a wooden board so that it doesn't burn the baize. I serve myself a healthy portion and even more aroma bursts free from the pie. I feel slightly faint as the steam hits my face. My stomach is suddenly alive with little cramps and gurgles and churnings. I cut a small piece away from the rest of the pie, making sure there is an even amount of fish and potato, and put that forkful of heaven in my mouth. What a complete moment it is.

I'm smiling all over my face now. I take another sip of beer and glance at my watch. Somehow the time has skittered away from me again and I see that it's now twenty past one. But I can't stop smiling because I know it's just enough time for me to finish the pie if I want to.

More sips of malty beer. More mouthfuls of pie. I'm surprised to find that tears are escaping from my eyes and I realise it's because I'm so happy. I'm filled with warmth from the fish pie and clothed in the warmth from the sun. But as I chew and sip it seems that a cloud has passed between the earth and the sun, a permanent shadow. There is a certain chilliness now but I am warm inside because of the pie.

And a true night is finally falling.

E. J. SWIFT

THE COMPLEX

THOSE WHO GO mad do so when the sun rises. Gill told me this on my first day, over forty years ago now. I've been awake through the night, sat by the window, listening to my lungs wheeze and thinking about tomorrow's hearing. Now I watch dawn seep through the darkened glass. I imagine, on the horizon, rows of tiny figures going mad. What do they do, the chosen ones? They hoot and hop, lift their hands to the sky and sing worship to the red dunes. Or they lie quiet, prone, as the whistling wind covers them with sand. First the feet and hands are buried, then the torso, then the neck. Those who go mad do so when the sun rises, because in the night it is possible to hide. But in the day, this planet is a vast, barren rock.

Nine o'clock. Hum of the air conditioner pumping air through the complex, but it's hot, always hot. My t-shirt sticks to my back. The three of them face me. On the left, the Warden, grey haired and austere. The woman, Karrow, is younger than me. She's a native. The third man I do not recognize. He must be from the Cities. They like to have an outsider at these meetings, for validation.

I sit in my chair with my hands resting on my lap, palms upward, to show that I pose no threat. The faint glow from behind is my file on the wall, backlighting me. Age: fifty-five. Height: one hundred and sixty centimetres. Lung capacity: I do not need a figure. The tightness in my chest tells me everything.

Karrow's eyes flick up and around me, scanning the information I cannot see.

'How do you feel, Yun? Physically?'

'I feel well,' I say.

Karrow and the Warden exchange barely perceptible glances.

'The next ship is due this month,' says the City dweller. 'We expect its arrival within two weeks.'

'Two weeks?' I have to suppress my dismay. 'That's sooner than I expected.'

'You will be allocated a bay for the return passage to Earth.'

'I would like to stay here.'

'Yes, we have noted your request.' He frowns at me. There is a tickle in my throat and I bite down on it. I feel as though they can see the red dust lining my lungs, as though my contamination is fluorescent. I wait.

'There is no provision for ex-convicts on Botoni, Yun,' says Karrow. 'You are not permitted to join the New Cities.'

This I know already. Nothing can be allowed to pollute the New Cities, not dust, not bad blood. I choose my next words carefully.

'I'd be content to remain in the complex and work for my board. To me it seems false economy to be preserved in abeyance for the considerable journey, when you consider the state of my general. . . health.'

The City man frowns and it is the Warden who speaks. He is a man for whom I have a distant respect, a tolerance, I suppose. He was young when I arrived.

'You have always been an oddity here, Yun. I remember your

rages in the early days, but it was a surprise to find murder on
your file.'

I keep my hands soft, my eyes lowered.

'With respect, I hope you will consider my request.'

After my hearing, even though the sun is lethal at this time of
day and my head feels light and giddy, I go and stand outside.
The white light strips the moisture from my lips and back. It
sears through the soles of my shoes. I squint at the naked sky.
I stand there until spots begin to appear in my vision. Then,
I retreat inside and rest my forehead against the dark glass.

The ship is due in a fortnight. I imagine its descent, the blip
in the sky slowly materialising into a silver bird. I imagine the
hatch opening, the procession of silver oblongs elevated onto
gravity carriers for delivery to the complex. They bring them
in at night, so we cannot stare, although of course we watch
from our rooms. Thus we arrived, thus we depart. We call them
coffins, though they tell us we are – we were – not dead inside.

Over the months of faster-than-light travel in my silver
coffin, my skin didn't sag, my muscles didn't atrophy, my
heart was still. I had no brain waves. Nothing in my chemical
makeup altered. But since they revived me I've wondered if,
in that act of carbon freezing, the flicker of consciousness that
makes me *me* underwent any change. The neuros say as your
cells die and replace themselves, you're a different person
from one day to the next. There's no such thing as personality,
they say. But if that's true then why are we given labels? Why
am I a criminal for forty years, and not merely for the day the
crime was committed?

It is dangerous to be fluid. To let yourself flow. I have
learned to hold myself in check.

Al finds me staring at the dunes. He's a kid, only six months into his sentence, ten years to donate. He was indicted for taking part in a protest.

'How'd the hearing go?' he asks.

'They've booked my flight.' Saying it aloud makes it real. My heart beats faster.

'Shit, man. That's come round fast.'

I nod. I haven't told anyone about my request. If it is not granted, I do not want them to feel sorry for me. And I am not sure they would understand why I have asked, that I had no choice but to ask.

'I'd kill to see proper water again,' says Al. 'Grass. Forests. Anything but this fucking red dust.'

'I don't taste it anymore,' I tell him. He looks at me dubiously, as if I'm old and potentially senile, but it's true. Even the little flecks you see in your food, or as sediment at the bottom of a glass of water, I don't notice them.

'D'you think they'll make rivers out here?' Al asks.

'Not in our lifetime.'

'The seas are so weird and lifeless, it freaks me out. Do they even know what's in there?'

'Only bacteria. It's too acidic for shellfish.'

'You are the Oracle, aren't you. Everyone says you are.'

I gesture vaguely. Up there on the horizon, is that movement? In the shimmering air, it is possible to witness false images, and speak to them too.

'I've been here a long time,' I say.

'And that you don't talk much. Everyone says that too.'

'I'm talking to you, aren't I?' He's right though. I don't talk much.

'And that you killed someone.'

'I've been here a long time,' I repeat.

'You don't look like a murderer.'

I see the shadow of my face reflected in the glass and I remember Gill's terror when she was due to go back. She was right to be afraid: once our sentence is up we have no purpose, and those back on what we should call *home* no use for us. To them we're no better than robots. In fact, our stock is worth less than a robot, because we're damaged. Gill was convinced that the silver coffins or perhaps merely their contents would be ejected into space mid-flight, and she would be left to float for all eternity, not alive, not dead. If that's true, I told her, you'll never know the difference. But now I feel the same fear creeping over me. I don't want to go back in a box. Alive is alive and dead is dead. Frozen is something else.

In the evening I take a booth in the Pod and listen again to the last letter Shu spoke me. While I listen I imagine Shu's clear eyes and tiny, intricate braids. I remember the fingers, rough skinned but dexterous, that shaped those braids. Despite the photos she has sent I still think of her this way, this young.

Shu's voice is calm and fluid.

You know of course that the family will take care of you, but I've heard disturbing reports. The people who come back are not welcome here, even on Moon. There have been attacks. It is a peculiar thing when you consider that you were sent there to be punished, but it seems to me that this behaviour stems from a kind of jealousy. Everyone wants a pass to the New World. I don't know what they imagine your life is like. I have seen videos of the complexes and even now I struggle to picture you there, where they say it is so hot that the air seems to be alive and makes you see visions, or ghosts.

We will have to keep you a secret, Yun.

By the time I get back to Earth, Shu will be over twice my age, or dead. Time dilation makes it impossible to know until I get there. And now my time is up I do not want to know. I do not want to go home and find a sister riddled with age or worse, a stone in the ground.

That, or else this planet has bewitched me. But is it not better to go mad than to go home, to lead at worst a reviled, at best a dwindling life, creeping about like a shadow?

In the week following my hearing I work in the kitchen, although my sentence expired six months ago, and I am not required to. I do not know what I would do if I did not labour. I don't think my fellow convicts would resent my freedom, although since Gill went I have cultivated no new friends, and perhaps I am mistaken and they would look at me jealously, even hatingly, if I spent all my hours in the Pod, lulled by Shu's voice.

My mind is skittish and I am glad of mundane tasks. Today I prepare greenhouse potatoes for the cook. They go into a stew with protein supplement. There is a rumour that in the Cities they have managed to breed livestock successfully, and that there is meat. It pleases me to believe this; that Botoni is making progress.

The cook bangs dishes around me. He is fond of banging things; it is his way of exerting authority, of making himself more than a chef for Earth's scum. As I scrape dirt from the potato skins I remember what Al said about the seas here and I think about the few occasions I ate fish, about the silvery scales crisping on a hot grill, the white flakes falling out hot and delicious and their salty tang on my tongue. I would say I miss fish, but I suppose I do not really miss it because none of these sensations can actually be recalled, except as concepts.

I wonder, if I go back, if there will still be fish.

'Chef?' I say, meek and respectful. Shu would not recognize this timid woman.

'What?'

'You could do with an extra pair of hands, couldn't you? On a more regular basis, I mean.'

He snorts.

'Got someone in mind to replace you? Want a soft job, do they? It's a fucking joke.'

I freeze.

'What do you mean?'

'Ship's due isn't it? You'll be off in a silver box.'

For a moment my old anger bubbles up and I imagine what it would feel like to stab the chef, to feel his blood in my palm. I take a knife and slice through the potatoes, making clean, exact quarters.

In the evening I serve the food I have helped to prepare in the canteen. I like doing this. It allows me to study the other inmates with the most cursory engagement, and then I can go and eat without being disturbed. But towards the end of the queue, I notice a pair of severely shaking hands. I look at the man's face and see the hallmarks of a shock-gun episode. I take his bowl myself, fill it, and hand it back to prevent the stew sloshing as best I can.

When the line has ended I go to sit next to the victim with my own dinner. His fingers are struggling to hold the spoon steady.

'Are you okay?' I ask.

His lips can barely form the words.

'It's barbaric.'

'I know.'

'They did it to you?'

'More than once.'

I remember the first time. I had dared to complain about something, the quality of the tools I was using perhaps. The foreman in my work party was on me in seconds.

'Repeat that?'

I repeated it. I was so full of rage in those days I could

barely keep my mouth shut. The foreman jabbed my stomach with the shock gun and my body convulsed. When my vision cleared I felt as though a hand had reached into my belly and scrambled everything inside me. I couldn't tell which way was up. My hands had switched places with my feet. I retched over and over, utterly disorientated.

'Get up!'

I couldn't move. I saw the gun approaching and tried to cringe away. He zapped me a second time, for longer. I was aware of all my limbs jerking frenziedly. I heard laughter and jeers. Then I lost control of my bladder and urine seeped down my trousers.

'Get up!'

Someone pulled me to my feet, pulled me along with her. A rough hand gripped my hair.

'Walk,' she said. 'Don't let them see you weak. Left foot. Right foot. Walk.'

Gill.

She rescued me that day, and many days after. I cannot rescue this man. I am leaving in a fortnight, unless they offer me respite. The man's story shakes me. Towards the end of my sentence, with my deteriorating health, they have given me less physical labour. I have forgotten the brutality of our treatment. I have forgotten that my body is still muscular, because gravity here is greater and the effort to do any small thing correspondingly so. I feel no ownership of this body. It's as if the planet has moulded me without consultation.

Why would they let me stay? And why would I wish to?

I became conscious on Botoni in a transparent box, with something beeping over my head, regular and insistent. Two white-clad figures on the other side moved slowly. I took a breath, my first. My lungs were desperate for air, I couldn't inhale quickly enough. I gulped and flailed until my breathing began to settle. When they took me out of the box the doctors had to help me with my first steps, one holding each arm, unused as I was to the stronger gravity.

Before I came here I had seen images of the complex, as everyone does. They are supposed to act as a deterrent. I had seen the glinting, silver domes; I had seen the endless red dunes. I could never have imagined the heat. Or the thick, stifling air.

The impossible silence.

In general they treat us well enough, in the sense that livestock are treated well. We serve a purpose: we need to be strong and healthy, get the right vitamins and stay clean. Each day, the bell pulled me out of bed at six. A wash at the sink with cold water. Six-fifteen: dressed and tidied. Inspection at six forty-five, breakfast at seven. Desert caterpillars took us out to the worksites; we could travel between ninety to a hundred and twenty minutes each day. Under colossal, wire rigged sunshades, we took raw materials and turned them into buildings.

We went in teams, rotating projects every six months. I dug canals, riveted pipes, mixed cement, placed bricks, pumped and sprinkled water, ploughed dust, planted seedlings, hoed soil, laid rails. I did these things until my hands were blistered, my body aching as if beaten, and then they ferried us back for the evening meal, and what remained of the evening, if we could stay awake for it.

As years passed, I began to see how Botoni might, one day, be beautiful. As the old world gassed itself to death, this place might become what Earth had been. It would take thousands of years. I was a part of it, willing or not. In the earth surrounding the complex we cultivated spindly plants from Earth seedlings. I planted a sapling. Every evening I went to water it. Year by year I watched it grow, and each day of its survival was a tiny miracle. I collected the leaves it dropped and hoarded them like jewels.

There were moments I stood on the edge of the complex and gazed deep into the desert, aware of a curious feeling in my chest: something like guardianship.

The nights here are quiet. I leave the window open. Sometimes I sit on the windowsill and look at the foreign constellations. My roommate sleeps like the dead. In the early days, the sheer weight of the things I missed would make me want to fall. I knew it wouldn't inconvenience anyone if I did. The paperwork is easy enough – failure to acclimatize, they would say. Other times I wondered what it was I did miss, and occasionally, the pan emptiness of the sky convinced me that none of it existed at all. On those nights I whispered to myself: *I must be going mad, I must have* gone *mad. I am not here. I am not anywhere.*

Sometimes the colonists pass by. Their vehicles glide on silver tracks that coil away into the dunes, towards other New Cities. They cannot be so far away, the Cities. When they pass we pause whatever we are doing and watch them silently. With their free, roving eyes, they are aliens.

Convicts do not run away, unless madness takes them. We are tagged of course, but that is not why. There is nowhere to run to and nowhere to hide. Violence when it comes is sudden; vicious and specific. I saw a woman twist a screwdriver in the eye socket of an eighteen year-old boy. She got up and there was blood all over her face, on her lips, her nose. She had been a lawyer in her old life. After that they put her in a white cell. White walls, white floor and ceiling and door. Soon enough, her mind was whitewashed too.

I am not the only one going back to Earth. We are twenty or so. A week before the ship is due, the Warden briefs us. I look around the room. The other faces reveal a spectrum of emotion from suppressed hope to genuine excitement. I have been here the longest.

The Warden clears his throat, and I wonder idly how far the dust has advanced with him. Some lucky people are immune – I say lucky, but those are the ones they take away to experiment on.

'As on the way out, you will be placed in abeyance for the duration of the journey. When you reach Earth, an officer will meet you. They will help you join your family.'

Amidst the ripple of anticipation, a lone voice calls out.

'What if we got no family? What if they're all dead?'

'Earth has a tried and tested system for briefing convict families. In the instance of the line expiring, a friend or acquaintance will have been named as your Rehabilitator. They will be alerted when the ship nears Earth.'

The man who spoke sneers but the Warden ignores him. The Warden will follow the line. He tells us that our families will help us re-enter Earth society. We will get jobs. We will pay rent. We will have free time. A couple of people nod: yes, yes! Some look dazed. Gradually they begin to talk amongst themselves, exchanging ideas. One woman is going to learn the guitar. Another wishes to study, physics she says. Even the sneerer admits he has a plan: he is going to build his own house in Greenland.

There is one man, older like me, who stares at the wall with eyes as vacant as the dunes. He knows, I think. He knows. After the briefing I notice him around the complex. In the dinner line. In the yard. Always the same, vacant stare.

I go back to the Pod and call up an old letter – I know them all by heart. I play Shu's voice.

Today I told my daughter about you. She had a lot of questions about Aunty Yun. What does she look like? Where does she live?

I said you lived in the sky. Can I go there? No, I explained. Aunty Yun will come back to us, but it might not be for a very long time.

One day I will have to tell her the truth, register her as your Rehabilitator after me, tell her to pass these instructions to her daughter and perhaps her daughter's daughter, for who knows which of us will be living when you return? It struck me, after talking to her, that it is most likely I will never see you again. Of course I have considered this before, but never with such certainty. With each year and each failed application for your early release, the odds are stacked against our reunion. Perhaps I should be glad that my children's children will have a chance to know you, Yun? It is difficult to be glad.

In this last week I am not sleeping and my breath is more constricted than ever. One night I see a sand cloud. It rolls along the horizon, changing its shape, stretching and retracting, breath like a dragon's. It is a sign, it must be a sign. I tap my tongue to the back of my front teeth, three times. Ward it off, whatever it is. Keep it from me, keep me safe. Keep me here. There is nothing good on Earth except for Shu, and Shu will be gone. At least if I stay here, her letters will keep coming.

She was always too good for me. I was a troubled child anyway, angry at the world I had inherited, angry at the restraints and the quarantines, the adults who had created such a scale of catastrophe that they chose to pretend it was not there. Instead they peered around the mess, around Earth and up and out into the stratosphere. The planet was a toy they had broken; now they wanted a better one.

We didn't have a bad start, my mother and my sister and I, until the Depression reached Antarctica. Shu was the conscientious one. Shu took jobs outside school when our mother started imbibing and her eyes turned dull. Shu dealt with the bailiffs. She found us a one-bed flat when we lost the house.

While my sister tried to save us, I went pick-pocketing with my co-conspirator T, a childhood friend who had grown up into a reckless and beautiful young man, and the only one who had stayed loyal through the bad times. I adored him. With T, I could make squalor a game. A dangerous game, because the law was harsh and prison penalties high, but a game nonetheless. I was fifteen, and as far as I could see I had nothing to live for but the excitement of breaking the law.

I still dream about him. T and I, running down the long white Antarctic beaches. T and I, paddling in the coral reef graveyards, collecting fish scales, shells, plastic bottles and Cocarola cans. T finding a sea horse skeleton held together by fragments of skin. When he scooped it up in his net, the bones crumbled to dust.

T and I, out on the city streets. T and I, watching for ripe targets to exit the sex clubs and the holomas. We worked as a team. Old perverts were the best. I'd distract them, rub onion in my eyes to make me cry, hike my skirt. *I'm lost*, I'd say. *I've got no money to get home.* When they put their hands between my legs, T would push the barrel of his gun into the back of their necks and they'd freeze and I'd knee their erection and take everything they had and then we ran. T kept the gun unloaded but they never knew that. T and I, criminal masterminds. T and I, doomed from day one.

The night it happened – it could have been any night, but it was a Tuesday, a dark February night. Our victim fought back, feistier than usual. T was on the floor and somehow the gun ended up in my hand. The guy was hitting T. I pointed the gun as T had shown me and pulled back the safety catch. I warned the man: *I'll shoot!* T was making awful grunting noises. I said it again. The man swivelled and kicked my legs from under me. I couldn't fire so I went for the next best thing, hitting out with the heavy barrel. When the shot exploded in my ears and the man jerked and went still I lay in shock, his blood soaking into my clothes. And I realized I had known all along. Of course the gun was loaded. Of course T would not be so stupid as to carry an empty weapon, even if he had told me otherwise.

'We just have to lie low,' said T.

But I knew we would be caught. We had left too much evidence, our fear was all over the scene. That night, I went to the police station and confessed. I wrote a full statement. I felt triumphant as I signed my name: I had done something noble. Because of me, T would be safe. Even after, in the difficult bit where I was allowed visitors, Shu, and when T came, I felt the strangest calm. I knew that I was strong enough to maintain my story.

'You can do some good in the world,' I told T, savouring my martyrdom, as I suppose I thought of it. 'You could be something. A doctor. An astronaut.'

T said he wanted to punch me. He said we should have sat tight. He said they'd send me to the convict planet. I didn't believe him.

'There's a new law. They can get people from fourteen now. Twelve if you're a boy.'

I was fifteen. They gave me forty years.

T never wrote. Over the years it was Shu's letters that I came to wait for, Shu's news that I craved. I came to know the woman better than I ever knew the girl.

Back on Earth, Shu goes to university and studies law. She promises to fight for my release and I know, even then, she will never succeed but I love her for trying. I become an aunt. The baby's name is Shui, for water, but she is known as Shell. The child's father is absent; Shu lives with her boyfriend who teaches scuba diving in the summer months. Shell gets bigger. A batch of photographs: Shell's first birthday cake, Shell's first day at school, Shell touching a turtle, Shell's nose pressed behind a diving mask, Shell with eyeliner and dyed blue hair. I gobble each titbit of news. I hug Shu's words to myself in the night, repeating them to my friend Gill in the day, happy that Shu is happy.

She writes steadily, steadfastly. *I hope I'm not boring you*, she says once, and I speak my response immediately, even knowing my letters are unlikely to arrive until she is elderly or worse, *No, please, tell me everything*, terrified of losing even a word. Shu and Gill are all I have. Had.

Day turns into night turns into day. Now there is grey in my hair. Now my lungs are clogged and I watch sand clouds roll on the horizon and dream about those who go mad.

In the morning over breakfast Al tells me there has been a suicide. I do not need to look around to know who is missing. It is the man with the vacant stare from the briefing room.

'How did he do it?' I ask Al. I ask because Al wants to talk about it; he's distressed and curious at the same time, but I barely listen to the response. I think of how I found Gill crouched in the bathroom with a razor, days before her own ship came. I remember the scratch on her inner wrist, not deep enough to draw blood, but a precise line along the veins. I remember the horror and relief in her eyes when I snatched the razor away.

'They're going to send me into space, Yun. I'll never make it to Earth, none of us will. Not dead, not alive, not dead. I should end it now. You should let me!'

Her shoulders shook when I held her.

'You're going back to Earth,' I said firmly. 'And when my sentence is up, I'll find you.'

'Promise me?'

'Promise.'

'Because fuck knows there's nothing else for me there.'

They allowed me to be with Gill when they put her to sleep. She was shaking and sweating. I knew she was terrified. The doctors must have known too. I held her hand, feeling like a traitor. I watched the needle slip under her skin. Then they took her away to freeze.

In her last years Gill had talked a lot about Earth.

'They didn't always send us back, you know. We were never meant to. I mean, would you ask a spider back into your house, even if it was all used up and looked harmless?'

'Where did we go then?'

Gill shrugged. 'The New Cities. We must have worked for someone. Must have died here. But those smug cunts in their pavilions by the sea don't want us either. They were the ones chose to start shipping us back.'

'I remember,' I said.

'What do you remember? You're just a kid.' Gill spoke with rough affection; she liked to say I'd been snatched from the cradle. But it was true. I did remember. I remembered images on the news, aged figures with ochre tinged skin disembarking from a spaceship. Placards and slogans.

Send them back! Send them back!

No room, no convicts!

Earth sent them to the moon colony. Them. Us. This, too, I remember, and Shu's letters confirm it is the case, at least in her lifetime.

They send us back because we are a civilized race. But it is not civil, not civil at all, and Gill knew it, and this man who has ended his life today knew it. Eventually, there will be no sending back. They will work us until we die or lose our minds. And that seems, to me, not illogical. Not unkind.

The ship is late. I ask the Warden if there has been a decision about me. He says they will let me know when the ship arrives. At night I dream that they force me into the silver coffin, stuff a tube down my throat and turn on the gas. I start to freeze from the inside out. Everything freezes except my mind, and all I can feel is cold cold cold. Endless awareness, endless cold. I want to scream, I want to thrash but I cannot move. Then the lid comes down, and it is dark.

I wake drenched in sweat, and I bend over the edge of the bed, my chest so tight I can barely inhale, convinced I will suffocate here and now. Slowly I regain control of my lungs and the panic subsides. But I am too scared to sleep. What if they come for me in the night? What if they decide to freeze me when I am unconscious, when I cannot struggle?

A month passes and still there is no ship. Hope flutters. Respite. In the kitchen, I assist the chef. At night I water my tree. I listen to Shu's letters. But it cannot last and it does not last. The day arrives. I come downstairs to breakfast and Al rushes up to me, breathless.

'Yun, the ship's coming down.'

Despite the heat I feel cold. I accompany Al to the front of the complex, where a small crowd has gathered. We watch as the atmosphere shimmers, as a glint becomes a silver colossus descending from the sky.

Sweat leaks over my body like an oil slick.

Now I can see the shape of the ship, squat and round. It moves ponderously downwards, landing wings and undercarriage extending, the air turning blue as its thrusters power towards the ground. I can hear it roaring. The sound is colossal. A horrible pressure builds against my eardrums. I don't remember the landings being this loud. The air around me seems to hiss as the ship touches down. Small vehicles are driving towards it, bouncing over the uneven ground. I hear a guard shout: 'Alright, get back to work!' I sense the crowd dispersing around me but my legs have become liquid and I am melting into the red dust, a part of it, taken.

I come to in the canteen, coughing up red mucus. A guard

takes me back to my room. Lying on the narrow bed, I feel frail. I feel as though the planet has crept inside me, and is feasting.

Nine o'clock. Hum of the air conditioner pumping air through the complex, but it's still hot, always hot. The three of them face me.

'I'm afraid your request has been declined.' The Warden raises both hands. 'We put in a word for you. But protocol must be observed. We cannot make an exception.'

'I'm sorry, Yun,' says Karrow. She looks sorry. Maybe she even is. They know what they are sending me back to.

After my hearing I go and stand outside in the terrible heat. I peer at the scorched horizon, searching for movement there. In a few days they will put something in my veins to make me sleep. Then they will freeze me.

Back on Earth, Gill is waiting. But perhaps she has made her own life by now, and will want nothing to do with me. Perhaps she was right to be afraid, perhaps they don't take us back at all, but eject us somewhere into the deep emptiness of space. I imagine how this place might look from out there: a huge sphere marbled with pink and brown, the occasional gleam of a shallow sea. Then I imagine Earth. Small and grey, cloaked in pollution.

For the rest of the day I speak to no one.

When the lights flicker off at night and the complex falls dark and silent, I lie on my bed and close my eyes. The breathing of my roommate lengthens, regulates. Once or twice she coughs, but does not wake. I get up and slip into my outdoor clothes. In the bathroom I hack up a compound of mucus, saliva, and red dust. I fill a bottle with water.

The corridors of the complex are deserted and lit with pale blue light. I walk outside. Nobody stops me. Why would they? My actions are insanity. I don't know how far it is to the nearest New City and there will be nowhere to shelter in the blazing heat of day.

I start to walk. The air is pleasantly warm and I remove my cotton shirt to feel it brush against my arms. I walk through the cultivated earth that surrounds the complex. When the ground softens and ripples underfoot, I know I have crossed the boundary into the dunes. I keep walking. After an hour or so the ground begins to slope upward and my breath shortens. I have to stop every few minutes, bent double and panting.

At the crest of the hill I turn and look back and see the faint blue glow of the complex in the valley below. If I turned around now, I could be back in my bed before dawn and no one would know I had been gone.

There is no wind up here. There is no sound except for my own slender breathing. I sit for a minute, burying my hands in the sand, letting it trickle through and over my fingers, burying them again. One day this will be soil. It will be rich in nutrients and yield Earth-born crops and the people that eat them will never think about those who came before. I have an impulse to press myself into the ground, leave some mark or impression.

I turn away from the complex and start down the hill, slipping and sliding in the sand. The sky is enormous and full of piercingly bright stars. I am covered in stars, wreathed in them. They stay with me until the night begins to fade. The world lightens, the world is huge. Now I can see nothing but white sky and rust dunes.

I wait for the sun, anxious for a moment that it might not appear. But no – here it is, the edge of the giant star creeping over the horizon, flooding the world with crimson. A beautiful, shimmering dawn. I feel the planet's heat infuse me, its dust lining my lungs. I kick off my shoes. At the exact moment when the light touches me, I raise my hands to the dawn and I begin to dance.

CAROLE JOHNSTONE

GOD OF THE GAPS

I'M EXPECTING IT – well, I'm expecting *something* – so when it actually comes I should be more prepared than I am. Instead, I almost scream out a lung and fling myself forwards, nearly knocking myself out against the lift's closed doors. Brian is shrieking too, but this concern comes far down a lengthening list that ends with possible concussion and began with the back wall of the lift being blown apart. There is much confused jostling – there were five of us in here a few seconds ago – and copious amounts of green smoke. I can't see very much (which, I'm guessing, is probably the point), but what I can see looks very much like a giant *xenomorph*: all crude spines and hissing teeth, rattling briefly around our tiny space before yanking up a screaming body and disappearing backwards into nothing.

There's a clunk – a loud one – and then the lift resumes its descent. A new hissing begins; one that dissipates the green smoke in seconds. Someone is still coughing, and Brian is still shrieking. I'm unsurprised to see that the body who went screaming out of the lift was our guide; Suse is cowering, choking in a corner, Jeff behind her. I swallow hard. 'Christ, that one was a bit much.'

Brian bounces over to me, mouth wide, fingers plucking

at my clothes. He wasn't shrieking after all, though his high-pitched yips of excitement sound exactly the same.

'Get off! I bloody hurt myself, Brian.'

He lets go of me and shuts up, though it's probably not out of obedience. I think he realises that excitable shrieks of glee probably won't do much for his chances.

My head is killing me; if I press a tender point above my left eyebrow, I can see white sparks. I hope it looks as bad as it feels. I try to catch Suse's eye, but she's still flat out on the floor. Jeff's helping her up, and probably copping a feel while he does it.

Our guide was a spotty sniffer called Vlado, and I'm not particularly sorry he's gone. After the last incident: a frenzied sprint through smoking, bass-filled corridors, chased by masked, white-haired creatures who bore more than a passing resemblance to the Wraith warriors in Stargate, our first guide ('Stuart, call me Stuey') had died a grisly death in a stairwell. Vlado had appeared at just such an opportune moment, whisking us away down another corridor, and then into the lift. He was twitchy from the start, and like I said, I had an inkling something else was afoot.

I lean back against the lift's doors as we go down, down. It's getting hot. Now that most of the smoke has been sucked away, I can see the remnants of the fake wall. The lift has two doors. Ingenious. Certainly more ingenious than what has gone before. Endless screaming chases and funhouse-style BOO!!!s through hidden doorways and around corners.

Brian is doing a bad impression of someone who is not excited. His fingers move in and out of fists, his eyes are wide and shining. I'm feeling a bit bad about shouting at him. It's not his fault that this is my idea of hell; that ever since the bus dumped us off outside the Arches under Station Bridge and its great big silver sign, I'd resigned myself to having a terrible time. This trip has by no means been the worst – there was the

Underage Festival in Kelvingrove, and a trip to Digger World that was pure, unadulterated torture – but I'm pre-menstrual, so it feels like it is. And that's not his fault either. The trip isn't for me anyway. It's for Brian and Jeff, and all the other twelve year-olds running and screaming somewhere else above us. We were first in the queue. Lucky us.

Suse finally manages to get back onto her feet. Jeff has definitely been trying to cop a feel, because her face is pucely furious, and Jeff's hands are hiding behind his back. Suse has even less interest in sci-fi than I do, so perhaps for her, this really is the worst trip yet. I'm about to say something to her, when the lift shudders to a halt. Brian lets escape a yip of glee.

I watch the lift door rattle and then slide open onto (quelle surprise) yet another dark and smoky corridor. Cue appropriately booming drumbeats that sound a bit like the Blue Man Group with their batteries running down (yet another trip).

'C'mon, c'mon!'

I let Brian grab my hand and haul me out. I'm trying to fake enthusiasm that was pretty lame in the first place, but the bass is hurting my sore head. The corridor stretches left and right into gloom. Without a guide, I'm not sure which way we're supposed to go, but I'm guessing that it doesn't really matter, otherwise there would be signs.

Jeff saunters out. He's a weird one. Suse told me the only productive thing that he ever does in their weekly sessions is stare at her chest. I suppose I should be grateful that Brian does actually try to read, even if it's only ever Motorcycle Monthly or SuperBIKES! Boring beyond belief, but at least he's getting the hang of words like chassis, titanium, traction-control and gyroscope. And expectation – every second word is expectation. Brian is very *big* on expectation.

'Which way, which way?'

I still have no idea, but he's pulling on me like he's a child. He is one, I suppose – a child I mean – but only just. Our

English teacher, Mr Payne, couldn't dish any real dirt on any of the kids we were mentoring, but I know enough to realise that Brian's got it pretty rough at home. He's from the East-hill Estate, which was probably all I really needed to know at all, but Mr Payne let it slip that Brian's dad isn't on the scene and his mum might as well not be. He's on a bursary and free school dinners, wears NHS specs, looks like he and his clothes last had a clean around the turn of the century, and I'm guessing that he's chronically bullied.

He's twelve years old, and has a reading age of about eight if he's lucky – maybe nine/ten if literacy was measured in ability to read aloud about superbikes. That's why I keep on letting him read those old magazines. I feel sorry for him. I feel sorry for him because no one else does.

'Which way, Miss Daisy?'

Mr Payne makes them call us that. Suse says that the way Jeff says *Miss Susie* makes her want to take a couple of hot showers. She doesn't have it that bad though. The Miss Daisy jokes got very old very fast.

We pick a direction – left – and start walking. It's like plunging into psychedelic fog. I haven't seen daylight in over an hour, and am regretting the half joint Suse and I smoked in the coach toilet on the way here. There's a sudden shrill scream, and half a dozen Greys slam up at us from behind a hidden Perspex window. Or they might be those things from that other Stargate – is it the Asgard? Something Lord of the Ringsey at any rate. One of them had a name that sounded like Haemorrhoids, I think. I only know this stuff because last year I went out with Gareth in the year above, and he's a nerd with a capital L. Cute bum though. And he's nearly eighteen.

Brian laughs like he's going to collapse, while Suse screams and Holy Christs like she's just been mugged. Even I'm beginning to get annoyed by her, although I should've expected it: she found Scary Movie 3 scary. We stopped having Saturday

DVD nights, because her dad thought it would be healthier for her to stand on a street corner drinking BO and smoking whatever.

Behind us, the lift dings closed, presumably to go back up and have its fake wall fixed before picking up the next suspecting customers. We keep going, and the smoke gets thicker, though that doesn't seem possible. I'm getting that inkling again, and so is Brian – he's holding onto my arm like it's Christmas.

Something bursts growling out of a fake wall dead ahead of us, sending us back the way we came. I can't see anything, just a lumbering shadow in swirling smoke – presumably because this *alien* is as cheap and ripped off as all the rest we've been running away from.

Suse screams, shoves me from behind. Something skids out of a hidden corridor, collides with the wall (accidently, I think, because over the stoned Blue Man Group, I'm sure I hear it say fuck), and then starts barrelling towards us, while we're still running towards it. Suse screams again, so does Brian, Jeff stays as creepily quiet as ever. This alien looks like a bigger version of the one in the lift. A Queen maybe, circa Aliens. It's pretty massive actually.

I'm beginning to feel a bit unnerved – it's dark, it's loud, I can hardly breathe for green smoke, I've already whacked my head, so health and safety clearly isn't big here, and there are two giant fake aliens charging towards us front and rear – when (quelle surprise again) a wide corridor opens up on our left.

Suse takes it first, dragging me behind her. I'm dragging Brian, but only because he hasn't let me go. The aliens cross over at the corridor's mouth, and then keep on charging in opposite directions. The music stops.

'God, I hate this!' Suse is crying, and Jeff is taking full advantage: he has one arm around her shoulder and the other around her neck in what is trying to be a headlock. He has to stand on his tiptoes to do it – and worse still, she's letting him.

'Suse, come on. The music's stopped, we're alright.'

I turn back at a low growl – a low something at any rate – and Suse squeaks. There's a shadow standing at the smoky mouth of the corridor. Just standing there, looking at us. It's not moving, and I can't work out what it's supposed to be (a big person is what it looks like – a big person with very long arms). Brian finally lets go of my arm.

'Suse,' I say. 'They just have to get us to move before the next lot come down in the lift. Come on.'

We shuffle down the corridor, where the air gets easier again. I only realise that my heart has been beating very hard when it starts going back to normal. I wasn't sure how much a tenner a head would buy us, but I've a feeling – a very glad one – that we've almost used it up. I finger the silver name badge at my breast. Its ALIEN ATTACK!!! hologram has been blinding me ever since I was made to put it on, and it's probably left a bloody big hole in my shirt. Maybe I can take it off now.

At the end of the corridor, the lack of smoke reveals black-painted breezeblock walls. A giant green arrow has been felt-tipped onto lined A4, pointing left. There are bright overhead spotlights and what look like glass cases beyond it, and further than that I can make out another even bigger sign. SHOP.

'Not another exhibition,' Brian says. His hands are little fists. There have been a *lot* of exhibitions.

'Thank fucking God,' Suse mutters, and she's halfway along this new corridor before anyone can say anything else, Jeff sliding on behind.

Brian gives me his best pained expression. 'Daisy – *Miss* Daisy – please.' He's looking right instead of left, off into pretty much nothing as far as I can tell, but his eyes are shining.

'Pleeaase?'

Suse and Jeff are long gone, and I think that I can hear new screams as the lift starts rolling and clunking far behind us.

'Alright.' Partly because I hate being told what to do and where to go. Mainly because I feel sorry enough for Brian to want to spare him a shop chock full of over-priced crap that he can't buy, and a quicker return to a world that he probably hates. Or that hates him.

I still suspect that there's nothing up here though. The walls are bare and strip-lighted; there are no hidden Perspex windows or doorways; no smoke; no growling shadows. We walk and walk. Turn once into another corridor just the same, and then walk some more. Just as I'm about to suggest turning back, we come to a room. I'm hoping it's not a security guard's hangout – or worse, a changing room full of spotty Australians surrounded by plastic alien suits. It's neither. Instead, it's a bright, white-painted room full of display cases and stands. On the door, someone's written UFO MUSEUM in black marker pen.

'Cool!'

I don't see how a museum is any improvement on an exhibition, but Brian seems to think it is. He's through the door and pressed up against the first display case before I've had a chance to check if the coast is clear. It isn't.

'Hello.'

'Hi, sorry, I'm not sure we're supposed to be here.'

The guy grins at me, and then cocks it towards Brian, who's paying no attention whatsoever. The guy is tall, youngish, dressed in horrible brown trousers and a too-small white lab coat. A badge on his lapel says John. He has absolutely terrible teeth – grey, crooked tombstones.

'It's alright. Most folk don't find us down here. Feel free to have a look around; there's plenty stuff to see.' He sees me checking out his horrible clothes, and shrugs with an embarrassed smile. 'Just trying to look the part.'

I join Brian where he's still pressed up against the first case. He's looking down at what looks like a coil of black hose. I remember the sign on the door. 'Please tell me that's not what I think it is.'

John grins his tombstone grin again. He points to a small card at the front of the case. *Rectal Probe: Peter Wilson; Jan 2009; Lanarkshire.*

'Cool!' Brian's fingers have left overawed little prints all over the glass.

'Oh fuck off.'

'What?' John asks.

'Well, it's a bit big, don't you think? I mean I've seen the ones they use in the hospital – endo-whatsits – and they're about a quarter the size of that thing.'

John shrugs. 'It's a replica built to the specifications of Peter Wilson. He was abducted from Wishaw High Street one Christmas Eve, and didn't return until after New Year.'

I scoff again, wondering if Peter Wilson's wife bought that too. 'So, he described to you some rectal probe he had shoved up his arse by aliens in a UFO above Wishaw High Street, and you made it?'

John nods. 'To his exact specifications.' He moves us along to the next case. It's filled with all manner of what look like dildos: metal, matte and shiny; cylindrical, cone-shaped, pointed, bulb-ended. Every single one has a name, date and place carefully documented on little table cards like you get at a wedding.

'Anal probes.'

I make a noise in the back of my throat that is as disgusted as it is incredulous. 'As if they just stick it up there.'

John shrugs, unconcerned. 'They might be conductors of

some kind. Some of the abductees reported experiencing various types of stimuli.'

'What the hell for? What does electrocuting someone's arse prove? And why does everything have to be so bloody big all the time?'

John shrugs again. 'Are chickens stuck with anaesthetic before their throats are slit?'

I'd certainly always hoped so, though I don't see what that's got to do with anything. I remember Brian only when his nose squeaks against the glass of this new case. 'Right well, I don't think any of this is entirely appropriate.' I pluck Brian free, ignoring his protests. I'm aware that I've begun sounding a bit like my mum.

'Okay,' John says. He peers at Brian's name badge. 'Maybe Brian would like to see some real UFOs instead.'

'Yeah!'

Seeing real UFOs involves moving on to some glass-topped tables filled with fuzzy photos of what might be sky and what might be spaceships – or grey shadowy blobs – interspersed with artist impressions of flying saucers sporting more under-lighting than the average sixth-former's Ford Fiesta. Brian oohs and ahhs a little less at these, and I can hardly blame him. Once again, each photo or drawing has a name, date and place attached.

'Right, shall I tell you what I don't get – *one* of the things I don't get?' I stab at the glass. 'Why do they always have to be so obvious? Why does every alien buy their ride at the same showroom, and why do they always arrive lit up like a Christmas tree, only to abduct the local drunk or hillbilly, instead of, oh I dunno, the local chess champion or whatever? 'Cause it's crap, that's why. Any alien worth their salt would at least try to disguise their arrival, and I dunno, come as a hot air balloon or something – you know, hide in plain bloody sight. Don't they do recon? Don't they ever debrief?' I'm now aware that I've begun enjoying myself.

'Look, I'm just the hired help, okay?' John hides his horrible teeth long enough to point out a dejected looking Brian. 'Maybe you want to tone down the scepticism a bit.'

I suddenly feel a bit guilty, and it makes me mad. 'So is there anything here that isn't replica?'

'You mean besides the photos?'

'Right, yeah, apart from them.' I roll my eyes – but only so John can see.

'Well, obviously there's not much. I mean, it's not as if you're going to be allowed to beam back down while you have a rectal probe hidden up your jumper.'

I resist rolling my eyes again – but only just.

'I've got a question!' Brian shouts. It sounds very loud in the quiet. 'Why do the aliens let them go at all?'

'What are you on about, Brian?' I think we should go now. I'm probably already in the shit.

'Well, at school right, we chop up frogs to see what's inside them, to see what's going on, like in those animal experiment labs.' There are bright red circles of excitement or embarrassment (I can guess at which) high on Brian's cheeks. 'And in Roswell, they cut the alien up, didn't they? To find out what was what.' Brian is sneaking past the table cabinets and further into the room as if he thinks I can't see him do it. 'So, my question is why? Why don't the aliens just cut people up? Why do they let them go?'

'That's a good question, Brian. In fact, it's a brilliant one.' John beams. 'You're right. It stands to perfect reason that any race would seek to further their knowledge of another through a combination of dissection and controlled observation. And it leads me to what I was about to show you both. The only other non-replica display in the museum.'

I reluctantly follow an animated John and almost apoplectic with excitement Brian to the other side of the room. There is a vast glass cabinet, and behind it a tall gunmetal case, its doors shut. Next to this is a small coded lock. John produces a key from inside his shirt with much dramatic flourish. It's very small, and attached to a piece of string around his neck.

'There are two possible answers to your question, Brian. The first is that those abductees who get sent back are the lucky few. In other words, they, for whatever reason, are let go, while the rest are dissected or stuck inside the equivalent of rat cages. And the second, which could be just as true if not simultaneously true, is that those who are sent back *have* been dissected. Just in a way that they could never guess.'

He turns back and winks at me. 'Too distracted by the memory of anal probes.'

John pushes the key into a tiny lock at the side of the cabinet. The glass door makes a nasty grinding sound as it's slid back on runners. As he keys the code into the lock fixed to the gunmetal case he winks at Brian, who is now hopping from foot to foot as if he needs to pee. John pulls open the doors to reveal a dark interior lined with shelves. We peer in. Brian immediately stops hopping, and I can see why. There's not much in there. Despite myself, even I'm a bit disappointed.

'What's that?'

'It's a specimen pot.'

'What's in it?'

John brings it very carefully out of the massive case. It looks like a tall jam jar with a plastic screw-top lid. There's a small label running around its base. I imagine something like *Strawberries; Back Garden; Jan '10*.

'Nothing,' Brian says, sounding dejected rather than cheated. 'It's empty.'

John shakes his head, grins his tombstone teeth. 'Not empty. Come closer, Brian. Look properly.'

Brian does as he's told, eager to be proved wrong. He peers

in at the empty jar, eyes screwed. They blink, big and distorted through the glass, finding me on the other side of it.

'Right well, so the only non-replica thing you have in this entire museum – apart from the bloody photos – is a jam jar filled with what?' I pretend to think, and then click my fingers. 'Alien air from inside an alien spaceship? No, I know: an alien's breath. Alien words!'

I've never seen such crap in my life. I'm aware that I'm spoiling things for Brian. I'm also aware that we've stumbled into a place that isn't for kids, hence the green felt-tipped arrow. Maybe this is for the evening sessions, just like the bar upstairs. Or for keeping the madman in the basement. I really don't want to get into shit (even though I think I definitely am now), because I really need the extra-curricular points that mentored reading gets me. John is beginning to look pissed off with me. But, I'm sorry, this is just ridiculous. Even Brian isn't buying it, and he *wants* to.

'Can you see anything, Brian?' John asks. 'Anything at all?'

'No.' Brian sounds morose. He starts fiddling with the jar's lid.

'Don't open it!' John bellows, practically snatching the jar out of Brian's hands before recovering himself. He takes a deep breath; slides his palms down those horrible brown trousers.

'Good grief,' I mutter.

'Look properly, Brian. Look closer, deeper. What can you see?'

'I can see something! I can see something!'

'No, you can't, Bri.' I'm no psychologist, but it doesn't take a genius to work out what's going on here.

'I can see colours – it's like a rainbow, a smoky rainbow!'

Despite myself, I look back at the jar. Nada.

'Deeper, Brian, what's behind the colours?'

Brian's breath hitches, recovers, hitches again, longer this time – long enough for me to worry whether he's suddenly forgotten how to breathe. He pushes the jam jar back towards John. His breath comes back in a fast rush. 'It's dark, I don't like it.' He shudders from head to toe, like a big spider's just run across his face. 'I don't like it.'

John carefully places the jam jar back inside the gunmetal case. He looks pleased and concerned all at the same time – though significantly more pleased than concerned. 'Yes, that's not one of the better ones, sorry, Brian. We routinely alternate which one we have on display, and you got unlucky.'

'How many empty jam jars do you have in your collection then?'

John cocks a mild eyebrow in my direction. 'None. But we have one hundred and fifty two *specimens*.'

'What *are* they?' Most of Brian's enthusiasm is back, but his face is still grey and I can see a few beads of clammy sweat on his forehead.

John beams. He takes his time closing the case and then the glass cabinet, dropping the key back inside his shirt before fixing us both with an earnestly sincere gaze. 'Souls.'

'Cooool.'

'Oh please.'

'Souls of people who have been sent back. Not their own souls obviously.'

'Obviously.'

He's ignoring me completely now, and addressing only Brian. 'Other people's.'

'Aliens give the people who go back other people's souls?' Brian frowns, confused. 'What, as presents?'

John shrugs. 'Maybe, who knows? But I doubt it. More likely as an experiment.' He sighs, purses his lips. 'I've been studying the idea of the *soul* ever since we were given our first specimen – this was a few years back. A young Italian guy called Alfredo

84

was abducted from his bedroom and gone for two months. When he came back, he had someone else's soul.'

'In a jam jar?' I scowl.

'In his hands,' John scowls back. 'And when he brought it to us, it was in a Tupperware.'

I try not to laugh, but I don't try very hard.

'He believed that the aliens had taken his soul and given him someone else's to hold.'

'How did he know?'

John smiles at Brian. 'He saw it happen. Most people who come back remember little if anything of their experiences – and what they don't remember their mind invents. I doubt any abductor needs to memory wipe or implant false ones, because the subconscious will wipe itself clean of any and all horrors, and then make up its own shortfall with little grey men, flashing lights, tractor beams and rectal probes.' He winks at me. 'And who believes that old crap? If you're interested, Brian, there are some fantastic books of personal accounts in the shop.'

Brian dismisses this last suggestion out of habit. 'Why did he give it to you?'

John shrugs. 'He didn't want it.'

'Why not?'

'It wasn't his.'

Brian starts gingerly poking at his own chest. He leans conspiratorially towards John. 'Where does *it* live?'

'The *soul* is located behind the nose just beneath the eyes.'

'God!' I'm bored rigid now. 'There is no such thing as a soul – same way there's no such thing as a bloody alien! This is stupid.'

John turns to look at me, and there's something in his eyes that suddenly makes me acutely aware of just how isolated we are here. No one knows where we've gone.

'What is the soul? Esoterically, it's always associated with life, and life with breath. The Latin *spiritus*, to mean breath; Greek *psyche*, to breathe or blow; the Sanskrit word *prana*, which is taken to mean the universal life force, literally means breath. If you're dead, you don't breathe. Spirit – respiratory, get it? It's got bugger all to do with that at all.'

John is staring off into space now. Glancing at a still engrossed Brian, I decide it's easier just to wait this freak ride out.

'The Chinese *qi* has it, I think. Energy flow. In Islamic Sufism, there is a low, base soul and a higher soul, and humans spend their lives tempering that primitive soul, trying to achieve higher knowledge through the teachings of the Qur'an. But they too, buy into the energy idea. What happens to the soul at death? What did Sir Isaac Newton say?'

He's looking at me. It's probably quicker just to answer. 'Energy doesn't disappear, it only changes form.'

He grins those tombstone teeth. Seems I'm forgiven. 'Exactly! Energy is transferred but never lost. Same theory applies to ghosts. Ghosts and souls. Like a magnet, right? A magnetic field can only be seen by its physical effects on other things. Otherwise it's invisible; is seen to be doing nothing at all, not even existing. Do you understand?'

I think about shaking my head, but I can't be bothered – it might invite an even longer-winded, more dizzying explanation of life, the universe and every bonkers theory in between. Brian, who I'd be willing to bet understood nothing after the behind the nose and beneath the eyes bit, is nodding furiously.

'Radiation and microwave field theory, EMF, all of that. Auras, rays, vibrations. Even dark energy: the negative energy of empty space. All of it! The soul! And when the human body dies, the base *Devil* soul is cast off to be recycled and reused, while the *Ruh* ascends.' He winks at me, very pleased with himself. '21 grams.'

I think about asking him if he's ever weighed his collection of jam jars, but again, I can't be arsed. What started out as a diversion and a good deed is now growing very old very fast.

'So, to answer your long ago question, Brian, I don't think that abductors need to dissect the physical much anymore. But the soul! That's much more of a challenge. And you know, a lot of my specimens are like the one you touched, Brian. Dark, bad, not very nice. I think the abductors are dissecting the human soul. Separating good bits from bad. Getting rid of the bad souls entirely. Seeing what happens when the soul is separated from the host. Seeing what happens when that soul is sent back with someone else – someone whose own soul is no longer in residence. See? It's fascinating.'

I think he's barking mad.

'God of the Gaps.'

My head is hurting again. 'What?'

'God is confined to the gaps in scientific knowledge and discovery. The abductors want to crush him completely. Want him gone.'

'Right well, this is fascinating stuff.' I grab hold of a reluctant Brian. 'But we have to get going now. The bus'll be waiting.'

John looks suddenly crestfallen. 'Okay, sorry, I've gone on a bit, haven't I? I tend to do that. Look, wait five minutes, I've got one last thing to show you – just one.' He grins at Brian. 'It's another replica, but it's a doozy. Wait 'till you see.'

I take one look at Brian and know I can't refuse. We start walking towards the back of the room, and when John turns back to me, he's got his earnest face back on.

'You know, the incidences of soul-stealing or *soulectomies*, as I like to call them, are very well documented. I know you think I'm barking mad, but they are.' He shrugs. I hate that shrug.

We come to a door. Hilariously, it is accompanied by a very Star Trek panel of buttons, and when John presses one, the door slides inside the wall with an even more hilarious whoosh.

'Cool!'

Inside is all white. After the dimmer fluorescents of the museum, it takes a while to adjust. The room's dimensions are relatively small, and the walls look soft, like in a padded cell. I momentarily wonder whether we've stumbled into the local loony bin, can't think why. There are no windows, and no other door that I can see, only low, white shelves and weird contraptions that look like familiar things and then don't. At the room's centre is a high, white bed. It looks like one of those toning tables you get in posh gyms.

John spreads his arms wide ahead of his masterpiece. 'It's a replica interior of an experimental lab on board a UFO. Obviously, it's not quite to spec. It's an approximation of dozens of accounts, though all remarkably similar.' He pats the bed's head end, where a pair of white, torsion-controlled manacles is dangling. 'Want a go, Brian?'

'Yeah!'

Up he scrambles, wriggling about, prodding this and that, eyes a-goggle before stretching out, slipping his hands inside the manacles, and mock-sobbing, *'Don't take my soul!'*, while John indulgently chuckles and winks at me like we're Brian's mum and dad.

'Right, come on now, you've had your fun.' I'm not sure which of them I'm talking to, but Brian's wrists are beginning to look pretty constricted the way he's bouncing around.

To his credit, John immediately unfastens Brian and helps him down. 'You want a go?'

'No, I bloody don't.'

'Aw c'mon, Daisy,' Brian wheedles.

'*Miss* Daisy,' I say. God, I can't believe he made me say it.

John even takes my refusal in good humour. That shrug comes again. 'Alright then, time to go.'

We start walking back to the door.

'Do you want to write in the guest book?'

'No!'

'But everyone writes in the guest book,' John frowns. 'Just your name. You don't need to write your full address if you don't want to.' He winks. "Case I'm a mad stalker.' He rolls his eyes at Brian in what I'm guessing is his impression of a mad stalker. 'And a few comments about what you liked and didn't like et cetera.'

'Who has a guest book for a bloody museum?' But it's already been thrust under my nose, and for the sake of peace, I do it. So does Brian, but his enthusiastic comments scribbling has me almost pulling my hair out in frustration. 'Come on, Brian!'

John gives me one last, long and hopeful look. 'Are you sure you don't want a go?'

'C'mon, Miss Daisy, do it! It's fun!'

I can't bear refusing any longer. Not because I care much anymore about making Brian happy, but because it seems like the path of least resistance, and I'm so worried about being in the shit now it's not funny. 'Fine, let's get this over with.'

I stomp back to the bed, realising that my stomps make no echo. Maybe that's to do with the loony bin walls.

'D'you need a hand?'

I shake John off. His hands are cold and a bit clammy. I quickly realise that I do probably need a hand though, as the bed is ridiculously high. Halfway through an undignified clamber, I feel hands pushing at my arse. The boost gets me onto the bed, and when I turn back to have a go at John, I realise that it was Brian instead. Maybe he's been taking tips from Jeff.

The bed feels weird – not in a bad way, in fact, in quite a good way. It's soft enough to make me feel like I'm sinking, but when I look down I've barely made a dent in its surface. It's incredibly comfy. Maybe John should get out of the basement museum game and design beds for a living instead. I also feel impossibly high, as if I'm twenty feet off the ground when I know that I'm only about three. I feel like the princess and the pea. Minus the pea, obviously.

'Try the manacles, Miss Daisy!'

God. I dutifully slip my wrists through the plastic loops. Immediately they pull tight, startling me into a yelp. It doesn't hurt though; doesn't even pinch. Much.

John and Brian are looking at me like gleeful children.

'D'you like it, d'you like it?' Brian yips. 'It's amazing, isn't it?'

'Yes, very cool. Can I get off now?'

John's still grinning, but it's a bit calculating now – a bit too over-excitedly expectant. My older brother used to look at me like that, right before something landed on my head, or the other one jumped out of a cupboard at me, wearing a sheet. Oh yes, I definitely have another one of those inklings, just like in the lift and in the corridor after it. Something is about to happen. Another ALIEN ATTACK!! special. And I've volunteered to manacle myself to a replica alien bed, instead of bloody leaving while I had the chance.

'Want to see something even cooler, Brian?'

'Let me off, John. Get me out of these things!' I hear another of those Star Trek whooshes, and then two white bands of what look like plastic poke up from the end of the bed and curl around my ankles. This time Brian doesn't laugh – I think even for him, this is a step too far. Which scares me even more than suddenly finding myself shackled and spread-eagled in a fake experimental UFO lab, in a hidden away basement museum, in a fake alien 'adventure experience', in an old warehouse under the Station Bridge. I suddenly feel very, very claustrophobic.

John comes up alongside me. He grins his tombstone teeth. I absurdly notice that his eyes are strange. One is bright blue, the other almost black, its pupil dilated. Like David Bowie. 'Not as bad as you expected, is it?'

'No, it's – it's alright. Can you let me up now though, John? Please.'

He slowly, regretfully, shakes his head side to side. 'Sorry, no, Miss Daisy. Soon, but not yet.'

He disappears from my side, and I crane my neck around to see where's he's gone. The manacles wind deeper into my wrists as I do it. Brian is looking at me: wide, white eyes in a whiter face. John is humming to himself, moving up and down the white shelving, looking for something. I think of all those horrible contraptions and consider screaming. For a moment, I actually think I have, until I realise that it came from far away. Maybe the lift again. Any one of a dozen corridors. I close my mouth. The back of my throat is stinging and my eyes are starting to blur.

'John, what are you doing? What are you doing?' My voice sounds like someone else's; I don't recognise it at all.

He comes back. In one hand is a white coil of tubing; in the other, a jam jar. He really is barking mad. He's trying to copy the aliens. He thinks he can steal my soul. *God, this is awful*. And then I think of those eyes, those tombstone teeth. The ghastly brown trousers, the lab coat. His self-deprecating smile. 'Just trying to look the part.' I remember something else – something I said this time – about hiding in plain sight. And then I stop thinking altogether.

Brian is screaming. He sounds very far away. My ears are rushing with peculiar noise that I know is just inside my head (this must be what terror sounds like), and I don't really care what Brian is or isn't doing anyway. *He* can still run away.

John, still wearing that hideous apologetic half-smile, starts feeding the end of tubing inside my left nostril. He's muttering under his breath: 'Behind the nose and beneath the eyes.'

'*What are you doing?*' But of course, I know. The manacles

have constricted my limbs so much now that all I can do is thrash my head from side to side. John taps the sore spot on my forehead with a long finger, and I momentarily see sparks of white light. He shrugs, shrugs, shrugs.

'If you stay still, it won't hurt so much.'

But it does. As I feel that tubing wind itself in further and further, deeper and deeper, it hurts like nothing on earth ever has. I can feel myself getting smaller and smaller – retreating inside another me, until all I can see is John's tombstone teeth at the end of a very long, very dark tunnel. The pain and John's tombstone teeth are the only two things left in the world. I remember asking John why everything had to be so barbarically big. That's why.

The bus stinks of diesel. I guess that's because it's been idling for 'fifty bloody minutes, Daisy Miller! I'll be having words with your bloody mother and father this bloody time, mark my words.' And then presumably, Mr Payne recognised that was one too many bloodys for a school bus filled with twelve year olds, and let me sit down.

Our arrival was greeted with much whistling. Brian got a few back slaps that he studiously ignored. He sat down next to Jeff, who studiously ignored him, arms folded in jealous fury.

Now, as we're negotiating rush hour city traffic – also my fault – Suse risks Mr Payne's wrath by leaning across the aisle to talk to me.

'What the hell happened to you two?'

I shrug. Shiver, like someone's walked over my grave.

She leans closer, dropping her voice to a conspiratorial whisper. 'D'you want to finish the joint in the loo?'

'No, I'm alright.'

Suse blinks, frowns. 'Are you?'

'Yeah. My head's still sore from where I bumped it, that's all.' I look out the window at all the cars and vans and lights.

It's starting to rain; legs of moisture run down the window. It's a lie about my head. My head feels just fine. I look down at my hands. Feel one with the other, smoothing fingers over the skin and between the joints like I'm searching for something. I've no idea why. There's nothing there. Nothing different. Nothing new.

We stop, and the bus sighs and drops. Another set of traffic lights. I look out at nothing again. I feel indefinably empty, like I'm hungry, but I don't know for what.

Brian gets up on his knees and turns around to face me over his headrest. He looks like he's been crying. 'Miss Daisy? My arse hurts.'

I look at him while the back of Jeff's head chuckles. My lips feel numb, and for whatever reason, I'd really like to knock Brian's block off. 'I should be so lucky.'

Suse shoots me another of those bemused looks. And so she should. I look out at the rainy traffic. I have no idea what I mean. No idea at all.

CHERYL MOORE

CORSET WINGS

IT'S NOT THE sort of dream that can be made inside a brothel.

'Come back here you thieving Dollymop!' I run towards Fleet Street, in the clothes of the bloke who beat me. Old men his age can't run fast and I'm guessing it'll take him a while to make himself decent enough for the streets. I wasn't planning on running tonight, but Mrs. Harding told me if ever I needed her, I was to come in disguise.

She's one of those new age American types, with too much money and a curiosity that could get her thrown in the slammer if she didn't own half of New England. Her Daddy was some big industrialist in the North East, built Zeppelins and submarines, but I didn't care for her stories, to begin with, so long as she paid me.

I've had my share of female clients, but she mostly wanted to talk. Rambled on about women's liberation before she bedded me.

The old man wasn't so pleasant. Fell asleep after a few rounds of treating me like a bruiser, so I left him laying there, thinking he'd be out for a few hours. I misjudged him, can hear him bellow from across town, 'Stop that roller!'

I hear pig whistles, duck down a side alley, as the rozzers run past. It's funny how quiet they were when the old man was beating the shit out of me. Double standards, still I know these streets better than any of them, and Mrs. Harding's house is only a few roads away. I disappear into the back yards of Kirby Street, and slip by, guised like a proper gentleman. I'll fit in with the toffs around here, no problem. Although rich folks probably don't hide in church yards, like I'm planning, unless they're students from St Bart's, robbing the dead of their rest.

The whistles have stopped, but I hop over the fence. I like my man drag; it's better for scaling fences than any skirts I'm used to. 'Ain't so bad, Moll, eh!' I hit the grass, still in my bare feet. 'Well almost!' I wish my feet were as big as the old man's so I could have stolen his shoes as well. 'Can't have everything we want, girl!'

I laugh to myself as I sneak into St Etheldreda's churchyard. Sway along the stone path onto the grass. My feet don't thank me for the battering they've taken along the alleyways, but it's dark here and that's what matters.

I slip into the trees at the back of the graveyard, take out the note Mrs. Harding wrote, just to check I wasn't imagining her invitation. 'My dear, Margaret.' I stop. She wouldn't call me Molly, said it offended her appreciation of the English language.

'Bloody Yank!'

I roll my eyes and read on. 'My dear, Margaret. You strike me as an open-minded but somewhat restricted young woman.' I duck low as the pig whistles get near again. Hold the note like those Catholic beads my old Mum used to pray on, before she was taken by consumption.

The pigs shout, 'Oi, come here!' The whistles get louder and nearer as more rozzers take to the streets. That's a hell of a lot of whistles for one Ladybird like me. I hear the sounds of other men, a gang of toolers. They've been pick-pocketing toffs. I relax. Those whistles aren't for me.

I wait for the feet to run past the streets behind, and then open the note again. It reads. 'I have great capacity to see past the confines of this very limiting society, into somewhere more advanced. Somewhere liberating. If you want to know more, come visit me.' She wrote nothing else apart from her address and name.

I fold the note back into my pocket; look at the graves, at the sky, from what I can see of it, through the trees. It's beginning to rain. I don't feel safe slipping back to my flat, dressed like a man. People around Whitechapel talk. The East End's not as big as it seems when you've lived there all your life.

I walk quickly to the back of the churchyard, where there's a break in the fence, which hasn't been repaired yet. I curse, 'Bleeding feet!' and head towards Fleet Street, down a maze of tiny courtyards and passages, easing my escape.

Mrs. Harding's street is full of grand old buildings, but hers is particularly handsome. I stop outside, check the address. There's a sign outside, as if it's some place important. Typical for a woman with a high opinion of herself. It says, 'Dr. Samuel Johnson lived here.' And then some dates from last century. Mrs. Harding lives here now, but there's no plaque to say so. I feel my stomach rise into my throat and then knock. 'Mrs. Harding?'

The sound of footsteps makes me nervous, heavy and mechanical. She must have one of those protocol butlers the paper sellers have been shouting about. The door opens. I'm right, as a creepy looking seven-foot man-shaped thing stares at me through the steam, which powers its motors. It hisses, 'Come in, Margaret,' as if it was expecting me. Its mouth is full of smoke, which warms the hallway.

I ask, 'Where's Mrs. Harding?' It motions for me to follow it into the house.

I've never seen so many books, as I'm lead from the entrance, past a spiral staircase, through doors hidden in walls, rooms behind rooms and more staircases going downwards until I can feel the air getting thinner. The creature turns and points to another door and says, 'Mrs. Harding's through there.' It holds back, as if it isn't meant to go further than this room, but holds the door open; until I can hear more engines, feel a rush of cold air, like on the London underground. I can hear steam trains, echoing from somewhere in the distance, smell the grease and stale air.

I walk towards the door and ask. 'She's got a train track in her house?' The steam man doesn't answer. He just hands me a book from one of the many shelves. It's entitled 'Corset Wings, by Emilia Harding.' I open it up to the first page, a diagram of a strange looking flying machine is scrawled on it and underneath, written in her handwriting and inscribed to me, are a few words.

'Dear Margaret, I dream of turning corsets into wings, of building metal and brass around your bones, the skin of a new woman, released from something constricting.' I stop reading; feel a sudden urge to turn around, and run back out onto the streets, but the mechanical man pushes me through the door and slams it shut.

I feel a rush of cold air, as I pound on the closed side, 'Let me back in!' I'm in a tunnel, with oil lamplight; it's a train platform, completely abandoned apart from me. I holler. 'I'll call the police!' I claw at the edge of the door, to try and prise it open, but it's jammed tight. I drop the book, as it's no use to me, clamber down the embankment, figure the train track leads somewhere out into the London sewers. Better I return home covered in filth than a skin of metal and brass. I mumble. 'Lunatic!'

I don't need her stupid book or her creepy butler to find my way out of this place. I knew I shouldn't have come here. That mental cow's probably turned her old Man into that robot, for all I know. I shiver and give the door one last glare, as the light behind it is switched off. I don't plan on getting on Mrs. Harding's train after reading her creepy plans for me.

I wish I had shoes as I scramble over the track, in the opposite direction to where I heard the train. There's enough space at the sides for me to crawl behind if anything approaches. 'No rich lunatic's turning me into an experiment!' My old Mum always told me I got my stubborn streak from my father, but neither of them are any use to me at the moment, so I concentrate on not tripping over the track. 'You are an idiot, Molly Baker.' Serves me right for stealing the old man's clothes. I doubt they'd find my body if it ended up down here permanently, not that they'd look for it in the first place, being that I'm not that significant in the world above.

'Margaret! What are you doing down there?'

I look up at a woman standing on the platform, peering down at me. She's holding some gadgets in her hand, and blowing out cigar smoke as she reaches down to help me off the track. I step backwards. 'Mrs. Harding!'

She looks confused, from what I can make out through the gloom. 'Well, yes! Who did you expect?'

I motion to the door her butler pushed me through as she sighs and realises I'm not going to accept her gesture. 'I have rights you know, same as you. Now let me out of here.' She's a small-framed woman, and I'm used to fighting men if I have to. I clench my fists. 'I'll not ask you again!'

She glances towards the door, and walks, quite absently; as if she has no plans to turn me into a machine and picks up the book I left on the platform. She mutters, 'You dropped my book!' I begin walking further down the tracks, as she doesn't seem to have anything that can stop me.

I shout. 'This is ridiculous! And my name's Molly!'

She replies, 'Where are you going?'

I answer, 'Away from you!'

She waves the book at me. 'But I gave this to you!' I stop. She says. 'You'd better get off the track, you'll get squashed!'

I growl, 'I'm not coming near you after that butler thing slammed the door on me and left me here!'

She frowns, and raises her eyes, gives the door a hefty yank until it opens. 'This door? Well, I've been meaning to get it fixed! And these butlers are not really designed for semantics, so I'm afraid your cries for help wouldn't have been understood.' She motions towards the room, turns the light back on, and says, 'I heard you screaming from my laboratory, thankfully!'

I clench my fists tighter, in case she's tricking me, but she nods to her house, as if she is inviting me to leave. 'I thought you were more curious and perhaps a little more open minded than this, Molly, but don't let me stop you. I'm sure you have other plans out on the streets tonight?' I clamber onto the track, seeing my opportunity to make an exit, push past her, smell the cigar smoke as she stubs it out on the wall and extinguishes it with her boot. She frowns, I follow her eyes as she looks down at my feet and says.'You don't have any shoes!'

For such a clever woman she likes stating the obvious. I snatch the book from her and turn to the first page, read out her threats, so she knows I'm not frightened of her.

'Says here, you plan to turn my flesh into metal and brass!'

She puts on some reading glasses, and squints, a slight smile on her lips, as I put my foot in the door to stop it closing. 'Oh, that's so endearing and at the same time quite frustrating. You've taken my words literally. I can see now, why you look as if you're ready to grind my head into the wall!' She grins, 'I'm not keen on brutality, but I understand why a woman in your position resorts to that kind of behaviour. It won't be necessary, Molly!'

She pats my shoulder as if this is all cleared up, and says. 'You can leave if you like, I'll find someone else.' I stand in the open doorway, as Mrs. Harding walks away from me, as if she's forgotten I'm here, but she turns and mutters. 'If you want some shoes I think I have a pair in my laboratory, you can use.' She disappears back into her laboratory, leaving the door to slowly creak closed, but not enough, for me to remain uncurious about what's behind it. I sigh, curse myself for being so nosey, and place the book in the door to the house, so it doesn't close on me if I need to make a run for it later.

'It's a wonder you've reached twenty five, Molly!'

I peer into Mrs. Harding's laboratory. I've never seen one before, but I've read about them. This one looks cluttered, with bits of engine parts littering the floor, steam rising from half made contraptions, and Mrs. Harding running around frantically, looking for those shoes she promised me. She turns and trots over to me, quite thrilled that I've entered her workhouse and passes me some flat looking boots. 'These were my sister's, they should fit you!'

They look quite new. 'She doesn't need them?'

Her mind seems to wander, as if she doesn't want to think about my question too deeply and replies. 'She died.' I take the gift reluctantly, not quite sure how to accept a dead woman's shoes, or reject the offer, but put them on, as my feet are raw.

I ask, 'How?' hoping it has nothing to do with her experiments.

She lights another cigar, and waves me into the workhouse. Says absently, 'Accident at work, things go wrong, but without experimentation, no one gets anywhere.' She gives me a curious look, and touches my face, but not in the same way she did when she paid me. 'You've been in a fight?'

I nod. 'Bad customer, that's all. Nothing new!'

She removes her hand and says nothing else, looks slightly angry, but then begins to walk across the room, as if she wants to show me something. 'Before you go, you may as well see what I was making for you, had you chosen to stay.' I step over bits of engine; all types of materials lay haphazardly across the floor and worktables. I can see a large wing stretching outwards, made of soft red cloth, and a second, attached to what looks like a corset.

She points at it, her eyes not quite right, as if she is so absorbed and obsessed, she's forgotten the world around her. 'This is my new experiment!' Her eyes get crazier as she points up at the ceiling as if she can see things that I can't. 'Men and women use Zeppelins and large flying machines to conquer the skies, but think about what would have happened if poor Icarus hadn't flown too close to the sun? We'd be a world of bird people, free to fly unhampered by gravity and hopefully society. I deal in gravity as it's much more predictable than the people who govern us.' She begins tightening something loose on one of the wings. 'Imagine how vibrant the skies would be if Leonardo Da Vinci had lived in this age!' She can see from my expression, I think she's obsessed, but instead of stopping, she lifts up the corset and says, 'Try it on?'

The wings trail behind, like a bridal train, looking heavy in her arms. I must admit I spent last night wondering about Mrs. Harding's plans for me, in a bed full of bumps and broken springs. I look at the wings and admit, 'They do seem beautiful!' Strangely I begin removing the man's jacket and shirt, 'I suppose wearing it won't hurt!' She smiles as I raise my arms up, for her to wrap the corset, watch as she ties the strings, feel the weight of the wings, and ask, 'Where would you fly something like this?'

She smiles, and nods towards the workhouse door, to where the sound of a steam train gets louder, 'You want to find out?'

I really do hate myself for not running away, but she hasn't turned me into what I thought, in fact this is the opposite of imprisonment. I admit. 'I'm not going to fly this, you understand?' She looks hopeful, but nods, as the noise of an approaching steam train blocks out my voice. I look towards

THE BEST BRITISH FANTASY 2013

the door and peer back at the enormous wings, disabling my exit. Before I can ask her to remove them, Mrs. Harding rushes over to the doorway, turns a lever until the mechanisms unravel into a hatchway large enough for me to see out onto the platform as the train hisses and stops.

Without turning back to look at me, she rushes towards the train, so I follow her, my feet a little warmer in her sister's shoes, the wings surprisingly light, as if the weight has been balanced by all the mechanisms attached. The platform fills with steam, like the sea when warm tides mix with cold. Before I wonder how I'm going to fit on the train, Mrs. Harding unravels another door, until a gangway rolls down onto the platform, wide enough for me to step into the cabin.

The cabin is lit from inside, and there are other people, some dressed in modern clothes, others, like me, have strange contraptions fitted. Mrs. Harding hops on, buzzing, despite me saying I won't fly her strange device, she says. 'We've only got one stop, I want to show you a most liberating sight!'

I can't imagine anywhere liberating in London, but I humour her. 'These trains go to the moon or something?' I look around at the people; some of them look like they belong in lands quite removed from London. Maybe the moon isn't such a wild guess. Mrs. Harding doesn't laugh with me; in fact she sits down and motions for me to hold onto the handrail above.

'Better hold tight, this train goes fast!' I prepare myself for a bumpy ride, close my eyes as the train fires up, can smell the steam, hear the whistle from the chimney as the doors close.

'We're here, Molly, it's our stop!'

I open my eyes, onto daylight. I swear it was night time in London. There's a cliff outside, and the seaside, I can hear seagulls and smell seaweed. Mrs. Harding gets out of her seat and takes my hand, as the door opens and leads me out. No one follows, as we step onto the new platform. I can hear ice cream sellers and the sound of fairground rides. Mrs. Harding grins and points up at the sky, to where I can see others like me, human flying machines. She says, 'This is New England. My father owned this beach and left it to me after he died. You can stay here on the ground and watch if you like?' She motions towards a beach hut, and passes me a key. 'You can store your wings in there?'

I study the beaches; hear the drawl of foreign accents, similar to hers, 'I'm in New England?'

She nods. 'I told you the train moved fast!'

There's always a price, but she hasn't told me what it is, so I begin to unstrap my corset. 'I'd better go home!' She doesn't stop me, as I protest. 'This was a bad idea.' A woman who uses Ladybirds for sex probably has ulterior motives. I accuse, 'So what do you get out of this?'

She looks confused again. 'I told you. Possibility, a reason to live, a place to realise my passions. I want to share my inventions, Molly.'

She looks sincere, but distracted as a young man wanders past, eating ice cream, identical wings strapped to his own corset. He grins at Mrs. Harding and says in an American drawl, 'Hi, Emilia, you going to join us today, or go back to that stuffy laboratory of yours?' He glances at me, 'New recruit?'

She shrugs. 'Maybe not!'

The man looks me up and down, attempting to remain neutral, but I can see he thinks I'm a coward. 'Ah, the British are so conservative!'

I retort, 'Mrs. Harding find you in a brothel too?'

He frowns at me, as if he thinks I'm crude. Mrs. Harding simply looks at the sky, admiring her work, as if she isn't part of the conversation. A normal woman would have gone an embarrassing scarlet, by now, but not her.

The young man offers his hand to me, despite seeming unhappy with my manner.

'Zachary Turner.'

I reply, 'Molly Baker.'

He continues. 'I'm not a prostitute, although some think lawyers are lower on the social order than hookers, which is probably why I spend most of my free time on this beach!' I return his gesture, growling at his undertone. I don't like being accused of cowardice, and as he lets go of my hand, I realise why I took the train, why I didn't return to the rain, the dark streets of London, crawl back to my filthy bug ridden bed, dressed like a Ladyboy.

I turn to Mrs. Harding. 'I'll do it, Mrs. Harding!'

She looks a little shocked but pleased as I strap my corset back on. She helps me tighten it, and says. 'Call me Emilia.' And adds, 'We're equal here!'

I feel my arms tingling, the bones of a new woman, emerging from something restricting, a beautiful new creature, as the possibility of flight brightens up my dismal past life, and I leave the brothel far behind. 'Thank you, Emilia.'

STEPH SWAINSTON

THE WHEEL OF FORTUNE

TUESDAY MORNING IN May, bright sunshine. I came out of
the shop, carrying a pole to pull the awning down. I was whistling. The shop door banged behind me and the cat fled off the
step. The whole street was vibrant with the spring sun. There,
sitting on the pavement and huddled against the terrace wall,
was Serin. She was a pitiful sight, gin-dimmed eyes and head
to foot in gutter dirt. I had last seen her Saturday, on stage at
the Campion Vaudeville, and she was wearing the same dress
now, a voluminous costume made of gold foil. Her reddish
wings stuck out the back and bunched up against the bricks.
The feathers rustled when she moved.

I knelt next to her. 'Serin? . . .Are you all right?'

She shook her head and looked away. She was on the spiral
downwards, that much was obvious.

'What did they do to you?'

'It's the things they make me do,' she sobbed.

I stroked her hair, the crackling material of her dress. 'Did
you come here to see me?'

'Yes. To buy some scolopendium. Cat. Because people say
you sell it.'

'No.'

'Yes, you do. You do.'

'Not to you, Serin. You don't need it.'

'I want to.'

I pulled her arm gently. 'Come inside. I'll get you a cocoa; it's better than cat.'

She looked at me gratefully, drawing a little consolation from my touch. Her hair was so ginger it looked fake, and stiff as wire. Her green eyes would put a Rhydanne to shame, but her face was purple with dirt. It was a bizarre contrast. She began to wail. I hushed her and helped her inside the shop.

It seemed dim after the daylight and it took a second for my eyes to adjust. I flipped up the counter, guided Serin through it and helped her onto a stool by the till. I pulled my worn black jacket off the peg and wrapped her in it like a child. 'God, what did they do to you?'

'They don't pay me,' she sniffed, and wiped her nose on her wrist. 'For two weeks Crispy didn't pay me *at all* and the land-lord threw me out.'

'Have you been living rough since – ?'

'Saturday. Yeah . . . I got this dress.' She scrunched two handfuls of the skirt.

This city sickened me. I folded my arms and glanced at the shelves. She needed a bath and she needed a place to stay. 'I'll get you that cocoa,' I said. At that moment the green linen strips hanging in the doorway whisked aside and Dotterel bustled through from the passage. He looked over his glasses at the girl. 'Well, well. What in the name of pathos do we have here?'

'This is Serin, sir,' I said.

'Your partner in grime. Ha ha.'

Serin stared at him. I explained everything, omitting, of course, my drug dealing, while giving Serin a warning glance, and ended lamely by saying, 'I'm just going to get her some cocoa.'

'Cocoa. An excellent idea. And plenty of water, and a nip of brandy. And then we shall have breakfast. Do you have a hangover, Miss Serin?' He added something kindly in Awian and she brightened up and replied. Her tears had cleared white patches around her eyes and she looked like a reject doll. 'Light the fire and run the bath,' he said to me.

'Yes, sir.'

'Then come back and man the shop. This doesn't entail a day off, you know. Young lady, if you don't mind wearing a shirt and trousers until you can buy some clothes.'

'I don't have any money,' she said.

'Well, that just depends whether you can help run a shop.'

Her eyes shone. 'Do you mean . . .?'

'Yes, yes. Well, we shall see.' He turned and started taking down jars for me to make the day's pastilles. 'When one is caught in a tempest it is important to steer the ship, is it not? There's no point bewailing life's vicissitudes when they rise up, up, up as well as down. And you, young lady, are on the up. Do you know of the Wheel of Fortune? It is always spinning. You can climb it to the top, but those on top have to be careful, because it can carry them swiftly down again. And serve them right! If you languish at the bottom, bear in mind you can rise to the heights. In a city like this you need a firm place to set your foot.'

'She has a voice like a nightingale,' I said, and blushed. I don't know where that came from.

'Jant. Kitchen.'

'Yes, sir.' I slipped through the waxed green linen strips. As I coaxed the stove to life, and warmed the tiny pan full of milk until it frothed, I was kicking myself for saying such a weird thing. But it seemed to have effected the best introduction, for talking and snatches of laughter came through from the shop, and when I brought the cocoa in on a tray, I saw that both the stage grin and the blank stare had gone from Serin's eyes. Dotterel had managed to make her smile through her tears.

After breakfast I showed her how to make pastilles. She was wearing one of my shirts, tied with a scarf round her little urchin waist. We had taken menthol, sugar syrup, essence of peppermint and a little liquorice, and stirred it around in a mason bowl. I folded the mixture over into itself and it went quite stiff.

'This is the good bit.' I tipped the ball of candy out onto the clean work surface and rolled it into a sausage. It was transparent, and marbled through with the black streaks of liquorice. I let Serin pick it up and place it on the pill press, which is a ridged brass plate. A similar plate went on top, squashing the mixture, then with a quick motion I whipped it across and rolled the mixture into little balls of satisfyingly equal size. 'Cough drops.' I said. 'They set within the hour and then they go in one of these tins. But you have to keep the flies off them.'

'I see,' said Serin. 'What about scolopendium?'

'That's proper chemistry, not cooking.'

'Show me how to make it.'

'No. It's the hardest drug there is.'

But she'd seen my glance to the distilling apparatus on its mahogany-topped table alongside the wall. 'Do you use that?'

'Don't get involved.'

'Everyone says you deal it. Vance said you're in with the Wheel gang, and you give them scolopendium, and it's the best in the city.'

'I'm not in any gang.'

'But you sell them cat.'

'...Yes.'

'Cool.'

I shrugged and began to measure warm sugar syrup for the next batch. Selling drugs wasn't cool. I'd only wanted a little money to see out my apprenticeship, but the Wheel was like a whirlpool and every night sucked me further in.

'You want to dive straight into danger and drown,' I said. 'You can sing and you can dance. Stick to that.'

'At the Campion? It's not serious acting. It's like a sideshow at a whorehouse. I could be Ata in *The Mayor of Diw* if they'd let me.'

'Come on,' I said. 'Six drops of liquorice.'

I packed medicines with Serin all day while the city's shadows lengthened. The cat stole in, and leapt on the counter, and was shooed out again. I sold two ounces of clove oil for tooth-ache, camomile for stomach gripes and a dose of pennyroyal for carelessness, all decanted into stoppered flasks and carefully labelled.

Outside, the blue sky gave way to mare's tails, then thick cloud. A cold front battered in off the estuary and the temperature began to drop. It was colder still when we finished our meal and Dotterel retired to bed. Serin followed to sleep in the box room, but my day was just beginning.

I left the shop and walked out of Galt district towards the docks. The Moren Canal strides in there to meet the slovenly river at a basin full of barges. By day it's busy with the trade and shipment of all sorts of goods. Now at nearly ten o'clock it was deserted, except for a dull glow and rowdy conversation spilling from the dockers' Kentledge Arms.

All was silent as I followed the towpath below blind mill buildings and warehouses, deeper into the docks. Last on the wharf, by the mighty canal lock, the Fulling Mill's barred windows were as lightless as the cold expanse of estuary. Its great hammers that beat woollen weave into fine cloth were stilled for the night, and the enormous waterwheel that drove it stood motionless. It hung above its reflection, seen now and then on the murky water, when a few spare lights from the road picked out the ripples in black and white.

On the six spokes of the waterwheel the Wheel gang had nailed another of their victims. The body of a teenager hung there, arms and legs outstretched, head dangling. Six inch nails through his denim wrists and ankles held each limb to a different spoke. His blood had drained straight down, staining his jacket and the wheel's enormous timbers. Then they had used him for crossbow practice.

I passed with a shudder. The warehouse at the end of the quay looked terribly lonely. I slipped inside and found myself surrounded by tall shapes: neat piles of barrels that reached up to the corrugated iron roof. There were sacks of barley, crates of candles, bolts of cloth. I walked between them like a thief.

In the middle of the warehouse various members of the Wheel gang were lounging around on woolsacks. They had piled hundreds of these sacks into the shape of a tall throne, and high up on it, looking down on us all, sat a young man in an exquisitely tailored grey silk suit.

'You're late,' said Felicitia.

He reposed with his chin on one hand, the other hand dangling. He was adorned with the most expensive makeup and fine gold jewellery, his long hair combed down straight.

Debrah and Vance stopped playing poker and watched.

'Have you got the drugs?' he asked.

'Have you got the money?'

'Just give me the damn phial.' He slipped lightly down and landed in front of me. I took the phial from my pocket and gave it to him. At once he flipped its cap, poured it into a glass of brandy ready on the table and drank it down straight. Then eyelids flickered over wide-pupilled eyes. He caught a breath and looked at me shrewdly. 'Your payment is protection,' he said.

'What do you mean?'

'We caught two of the Bowyers gang hanging round your shop. Didn't we, Vance?'

'Yeh.'

'They won't bother you again.'

'Was that one outside on the wheel?'

'Yes,' said Felicitia.

'What about the other one?'

He beckoned to me and we went outside. At the edge of the lock he rested his arms on the railing and gazed down at the black water. Vance, the docker, spun an iron wheel and the water level began to fall. The water drained away and revealed a metal ladder bolted to the slimy wall. Tied to the ladder, and drooping away from it, was a pale and waterlogged corpse.

'Oh god,' I said. 'Oh, god.'

Felicitia leant his head on my shoulder. I could see the powder particles of his eye shadow and smelt his brandy breath.

'Stay, my dear,' he murmured. 'Stay the night.'

He steered me back into the warehouse. Vance pressed a glass of brandy into my hand. Debrah involved me in a game of cards, and I stayed.

I was asleep, lying on the firmly filled woolsacks below the throne. The last candles in a stolen crystal chandelier that hung from the airy warehouse beams had failed, and all was dark.

I was woken abruptly by an urgent hiss and a hand on my shoulder: Felicitia. 'What?' I asked, shrinking from his hand.

'Sh!' he said. 'Get up.'

What the fuck was going on? I thought that perhaps the Bowyers were about to attack, but lamplight leaking in from the docks illuminated an excited smile on Felicitia's face – far from the usual sardonic expression he affected to match his expensive clothes. He walked towards me and I backed off, over the straw-strewn floor until I walked into the chair in which Vance had been sitting. Its cold metal pressed against the back of my legs. Felicitia giggled, shaking his hair that was dyed in stripes, for god's sake. It reached to his shoulders and flowed into his black coat, so he seemed featureless, a strip of darkness sliced from the night. He moved with a woman's delicacy, did it better than a woman, more like a cat.

Vance stepped out from behind a pile of barrels and grabbed me with a hand on each bicep. I struggled to pull away but I had no chance. The greasy-haired bodybuilder tapped me on the shoulders and I sat down on the chair. He began to pull a length of cord from his pocket.

Felicitia watched with his head on one side. 'Why are you looking at the door, Jant? Even you can't move that fast.'

'What are you doing?'

'Tut, tut. If you're going to sound so terrified you should shut up.'

Vance looped the cord around my wrists, then pulled it appallingly tight across the back of the chair. I began to lose the feeling in my fingertips.

'Aren't you on our side?' I appealed.

'Yeh, well if I wasn't, you didn't put up much of a struggle.' He tied my legs to the legs of the chair; wrought iron against my shins and impossible for me to lift.

'Everybody in the Wheel has this done,' said Felicitia slowly. 'You want to belong to our gang, don't you? You want to be one of us.'

He brushed past me as he stood up and I felt his erection hard in the front of his trousers. Over the last year I had often glimpsed our symbol on Vance's shoulder and I had watched him carve it on Debrah's arm when she joined us, but I had always hoped the ritual would pass me by.

'Everyone has to witness it,' I tried to stay calm. 'You said so. You said we do scarifications in the Kentledge, in the beer garden.'

'Tonight it's just you and me.' He pulled the sheath off the blade.

'You never cut Layce,' I said desperately. 'Is that because you love her?'

A pained expression crossed his face. He poked the knife under my chin and lifted it so I had to meet his gaze. 'Well, I would fuck Layce. But I'd be thinking of you.' He stepped back and began to slit my sleeve carefully.

My adrenaline was hiking up, while he opened a bottle, dripped disinfectant onto a pad of lint and rubbed it over the blade. The light from his lantern gleamed along its edge. I was high on the peak of anticipation, teetering with the void before me. I knew if I tensed myself the agony would be worse, but I was rigid with fear. 'You goatfucking son of a bitch,' I spat in Scree.

'Keep talking. I love it when you speak foreign.' He rolled back his cuffs and spread his hands like an artist contemplating a canvas. He pressed the tip of the knife against my skin, which dented, then the knife sank deep.

I swear the first cut went straight to the bone. He put all his weight against the blade and dragged it through skin and muscle with a butcher's precision. I struggled, pulled away. The line he was cutting curved and he cried out in frustration. He seized my shoulder and held it still. He drew the circle deep into my flesh with the knife. He lifted out the blade, then began the first spoke. I clamped my mouth shut and never made a sound – I wouldn't give him the pleasure. I stared straight ahead into the warehouse. Three lines made six spokes: on the second line my vision went dark around the edges. Blue spots, then unfocussed black patches clouded it. I couldn't breathe enough oxygen; I dropped my chin to my chest. I could hear blood pattering off my arm, dripping off his hands. Felicitia hummed to himself and started the third line. I fainted.

At length I became aware of him slapping my face. My arm and my whole side were searing pain. He cut the cords because blood had soaked the knots too tight to undo. I fell out of the chair onto my hands and knees, and rested my forehead on the floorboards. Blood was running in rivers down my arm, over my wrist, and drying stickily on the floor.

Felicitia had never scarred any other gang member this deeply. Every spoke was a punishment for a time I'd rebuffed his advances. He stepped back and admired his handiwork, then slipped behind me. I felt him grope my arse and his hand sank into the crack. At the same time he reached round and deftly undid my belt buckle. In a trice I was up and glaring at him, squeezing my shoulder.

'Cool it,' he said. He pointed to the disinfectant and I picked up the pad and pressed it against the cuts, trying to staunch the flow.

'Get away from me,' I slurred.

Vance yelled at Felicitia: 'You go too far!'

'Everybody has it done. You did.'

'Not that deep!'

'I want to know what Jant will do in return,' he said softly.

I tried a step and the warehouse spun. I fell to one knee again and my hand went almost automatically to my stiletto knife tucked in the top of my boot. But when I looked up he was again pointing his dagger at me. And smirking.

'Fuck off, Felicitia.'

'Oh, stop giving me ideas. You are so very young . . . and so very pretty.'

I knelt and concentrated on the pain, thinking I was about

to die of it, or of blood loss, and I couldn't bring myself to move for what seemed like hours. He nudged me with his boot toe. 'Get up, Jant.'

'Can't . . .'

'You're a drug dealer, aren't you? Go and deal yourself some drugs. Roll up your sleeve and shoot some of that stuff you sell me. Hook yourself up with a dose of cat; I know it takes all the pain away.'

'Felicitia Aver-Falconet, you're living on borrowed time.'

'Promises, promises.' He stepped back and bowed, beckoned to Vance and they walked off without another word. I stood up carefully, hunched over my pain, holding my arm, and the warehouse was reeling as I made my way across it.

As I left the quayside, a figure began to trail after me, scarcely distinguishable in that stinking canal night. Well, let it: I was thanking god silently that the distance was not too far.

Dripping blood all the way, I staggered down the underpass that led beneath the watermill's conduit. It was desolate and stank of piss. Concrete stalactites hung from seeping cracks in the ceiling, and muddy footprints streaked the tiles. I hurried through as quickly as I could. At the crossroads by the Moren Bridge, street lamps cast my shadow long across the road. Two rats were fighting in the gutter. They snapped at each other like stunted dogs. I limped past them and painedly made my way from the docklands back to Galt, through the four a.m. landscape of twisted roofs and slippery pavements bordered with open drains, while the amber moon's sick light laughed at me.

I crossed over into Cinder Street, off the cobbles onto the wet brown pavement, past the Campion Playhouse, alongside its iron railings. I reached the chemist's shop, its shutters fastened for the night, and sighed with relief. I fumbled with the key, shouldered the door wide and stumbled inside.

I kicked the door closed and made my way by a combination of touch and memory across to the counter, and ducked underneath. The counter stood as an ebony barricade between the shelves and outside, the street still visible through the pane in the door. I lit a candle one-handedly and searched the shelves, which were lined with boxes and jars full of potions and pills. Painkiller, I was thinking. Felicitia was right that cat will work. That's what the addicts tell me it's like. The ones I sell it to: they care for nothing else. I knocked over a couple of little bottles, spilling some silver liquid; and the dregs of red powder from another, swearing loudly. I didn't expect Dotterel to be awake yet; he was far too old, and slept as if already dead. My moonlight customers and I were glad of that.

I picked up the bottle against my chest, but didn't have the strength to open it. I sat down, panting, and eased the stiffening sleeve of my shirt away from the network of cuts on my shoulder. This action made the bleeding start again. I promise I'll kill that bastard.

I smashed the neck off the bottle on the counter top, poured the drug into a beaker and drank it. The pain disappeared – it didn't ebb or dull, just snuffed out, like an extinguished candle.

I pawed my way through the shop, under the desk again, and unlocked the door that led down to the cellar, where I slept on a shelf. I made no attempt to bandage my arm, I didn't care for it at all. I even smiled, thinking how good this stuff was, and how perhaps the addicts I sold it to were correct, all their lax philosophy, all their contorted sense of time.

Hours wore on and fever set in. When the pain began to pierce the shell of the scolopendium I'd drunk, I sipped more, lay on my impossible bed with the beaker clutched in one hand and listened to my own voice whispering.

'Good, isn't it?' said a voice in the doorway. That feline silhouette lounged against the doorframe, its long, stripy hair now scraped back in a ponytail. 'It's the best drug in the world.'

Felicitia? Here? Or was it a hallucination?

'Felicitia . . .' I breathed. 'Did you trail me as well?'

'As well? As well as who?'

My mouth was dry and I gasped. 'The Bowyers . . . followed me here. They'll – '

'No, my love. I'm the one that was following you. I put a guard on your shop. . . you'll be safe.'

I squeezed my eyes shut in frustration and tears forced out the corners. He swayed up to stand beside me. 'You have such an interesting establishment. It belongs to us now – and so do you. Now we view the world in the same way, we should understand each other. Is there anything . . . at all . . . I can do for you?'

'Take me to the hospital, you bloody bastard.'

He raised an eyebrow and laid his hand on my thigh. 'In a while.'

A movement in the corridor made us both start. Serin rushed into the room, levelling Dotterel's crossbow directly at Felicitia. 'Who the hell are you?' she snapped.

Felicitia backed off at the sight of the gleaming bolt, but then he shook himself and assumed an air of smoothness. 'Jant, you didn't tell me you had a girlfriend.'

'*Who are you?*' yelled Serin.

'She must be quite something to have seduced our Jant.'

Serin closed her finger on the trigger. To her eyes he was one of the men who made her life a misery. She meant it.

'I'm the Governor's son,' he said quickly.

'What?'

'Felix. The son of Kalice Aver-Falconet, Governor of Haci-lith.'

Serin glanced madly from him to me, behind the crossbow that was far too big for her. 'From the palace?' she said.

'Just shoot him,' I said.

'Such hospitality. I – '

'Out!'

She kept him at crossbow point as he walked around her. He winked at me as he left, and she followed him out. I heard the shop door bang. In a second she was back, shaking with relief and dangling the crossbow. 'He's gone.'

'For now.'

'God . . . what happened to you?'

'This is what it means to join the Wheel gang,' I said through my fever. She bent close and helped me lift my fingers away from my wounded shoulder.

'He cut me,' I said. 'It needs dressing.'

'Show me how.'

She helped me up to the shop and I sat on a stool while she cleaned my wound and bandaged it carefully. The sky was brightening from misty grey to a deeper blue every minute and a soft, peaceful dawn trailed into this side of Hacilith.

In the shade of the shop, Serin traced with her finger the lines of blood that were starting to show through my bandage. Her touch was so light – and caring. She whispered, 'A circle with spokes . . . It's the Wheel of Fortune. We're at the bottom now, so the wheel will raise us up . . . won't it?'

'Out of the dregs.'

'Yes. We have to.'

A wheel takes more effort to push upwards than it does to spin downward. I was suddenly determined. I would set my shoulders against the Wheel of Fortune and shove.

'We'll get out of this terrible city,' I said.

Serin hugged me tight and kissed me. It was the first time I'd ever been kissed. An awed awakening broke upon me – she really cared! I drew close to her with an abrupt, fierce love.

'We will escape.' I promised. 'The Wheel of Fortune will turn for us. We'll turn it.'

THE ISLAND OF PETER PANDORA

PETER CAUGHT THE fly between his palms. The insect buzzed and tickled.

'Aren't you the jolly little irritant!' Peter parted his hands slightly and tried to peep in. When the fly flew out, he snatched at it. A trace of gore stained his hand.

'Funny bug.' Peter didn't bother to brush off the insect's remains, but picked up the wrench and plunged his hands into the Lost Boy's stomach.

'Those Rogues. They'll do for me one day,' said Nibs in his chiming voice.

'Ha! They'd have to catch me first, and Peter Pandora is not easy to tie down.' Peter lifted his sharp chin a notch. Locating the flywheel under the leather heart, he adjusted the torque. A squeeze of oil from a can and the gears moved smoothly again.

'I am nothing if not exceptional.' Peter slid the bolt plate back across Nibs' stomach. He cleaned his hands on a rag.

'You're the bravest and the best, Peter.' Nibs craned in his legs, rocked onto his porthole backside and got up off the grass. Steam oozed from his joints.

Peter nodded sagely. 'I am.' When the Lost Boys failed to

concur, he shot them a savage look. 'What say my men?' He bit his bottom lip.

The animatronic band wheezed into life at the command.

'The finest mind in the French empire.' Tootles cradled his fat bowl belly; Peter had fashioned it from a condenser casing and a girdle of steel ribs.

'Master of the fair isle of Tsarabanjina. We are loyal to the last.' Curly nodded enthusiastically, exciting the frayed wires that poked out his skullcap.

'The last! The last!' echoed the twin tinies who Peter had not bothered to name. They were rather a nuisance with their rudder flippers that got stuck in the sand or left visible tracks up the banks like turtles come ashore to lay their eggs.

'Slightly?' Peter adopted a grown-up's tone.

'I have a headache,' said Slightly as farts of steam escaped his back boiler. 'And with mother being on the gin and father having run away with the fairies.'

Peter crossed his arms. He considered Slightly's head which had been all but bashed off, with only a couple of wires attaching it to the body.

'The Rogues shall pay for their attack.' Peter unhooked the wrench from his utility belt and wielded it. 'What say my men?'

'The finest mind in the French empire.'

'Master of the fair isle . . .'

'Enough!' cried Peter, and apart from the taps of water pipes and the crackle of wood inside their boilers, the Lost Boys fell silent.

Three hours later and Slightly's head sat back on his shoulders. The iridescent blue of day was giving way to the black and oranges of dusk. Peter led his robot band through the tall reeds, kicking up crickets and newborn mosquitoes. The air was full of flavours – cocoa, coffee and sea salt; Peter breathed them in. This was his favourite part of the day, when the stars his father had loved so much began to wink overhead, and the rumble in his belly told him it was suppertime.

'Did any tuck survive the raid?' he called over a shoulder.

'Papaya, banana, sweet potato.' Tootles sounded proud of their haul. Peter had hoped for a fish supper, but he let things slide. His men had survived being attacked by the Rogues when collecting provisions earlier that day. Plus, they could always go a-hunting again tomorrow.

'A banquet fit for kings,' he managed. His spirits cheered at the sight of the raggedy tree house with its smoke stacks and the fat brass trunk of his father's telescope pointing skyward.

'Run on ahead, you and you,' he told the twin tinies. 'Get the water boiling under the supper pot. Light the lamps.'

The pair set off, rudder feet swishing through the reeds. A minute later, Peter saw the glow of lamplight at the windows. Smoke trickled from one of the tall stacks.

Peter entered the clearing. Tootles, Slightly, Curly and Nibs arrived alongside, oozing steam and sweating oil. Moths danced in the twilight like fairy folk. The detritus of scrub and husk made a noisy carpet underfoot. 'No creeping up on me,' thought Peter smugly.

He stepped onto a wooden palette, grabbed hold of the ropes and heard the winch start up. The ground dropped away and he sailed up to the tree house, that great nest of palm leaves, reeds, flotsam and jetsam, turtle shell, coral chunks and drift wood. Crawling in at the tarpaulin-covered entrance, he slammed a large iron lever forward and sent the palette back down to fetch the others.

Standing up and placing his hands on his hips, Peter took in the chaos of the room. The hairy trunks of seven coconut trees sprouted up through the living quarters. Golden Orb spiders nestled among the eaves, their sun-coloured silk forming a glittering canopy.

'Home sweet home.' Peter rocked back onto his heels and

separated his toes, planting them on the reed matting with a satisfying sense of grounding.

James and Wendy Darling had come to Tsarabanjina – a tropical island located northwest of Madagascar Main Island and forty nautical miles from Nosy-Be – in the year of our lord 1889. A twelve-man strong crew assisted them to offload the numerous tools of Mr. Darling's trade – spy glasses, constellation maps housed in leather tubes, an oversized compass with gold and ivory inlay, easels and other drawing apparatus; and, of course, his pride and joy, a giant brass telescope. Mrs. Darling, meanwhile, was content to haul ashore her own box of tricks – metal-working tools, saws, hammers, piping, sheet steel, and every conceivable nut, bolt and screw. And while many ladies would have protested at the steaming wilderness, Wendy embraced it. Befriending the tribe on the south side of the island, she enlisted those strong, cocoa-skinned men to help her build an observatory among the trees.

Peter had been four years old, his sister Bella, six months. Leaving behind the dreary greys of London for Tsarabanjina's endless blue sky and ocean, both children felt as if they had stumbled upon paradise.

Three years later came the Three Bad Events as Peter called them. First, a tremendous cyclone storm which sunk his parents' dhow offshore. Second – and by far the more devastating – the death of both his parents from Typhoid Fever. What made it worse was that both of these incidents happened within two weeks of one another. And third, the islanders muscling in on his and Bella's seclusion and insisting so kindly and so absolutely that the youngsters go with them. Peter had refused with every violent response he could muster. Bella, though, went with them. At the age of seven, Peter had found himself alone with only the sounds of the waves lapping the shore and the contents of his mother's workshop for company.

'Time to fill your cakehole.' Slightly stood at the brink to the observatory. His insides turned over with a faint clanking sound.

Peter peered into the telescope's eyepiece. Venus, the morning star and his father's life's work, shone in the night sky. 'Such an elegant turn of phrase, Slightly,' he muttered.

'Want me to put on false airs like Rogues?' Slightly elevated a backside flap and let out a guff of steam.

Peter slid the cap across the eyepiece and made his way across the room, weaving in and out the map stands and tables full of paperwork. He slapped Slightly on the arm, producing a hollow rumble.

'I really did use up the odds and sods at the bottom of the drawer when I created you, Slightly.'

The Lost Boy seemed pleased with the fact. His boiler bubbled softly as he led the way into the dinner den.

'Peter! So glad you can join us.' Tootles tapped the space on the bench next to him. 'Have a seat, there's a good chap.'

Peter eased in besides Tootles even thought the crueller part of him wanted to say, 'No, I won't. I shall sit opposite between the twin tinies just to show who is boss around here.' By way of compromise, he vowed to ignore Tootles for the evening.

'So what's the plan, Peter? How do we make those Rogues pay?' Nibs banged his fist against his stomach plate, a reminder of the torn internals he had suffered at their hands.

Peter spoke through a mouthful of turtle and sweet potato stew. 'We lure them in from their hidey hole and then we garrotte them.'

'Sounds marvellous,' said Curly.

'Masterful,' added Tootles.

'How'd we do it?' The twin tinies asked in unison.

Peter put his elbows on the table and lent in. The Lost Boys mimicked him.

'I am going back below and I'm going to raise the Ticktock.'

His animatronic companions ooh'ed then fell silent, the cicada song of the night punctuated by the whir and knocks from their steaming bellies.

It was Slightly who spoke up. 'What's the Ticktock?'

'What's the Ticktock?' Peter leapt onto his seat. 'What's the Ticktock?' He stepped onto the table, narrowly missing his bowl of fruit mush and the Lost Boys' flagons of oil and platefuls of grease. 'Only the bringer of destruction. It is the hand of God, the great leveller.' He knocked a fist off his breastbone. 'It was my mother, Wendy Darling, who told me of its power. 'Be careful, son, the Ticktock is not a toy. It likes to buck and spit."

'But you'll tame it, won't you, Peter?' Tootles showed his metal tooth pegs.

'Naturally. First though, I've got to commander the thing from the deep.' Peter danced up and down the table, upsetting a jug of rainwater and splashing through it as if he was jumping in puddles at the park. 'I do so love to go a-hunting!' he cried.

'Can we come too?' piped up the twin tinies.

'Only I.' Peter puffed out his chest. 'This quest requires cunning and lashings of cleverness. Besides. . .' He dropped to his haunches and ladled a mouthful of stew into his mouth. 'I'm the only one who knows how to swim with the Mermaid,' he said thickly.

Later, when the Lost Boys had completed their chores and joined in Peter's rousing rendition of Jolly Rain Tar; after which he had instructed them to stoke their boilers, wind innards and sup enough water to tide them over until the morning – then companions and master had gone their separate ways. The Lost Boys took up patrol duty on the tree house's vined balcony while Peter climbed onto his parents' reed-stuffed mattress, beneath a canopy of mosquito netting. Besides the bed was the gramacorda which his father had used to archive his discoveries. A few times, his mother had thought it amusing to speak into the horn and record the bedtime stories she told Peter onto one of the foil scrolls. While the heat had warped the greater part of his father's recordings, three of his mother's tales still played. That night, Peter selected her rendition of The Tin Soldier. Lying back on the bed, he had let his mother's spirited narration lull him to sleep.

He was woken once during the night by the sound of footfall on the ground below. Peter imagined he heard a chilling, all too familiar grunting, but sleep overtook him again.

The sun was high in the sky when Peter awoke. While the Lost Boys breakfasted on their oil and grease, their creator tucked into spiced fish baked in banana leaves. Soon the conversation turned to the night watch. The Lost Boys denied any sign of intruders. Peter remained haunted by the conviction they were wrong.

'Rogues have curdled my dreams long enough.' Peter fastened his utility belt at his waist and slammed his hat down on his head. 'Time to fetch up the Ticktock.' He knocked a hand off his brow in salute. 'See you later, alligators.'

Half an hour later, and having battled his way through the mosquito infested reeds, Peter arrived on the north shore. The sand was toasty between his toes. Waves foamed at the shoreline. The clear blue ocean stretched away to tiny islands known as the Four Friers. Two large rocks 'kissed' a little way out to his left. His mother's workshop burrowed into the cliff to his right.

At the entrance, Peter cocked his head and leant in, drinking from the fresh water, which streamed down the rock. He stepped inside the workshop, blinded by the sudden transition from brilliant daylight to shadow. It was dry inside –

precisely the reason his mother had selected the cave – and battened with wooden shelving. Peter lit oil-filled dips in the rock. The makeshift sconces flickered whenever he walked by, causing his shadow to dance over the walls seemingly of its own accord.

Numerous engineering supplies had gone down with his parents' ship, but the workshop was still well stocked. Several shelves were dedicated to trays of nuts, bolts, screws and nails. Giant bobbins were wound with rubber pipe while tinier versions held various gauges of copper wire. Two workbenches stood on stilts on the uneven surface; one was stained with oil, the other with blood. Tools hung off nails between the shelves – hammers, bow saws, hand drills, chisels, scalpels, vices and tourniquets. One basket held clean bandaging, the other soiled.

Standing in his workshop surrounded by the tools of his labour, Peter was glad he had come alone. As much as he enjoyed his elated status among the Lost Boys, there was a tendency for their restricted audio to grate. More than anything he longed for the stimuli of sentient conversation. But his efforts to create companions had birthed all manner of dark breed among the Rogues, he reminded himself, gaze lingering on the bloodstained bench. One of them worse than all the rest; Hookie, the ape-man. Had Wendy Darling known that, in introducing new animal species to the island, she would provide her son with the raw materials to investigate and reinterpret life, she might just have tipped her caged specimens overboard on route and drowned the lot. Instead she was the enabler for Peter's experiments, having left behind science books, engineering diagrams, pencilled notes and a veritable operating theatre.

'Much good it does me!' Peter protested out loud.

Not that he had any intention of moping around and feeling sorry for himself, Oh no, Hookie and crew had played their final trick on him. It was time to deal with the Rogues like any other group of wayward children.

A long tarpaulin-covered object occupied the far end of the cave. Peter pulled off the cover. The Mermaid's polished wood shone in the greasy lamplight.

Pitched between the perfection of motherhood and the gutsiness of a Rogue, Wendy Darling had always demonstrated a soft spot for the underdog. In engineering terms, her pet favourite was an untutored Catalonian inventor called Narois Monturiol I Estarrol. To the young Peter, his mother's daytime stories were as engaging as her bedtime stories were soporific.

'Imagine it, Peter,' she would say, a glint of passion in her eye. 'While his competitors were busy developing submarines for military purposes, Monturiol was a communist, a revolutionary, a utopian. He saw his machine as a way of improving the lives of poor coral divers. Here, Peter.' She would lay the open book before him and stab a finger grubby with oil at the illustrations. 'Such a beautiful design. A wooden submarine supported by olive wood batons and lined with copper. Why copper?' She would shoot the question at him like a bullet.

'For structural support?'

'No, Peter, no. To stop shipworms from eating the hull.'

Even as an intensely intelligent child, Peter had been haunted by images of giant worms chomping down on the wooden submarine. And while he was nonchalant about Monturiol's morality, he did appreciate the inventor's design ethic and had proceeded to apply it to a solo submersible he nicknamed the Mermaid.

A pair of polished wooden sleds allowed him to push the Mermaid out of the cave and through the sand to the water's edge. He paused for breath and mopped his forehead with a forearm. Seeing it in the sunlight, he was reminded just how perfect a machine the Mermaid really was. The 'head' was a wood-staved cabin with a broad strip of glass tied around its middle like a ribbon. This cabin housed the controls and a driver's seat, which revolved to allow for a 360-degree view through the glass. The boiler was built into the torpedo-shaped 'body' and heated via a chemical furnace; the compounds potassium chlorate, zinc and magnesium dioxide were from his mother's dry store, and while their combination produced enough power to heat the boiler, it had the added bonus of generating oxygen to supplement the supply in the cabin. The true magic, though, was in the Mermaid's tail – five feet long, covered in wooden scales, and tapering to a brass-plated rudder.

Pushing the Mermaid offshore, Peter held his breath and ducked under the water. He swam beneath the submersible and emerged in a small moon pool to the rear of the cabin. Securing himself in the driver seat, he twisted a stopcock to flood the boiler and began to work his way through the operative checklist.

It was the 28th of February 1893 when the storm hit. Peter's family had been living on the island for eight months, and while numerable supplies had been brought ashore, some larger items were stored in the traditional 'dhow' boat moored offshore. As Peter had learnt since, December to March saw violent cyclones bombard the island and its neighbours, the usual tropical serenity giving way to torrential rain and clockwise circling winds. The dhow was well made, used to carrying heavy loads up and down the East African coast. But even with its lateen sail lowered, the dhow could never have weathered that assault. Sometime between dusk and dawn, the ship tore loose of its anchor, drifted and sank near the second Freir. His parents had called it the devil's work. Peter had come to view the shipwreck as a treasure trove.

The water was fantastically clear as the Mermaid dipped

below the surface. Peter moved the weight along the line by his right shoulder, adjusting the angle of the Mermaid's descent. The smooth action of the tail drove the submersible forward at a steady rate of four knots. All around him, shoals of fish danced, their brilliant colours transforming the ocean into a fairyland. Corals burgeoned below like giant fleshy roses. A solitary turtle drifted by, buoyed on an invisible current. Once the creature stirred the water with its front flippers then drifted once more – the nonchalant old man of the sea.

Lying besides a great crease of volcanic rock, the dhow's sharply curved keel reminded Peter of one half of an eel's open jaw and he felt the jolt of discomfort he always did at the sight. The feeling gave way to excitement; Peter wanted to fly out among the wreck and peel strips off it for no other reason than it might please him. The rational side of him argued that the wreck was best preserved for future foraging.

One thing he did intend to secure that day was the Ticktock. His mother's ledger listed it under 'Weaponry/24 pounds of copper.' He knew the Ticktock had been stored in a large chest with a skull and crossbones etched on top – his mother's idea of a joke, given the Ticktock's practical application. That box now lay at the bottom of the ocean, wedged between the crease of rock and the ribs of the dhow. Up until that moment, he'd had no need for such an item, but Hookie and the rest of the Rogues had become a damnable pest. They needed swatting like sand flies.

The boiler to the rear of the cabin mumbled soothingly. It was hot inside the Mermaid but Peter didn't mind. Yes, he risked drowning or being baked alive in his handmade submersible, but he'd always entertained the idea that to die would be an awfully big adventure! He pulled on a leather strap above his head to regulate the heat off the boiler and stabilise the craft. A small adjustment to the sliding counterweight and the submersible hovered alongside the large chest.

'Peter Pandora. You possess the cunning of a crow and you are as wise as the stars,' his father used to say.

Peter sucked his bottom lip. 'Indeed I am, father,' he whispered. Scooting his seat forward on a greased wooden rail, he took hold of a pair of iron handgrips. His fingers pressed down on ten sprung-levered valves. 'Arms' unlocked on the front of the cabin; each metal limb was tipped with a grabber. Peter manipulated the handgrip valves to open and close the grabbers and secured a hold on the handle of the chest nearest the curl of rock; the other handle was trapped beneath the boat's mast. And while the arms siphoned off power from the boiler, magnifying his strength three fold, he still got slick with sweat as he tried and failed to pull the chest free.

'Move, you bloody thing!' he cried, irritated at the situation but pleased with his use of the swear word. The chest stayed wedged beneath the mast and he had to break off trying to move it and catch his breath. Water pressed all around, muffling the sounds of the boiler and the churn of the engine.

Peter stretched out his fingers and was about to work the handgrips again when something large crashed into the cabin's exterior wall. He spun around in his chair, staring out the window strip. Legs disappeared from his eye line, the soles of the feet like black leather. Peter whipped his head the other way and caught a glimpse of horns, thighs like fat hams, and a snout. When the Mermaid began to rock, water lapping at the moon pool and threatening to flood the cabin, Peter knew he had attracted company – and not that of a whale shark or a mantra ray. The hands rocking his craft were strong and animaltronic, with claws that scraped the hull.

'Rogues.' Peter bared his teeth gleefully. 'You're no match for Peter Pandora!' he cried, kicking at the sides of the cabin to add his beat to theirs. He concentrated on the hand-grips and tried again for the trapped handle. Bodies hurled themselves against the submersible. Peter was grateful to have a grip on one trunk handle since it helped anchor the Mermaid.

'Wild things!' he called out to the creatures pestering him. 'To catch a fellow unaware. But that's the nature of Rogues, isn't it?'

Faces appeared at the glass. Part mechanical, part animal, the Rogues stared in with colourful glass eyes, which reminded Peter of Christmas baubles. One Rogue had goat horns grafted onto his iron-plate skull. He butted the glass and blew bubbles out his ear canals.

'All bluster and no backbone' Peter stuck out his tongue. By way of reply, one of the Rogue crew tried to come up through the moon pool; Peter stamped on the creature's skullcap. It sank down and swam away, air escaping from steam-release vents at its knee joints.

He'd scared one off. The rest appeared perfectly happy to continue rocking the submersible. Meanwhile, a dark shape was materialising through the dust cloud kicked up by the Rogues. The figure swam with broad, confident strokes, the scythes that served for hands sweeping out in glittering arcs.

Peter slammed one hand forward, driving the correspond-ing grabber hard at the mast, splintering the rotten wood. Hookie drew closer at speed, the sweep of those long, mus-cular arms matched by the frog-like pump of his huge legs. Underwater, Hookie's fur was dark and sleek. His silver teeth shone.

At last, Peter got a lock on the other handle and lent back in his chair, pulling the handgrips towards him. Secured in the Mermaid's arms, the chest lifted off the ocean floor. Peter pressed a foot pedal to lock the arms in place then released the handgrips. Adjusting the weight counterpoint to allow for the burden, he raked a hand across the bank of switches to release the sand ballast in the storage cylinders and unleash a fresh head of steam to drive the engine. He engaged the throttle and powered up, Rogues tumbling aside in the submersible's slipstream. All but one. Hookie maintained his hold on the craft. Buffered by the pull of the water, he brought his great muzzle to the glass and stared in before letting go, seemingly of his own accord. The last thing Peter saw as the Mermaid ascended was Hookie dropping away into the darkness.

'You must stay with us now. My wife will care for you well. We are a good family and, together with the rest of the village, we will feed and clothe you.' The islanders' representative had appeared kindly and concerned. He'd smiled and clapped a hand on Peter's shoulder.

Seven years old, Peter had surveyed the horseshoe of islanders. Bella's hand had gripped his – not because she was scared of the Malagasy with their open faces and choppy way of talking but because, even at three and a half years old, she'd known he wouldn't stay.

Over the years, Peter hiked to the south side of the island on occasion. Hidden at the forest's edge, he spied on the villagers and his sister. The malady Bella had been born with was as much a gift as a trial and one that suggested she was only capable of registering one emotion at a time. On occasion, she would kick and wail in blinding rage. But there were also calmer moments when she would concoct detailed puzzles from the rows of shells she painstakingly arranged. Sometimes her laughter was high and tinkling. Sometimes she sat and stared out at the sea for hours, as if her mind had flown far away. Then Peter would see one of Bella's Malagasy brothers come and take her hand and sit with her awhile. Perhaps her new family thought her enchanted. Peter was pleased that Bella was happy. He was also sick at heart and resentful.

For the most part, Peter had been left to his own devices on the north side of the island. He didn't interfere with the fishing trips or beach BBQs or Famadihanna ceremonies where the Malagasy would exhume the remains of their ancestors, wrap them in silk and entomb the bones once more. In return, the Malagasy left him to play puppet-master with his band of loyal Lost Boys and itinerant Rogues – the later steering clear of the islanders ever since one inquisitive specimen had been speared in the chest like a giant turtle.

There was one exception to the rule though. Two days after his underwater expedition, Peter was holed up in his workshop with the Ticktock when he caught a glimpse of movement at the mouth of the cave.

'Tigermaw. I can see you.' He waited, staring out from the gloom. All he heard was the noise of the ocean.

Satisfied that his mind was playing tricks, Peter gave his attention back to the Ticktock. Dipping a small scrubbing brush into a coconut shell containing a solution of salt and vinegar, he set to work removing the patina from the brass.

A stone struck him on his left temple.

'Damnation!' His eyes flashed aside. This time he saw feathers of afro hair poking up from a crop of rocks at the cave's entrance.

'Go away before the Rogues get you, girl!' he called, slamming down the scrubbing brush.

As quick as Peter liked to think he was, his reactions didn't compare to Tigermaw's. She fired off two more stones from her slingshot. One struck Peter's thigh. The other nicked his ear.

'Enough, Tigermaw! Don't start what you can't finish.' Using a ruler as a makeshift catapult, he sent two slugs of nails towards the rocks. Apparently the scattergun approach worked. He heard a gasp.

'Peter Pandora, you are a sorcerer. You deserve a hundred stones upon your head,' came the cry from the rocks.

'And you are slow brained, and a savage to boot!'

'What are you cooking up today, evil boy?' demanded Tiger-maw, standing up suddenly and striding inside the cave. She approached his workbench, hands on hips, lemur-large eyes blinking as they adjusted to the dark. *How fantastically fearsome she looked*, thought Peter. Her face painted with white swirls. Her afro hair spread high and wide like wings. The shift she wore was a faded rose pattern. Her feet were bare.

Tigermaw pointed at the copper barrel of the Ticktock. 'Will that be a tail or a nose?'

'Neither. It is a method of upping the stakes against the Rogues.'

'Ah, so it is a weapon.' Tigermaw glared, daring Peter to deny it.

'It is *the* weapon, savage girl. I'm going to fill those Rogues with so much lead they won't have brains intact to bother my Lost Boys and me ever again.'

'By Rogues you mean the demons you yourself conjured? They are mischief-makers, but nothing more serious than children in need of their father's affection. But instead you cast them out as failed experiments.'

Tigermaw leant in close. Peter felt her breath on his lips. It made them tingle.

'Would you have us behave the same with your sister, Bella?' She stabbed a finger up at the roof of the cave. 'Bella is angry with her maker for taking away her parents, making you a stranger, and giving her an unusual nature. Should she be destroyed too?'

Peter folded his arms across his chest. 'What do you know about my inventions? You have no more right to apportion feelings to a Rogue than to a Jackfruit. As for Bella, she is a free spirit who must be allowed to fly. Your people should not try to contain her, else she might just rise up and bite you on the nose.'

'Ah, Bella is a good soul,' said Tigermaw with a dismissive flick of a hand. 'The only bad around here is a little boy who plays with flesh and machinery over choosing a normal life living alongside his sister.' The girl's big black eyes softened. 'My family will still take you in, Peter. You can have a home.'

'And see my life drain away until I am old and wrinkled, just another bag of bones for your people to cherish. No thanks. I'd rather stay here with my Lost Boys.'

Tigermaw sighed; to Peter, it was a sign of submission and he put his nose in the air.

'And what about the Rogues?' It was Tigermaw's turn to cross her arms. Under the lamplight, her white war paint was luminescent.

Peter picked up the scrubbing brush and attacked the Ticktock's patina again. 'I'll kiss each and every one goodnight with this then fashion myself a grandfather clock from their remains.'

Tigermaw stared at him, and for a moment Peter saw himself through her eyes as the true monster. He started scrubbing again. When he next looked up, the girl had gone.

Lying in bed listening to his mother's bedtime stories on the gramacorda, Peter would occasionally feel the pinch of loneliness. At such times he would question the ethics of his companion machines. Life was his to give or take at the flick of a switch or the turn of a key. But where he had really strayed from the moral path was in his creation of the Rogues – in particular, Hookie. Most Rogues owed their origin to the livestock his parents had introduced to the island – pigs, goats, sheep. Hookie, though, was a rangy old orangutan his mother had rescued from a street performer in Borneo. Shot through with arthritis and pining for Wendy, Peter had decided to put the creature out of its misery. But had the family pet deserved vivisection and animaltronic rebirth? Had any of those poor dumb animals wanted the gifts he had bestowed – intelligence, conscious thought, and all the suffering that came with an awareness of one's own mortality.

That these moments of lucidity were rare testified to Peter's absolute self-belief. Secure in his divine right to mix, mess and mesh, he'd created monsters. Now it was his choice to destroy them.

Evening settled around the circumference of the camp. Tootles had done an excellent job of collecting dry wood. The fire pit roared, spitting sparks like orange shooting stars. Slightly had unfastened a little at the neck again. He walked to and fro, muttering, 'Midnight feast, he says. Go cook it up, he says. What from, say I? Fairy dust?'

In spite of his limited larder, Slightly had magicked up a decent spread of deep fried hissing cockroach with its greasy chicken taste, vegetable and coconut curry, a platter of bright orange jackfruit pieces – resembling dragon scales laid out on a knight's shield – spiced rice, and crab claws.

In lieu of a table, Peter had instructed the Lost Boys to bring up a bench from the workshop. No one had bothered to clean it so they ate amongst sawdust and iron fillings.

The moon was fantastic – pocked and shimmering like a cherished half a crown. Everyone tucked into the feast, Peter crunching up cockroaches and greasing his chin with crab juices; the Lost Boys taking great mouthfuls, swilling the useless matter around their jaws and disgorging the lot into personal spittoons. Peter didn't mind. He had his feast. Now all he needed were a few extra guests.

Ten more minutes passed. The Lost Boys were in danger of mauling all the food.

'Leave some to attract the blighters,' he shouted. His

mechanical companions froze mid-grab. They brought their arms back down slowly and fell silent.

'They should be here by now.' Peter bit his bottom lip, scowled and forced himself to drop the childish expression. 'Fetch the gramacorda, Curly, and don't get your hair stuck in it this time when you wind it. Twin things, bring the music scrolls.' He crossed his arms and stared out at the velvet dark. 'Come out, come out, wherever you are.'

Before long, Curly and the twin tinies descended from the tree house on the elevator platform. Curly set the gramacorda down on one end of the workbench. Each twin carried a number of cylinders.

'What song shall we have?' demanded Peter. '*Whist the Bogey Man? Jolly Little Polly On A Tin Gee Gee?*'

'*Daisy Day!*' cried Tootles, patting his tin-pot belly contently.

Peter ignored him. '*Maple Leaf Rag*, it is.'

Curly saluted at the order. Locating the right cylinder, he slid out the foil sheet, fed it in then cranked the stylus into place. As he worked the handle, his wire hair bobbing, he became just another extension of the machine.

The ragtime tune plinked and plonked, cutting through the peace of the forest like swords through reeds. Peter tapped his feet to the music while watching the peculiar lurching dance of the twin tinies in the centre of the clearing. They made for pleasant little morsels of bait, he decided, his eyes sharp and his mouth tight. Curly sent the crank round and round, keeping up the tempo. Tibs forgot his sentry duty and belched steam from his mouth as he tried to recreate the musical notes. Only Tootles remained seated, no doubt eyeing up the last dregs in the oil can.

Peter strained to listen past the music and the mechanical orchestra. Was that the drag of scythes across tree trunks?

There was no wind but something whistled out among the reeds.

'Hush now, Curly.' He glared at the Lost Boy who let go of the crank and steeped away from the gramacorda as if it was nothing to do with him whatsoever. The rest of the gang fell still and the silence pressed in.

Yes, there it was – the distinctive yo-ho-ho of Rogues' pistons and the swish of their footfall. They came through the reeds, fifteen not-quite-anythings – his animalisations. Bred on steel skeletons with nerves of copper wire and clinking steam-driven insides, the Rogues were the monsters to his Frankenstein.

Stepping out from the reeds, the creatures spaced themselves out around the edges of the clearing. Each carried a makeshift weapon of a long wooden spike or a rock hammer. They showed their silver teeth and breathed heavily.

Lastly came Hookie, two pig Rogues moving aside to make way for him. The Lost Boys seemed to understand the point of the feast – that big shiny homing beacon – and stood up straight, chests plumped. Peter had not built it in them to know fear -which was not to suggest either the Lost Boys or the Rogues had turned out as pliable as he might have imagined. This was especially true in Hookie's case.

'Peter Pandora.' The ape-man spoke slowly, feeling the weight of each syllable. His tremendous, muscular shoulders were matted in orange hair. His metal breastplate reflected in the moonlight. 'What a wonderful feast. And music too. Are you holding a party for us?'

'A party for Rogues? What a notion! No, Hookie, I am throwing you a wake,' hissed Peter.

Hookie's long arms swung by his sides. The huge scythes serving as hands glinted.

'In which case, I must apologise, for I have made the intolerable faux pas of attending my own wake while still alive.

Which, I have to say, seems an idea worth prompting. After all, there ain't a man alive who wouldn't risk a breech of etiquette under those circumstances.'

'Except you aren't a man, are you Hookie. So how could you know?'

'Ah, that old chestnut. So you can give an old ape a voice to speak but refuse him humanity on the grounds his nose is a little too bulbous.' Hookie gestured to his hairless grey face. 'Or his hands a little too extraordinary.' He held up his scythes.

'You gave me a headache,' said Slightly, lunging forward. He stopped short of the ape-man, his motoring whirring inside his chest.

'I did? At least your master was good enough to put you back together again. I wonder if he would do me the same kindness.' Hookie's seven-foot frame towered over Slightly's four. Peter had always liked to experiment with proportions.

'Poor Lost Boy. A windup doll without a soul.'

'Don't go claiming a soul now, Hookie. You are an animal with a metal spine at best.'

Peter was pleased not to flinch when Hookie knocked Slightly aside and ran at him, one scythe stopping an inch short of his throat.

'If that is all I am, it is of your making. I have begged to continue my education under your tutorage. But no, the second I show a mite of interest in your precious books, you banish me and my kind from the only home we've ever known.' The sickle hand shook slightly. 'Well, if you don't mind awfully, the Rogues and I are inclined to move back in and boot you and your Puffing Billies out.'

'You can try, Hookie.' Peter stepped back and grabbed hold of the ropes, activating the platform winch. He rose rapidly towards the tree house, leaving the ape-man behind. Looking out, he saw Hookie beat his scythes against his breastplate and let out a deep bellow. Peter responded in kind, beating his chest with his fists. It was invitation enough for the Rogues to attack. Two pigs took on Nibs and Slightly, their spears clattering off the Lost Boys' chest plates. Not that Rogues were discouraged that easily. They drove the spears at Slightly's skull and Nibs' tessellated arm panels. Slightly lost his head. Nibs shed scales, exposing his inner workings.

The twin tinies fared better against the reanimated goats. Forming tight little balls, the twins propelled themselves at the goats' legs. Horns battered off them, ineffectual against the rudder feet and steel bellies. While Tootles belly-flopped the sheep, Curly added his muscle to the assault, spiking the Rogues with his wiry hair and pulling their tails.

'Ah, my fine men. Show no mercy to the Rogues!' Peter smiled. It felt phenomenally good to witness the carnage below. He was a god ruling over a universe of his own making.

'Do we honour you with our split guts and flesh wounds?' Hookie called up from the base of the largest coconut tree supporting the tree house. Unlike the rest of Peter's creations with their colourful glass orbs, Hookie retained the deep brown eyes of the orangutan. Peter felt a pang of longing for the companionship of the wise old ape he had murdered.

'You are to leave the island and swim far far away,' he told Hookie. 'No more night raids, no more crying at the moon, no more effort to be what you are not.'

'And what is that, Peter Pandora?' Hookie drove the scythes into the trunk of the tree and began to inch his way up. 'I am not to be intelligence, and yet you built me so. I am not to behave like an animal and yet you insist I refrain from bettering myself.' The scythes scraped up and in at the trunk. Hookie's grey muzzle moved closer.

'You are missing the point of servitude,' spat Peter. 'You want to question and learn and exceed your master.' He danced off to the back of the platform and ripped down the tarpaulin. The sight of the Ticktock set him aglow. With its copper

barrel restored and polished up, the steam-canon looked like
a piece of the sun. One end was enclosed in a chemical furnace
chamber, the other loaded with gunshot.

Peter stood behind the canon, hand going to the firing valve
just as the first of Hookie's great claws appeared over the platform's edge. The ape-man's shoulders rippled with muscle
mass as he hauled himself up and got to his feet.

Hookie's deep brown eyes settled on the Ticktock, which
clicked over in anticipation of being discharged.

'I ask for books and you give me bullets?'

Peter jutted his chin. 'You should have towed the line,
Hookie.'

'And you should have left me an ignorant ape!' Hookie
lunged forward, scythes whirring. Peter tripped the firing
valve; water gushed into the trigger chamber, evaporated in
an instant and discharged the canon. A starburst of gunshot
escaped the barrel. As the ape-man fell, the tip of one of his
scythes nicked Peter's cheek. He lay at his creator's feet, blood
escaping his flesh parts. His metal guts wheezed and spluttered.

Peter rolled the ape-man over to the platform's edge. He
rested a foot on the creature's bloodstained breastplate.

'Goodbye Hookie.'

He pushed the body overboard.

Seeing their captain defeated, the Rogues took flight into
the forest. Peter didn't mind. He could always pick them off
another time. Below, his Lost Boys had suffered rather badly.
Slightly's head lay a foot or so from the rest of him, mouth
flapping like a fish out of water. Tootles wobbled about on
one spot, belly skewered by a spear. Nibs had split open
again, wires and cabling erupting from his chest plate. Curly
appeared to have been scalped. Only the twin tinies looked
well preserved as they circled the clearing, fists raised, rudder
feet flapping.

Peter put his hands on his hips. He nodded in satisfaction. Victory was his. Letting his head fall back, he opened his throat and crowed.

It took Peter three days to repair his Lost Boys. Rather than drag their hefty machinery down to his workshop, he chose to bring his tools to the clearing where he worked beneath the glare of the sun and well into the night. He constructed a canopy from palm leaves, which he strung together. In the evenings when the temperature was still intense, he stacked the fire pit high, more for company than any other purpose. Watching the flames, he would fancy he caught the gleam of eyes out among the reeds. Sometimes he thought they belonged to animals gone Rogue. Other times, he believed they were bright black – Tigermaw's. Once he thought he saw a glimpse of yellow hair and he called out Bella's name urgently, like a lost sheep calling for its mother. When no answer came, he cursed his stupidity and returned to tinkering with his toys.

At last, his band of steam and clockwork men was put back together again. Slightly uttered those now immortal words, 'I have a headache', before stalking off to the platform and setting the winch in motion. Soon he was installed in the safety of his kitchen, putting Curly to good use as his commis. Tootles broke out into an idiotic monologue on the mating habits of lemurs and Peter was sorely tempted to smash him up again. Nibs and the twin tinies seemed unaware of any time lapse and spun round on the spot, fists wielded as if still engaged in brawling. Peter sent the three off into the forest to hunt, their clanging and hissing gradually receding until the night fell quiet again. Cicadas pulsed in the grasses. He could hear the ebb and flow of the ocean. It was all very beautiful, and all very dull. Not for the first time since the great ape had fallen, Peter found his gaze returning to Hookie. Flies had bothered the remains all day. The creature's muzzle was mud grey, the jaw open, the protruding tongue still and mollusc-like.

Peter approached the body and gave it a firm prod with his toe. He crossed his arms and stared up at the blanket of stars overhead. For an instant, he felt the magnitude of his insignificance next to that heavenly expanse. Pointlessness threatened to crush him alive. He hated the thought and forced it aside. He needed more than the Lost Boys. He needed someone to truly show him the meaning of love and of hate.

His gaze returned to Hookie. Dare he attempt to reanimate the ape-man's decomposing corpse? It struck him as a dark art but no more so than the acts of a twelve-year-old boy who creates living creatures out of flesh and metal. And didn't all heroes need a foe to fight?

By the light of the moon over a far away island, Peter Pandora went off to fetch his tools.

CATE GARDNER

TOO DELICATE FOR HUMAN FORM

A TRAIL OF dead goldfish wound towards the pool where
Jenny's aunt drifted face down.

Her aunt's silver chain, its pendant an iron key, dangled
from the prongs of a leaf rake. Jenny put the chain around
her neck and wondered if the fish had tried to save her aunt
or themselves. The iron key dangled between her breasts,
irritating her skin. She followed the trail back into the house,
she phoned for an ambulance. To the coroner, the fish were a
suicide note. To Jenny, they were family.

The world blurred. Rain lashed the funeral car's windows
turning the graveyard into a sodden watercolour painting –
greys, browns and greens bleeding. As the car pulled away,
Jenny imagined the palette to be a collection of mourners.
Goldfish ghosts gathering in their human form. Beside Jenny,
Coral pressed her nose to the window trying to swallow the
rain. Her elbow knocked the window button and it rolled down
allowing Coral to lean out, her red-gold hair fading to blonde
in the squall. Spray hit Jenny's hand. She scratched the patch
of inflamed skin that ran from her thumb to her elbow.

She should have left Coral in the tank at Cloyster Fishes. She shouldn't have tried to make a friend of her own.

Cloyster Fishes specialised in goldfish. Over the years, Aunt Lou had bought a variety – the bug-eyed Celestial Eye, the Black Moor, the Shubunkin, otherwise known as Gabe, Hassan and Marvin – but Jenny had always wanted a Veiltail despite her aunt's warnings that the breed were too delicate for human form.

'I heard about Lou's fish,' Adam said when she entered the shop.

Not about her aunt, about her fish.

'It wasn't purposeful,' Jenny said. 'She wouldn't have harmed them. She wouldn't have harmed herself.'

'I didn't mean . . . Lou treated her fish like family. Better than.' Adam's eyes met hers and then he glanced away, busying himself with the fish food display. 'New brand. Of course, you don't have any fish to . . . I mean . . .'

Jenny crossed the store to the tanks. Black Moors skulked around the bottom of the tank adjacent to the Veiltails.

'I want just one,' Jenny said.

Adam slid aside the tank lid and gathered the net and a plastic bag. 'Do you have a favourite?'

'If I had the energy, I'd take them all.' Jenny pointed to a fish with the longest, sweeping tail. 'She's so beautiful. I need a new tank too. It wouldn't feel right using Aunt Lou's; it belonged to them.' She didn't add that Gabe had shoved the tank off its stand the night before they all died. 'Or maybe I'll put her in a bowl.'

As she left the store, Jenny said, 'I'll name you when we meet. You never can tell who a fish will be.'

The Veiltail swam within the bath, circling its bowl and peering into its concave hollow. Jenny pulled her aunt's chain from beneath her blouse. The wooden box of fish food rested on the bath rim. This was it. She drew a breath, opened the box and took a pinch of magic flakes. She sprinkled them into the bathwater.

The fish gobbled the food. It took a moment for the transformation to take shape. First, the gills bulged and the body swelled until it seemed the fish would burst and then, its fins flapping so fast the fish blurred, the goldfish morphed into a girl. The girl shot up, spraying water across the bathroom. She gasped for air. Once her lungs were full, she turned to Jenny. Her mouth flapped open, unable to form words.

'It's okay,' Jenny said.

It probably wasn't.

Jenny helped the girl out the bath and into Aunt Lou's dressing gown, conscious of her ravaged patches of skin against the girl's newborn flesh. Flakes of Jenny's dead skin clung to the bathrobe. If Aunt Lou were here, she'd take a metal brush to Jenny's skin and scrape it until only raw skin remained.

'Who . . .?' The fish-girl peered into the mirror. 'Who . . .? Who am . . .? Who am I?'

'Your name is Coral.' Stealing her aunt's line, Jenny added, 'You bumped your head and forgot everything that happened to you.'

'Who . . . are . . . you?'

'I'm your best friend, Jenny.'

Coral's hand flapped to her forehead. Sweat dripped. *Don't be sick.* They'd known a Fantail (Eduardo) who only lasted a few hours. Perhaps she should have tried to live without someone – Aunt Lou had said people did it all the time. Maybe it was easier to live when there was no one to lose.

Or harder.

'I'm Coral.' Coral nodded at the mirror and her reflection agreed with her. 'I'm Coral.'

Jenny lay next to Coral, fighting sleep. She wasn't certain how long Coral's first transformation would last. Each fish was different. Countless times, Jenny had sat and watched the revelries afraid to go to bed. When Aunt Lou was drunk she'd forget Hassan, Gabe and Marvin were fish and that they could lose them at any moment. She grasped Coral's hand and held it to her chest.

Her dress for the funeral hung from the bedroom door like a shroud. As Coral's hand slithered away, Jenny choked back a sob.

Transformed back into a fish, Coral squirmed across the pillow, gasping for water. Jenny scooped her up and dropped her into the fishbowl. She'd bring her back in the morning. Coral pressed her fish eyes to the bowl, staring out at Jenny.

'Do you remember being human?'

She hoped not.

'Who am I?' Coral asked, water dripping from her hair.

'You're Coral. You bumped your head and forgot . . . me. It's Aunt Lou's funeral today, but you don't have to wear black.'

Aunt Lou would appreciate that a fish attended her funeral. Jenny fussed with the neck of her blouse. It irritated her psoriasis, but she shouldn't scratch. Scratching only made it worse. If Coral would move away from the bathroom cabinet and its mirror, Jenny would open the door and slather cocoa butter onto her neck to calm the itch. Her aunt disapproved of creams, said it made her skin reliant.

Coral pressed her fingertips to the mirror. 'I forgot everything.' Then she turned and ran from the bathroom, trilling, 'I forgot everything. I forgot everything. I'm Coral. I'm Coral. I'm Coral.'

Jenny's neck burned red. 'I'll always be Jenny.'

Something shattered in the bedroom. Coral stood amid the ruins of the fishbowl. Water dripped from the bedside table, pooling on the floorboards. Downstairs, the doorbell rang.

'Stay here,' Jenny said. 'And mind the glass.'

When she opened the door, a dour group greeted Jenny. The undertaker tipped his hat. *Aunt Lou's home*. Along with Gabe, Hassan, Marvin, and an assortment of fish she'd never met but who had formed a trail from pool to kitchen. The undertaker had allowed her to place a fishbowl, sans water, in the coffin. *Home*.

'I just . . . Can you give me a moment, I need to . . . We're not quite ready.'

Was anyone ever ready for death?

'Of course,' the undertaker said, stepping back.

Coral stood in the wardrobe doorway, running her hand through Jenny's clothes. She chose a red summer dress that Jenny had never worn. It came to just above Coral's knees. Watching the girl dress, Jenny knew that Aunt Lou would have loved Coral, as would have Gabe. Coral twirled, causing the skirt to fan out like a tail. Did Coral remember her fish tail? Did it bother her like a phantom limb?

'We're going to a funeral, Coral. You're very sad.'

'Am I?' Coral said. 'Should I cry?'

Jenny balanced at the edge of the bed. At her feet, glass shards glistened. Her toes scraped at the floor just above them. If she stabbed her foot, she wouldn't have to stand at the graveside and see her aunt lowered into the ground. A sob caught in her throat. Best if she thought of the coffin as an empty box. If only they sold magic flakes to change the dead into the living.

Downstairs, in the hallway, someone coughed. Jenny gathered her courage and Coral's hand. *Stay human*.

'We should go.'

'I'm very sad,' Coral said.

Please, don't turn into a fish. If Coral changed mid funeral, she'd have nothing more than a rain puddle in which to swim. Then there was the matter of how Jenny would explain the transformation to the priest and the undertaker. As if she were an anchor to human life, she didn't let go of Coral's hand until the funeral mass and burial were done.

Sitting in the back of the car, with Coral leaning out the window gobbling raindrops, Jenny had never felt so alone. The undertaker watched them through the rear-view mirror. Jenny pulled Coral away from the window and wound it shut. *Stay with me.* At the house, Aunt Lou's house, Adam Cloyster waited at the door. He carried a bag containing a goldfish. Jenny shivered.

'Everyone needs a friend,' Adam said, then blinked as Coral emerged from the car.

'Oh, it has nowhere to live. How sad. I smashed the goldfish bowl because it bothered me,' Coral said.

'Did you put the fish in your aunt's aquarium?'

Jenny jabbed the key into the door. 'It's . . .'

'Oh, there wasn't any fish,' Coral said.

'The fish is in the bathtub,' Jenny said, opening the door.

'Oh, but I was in the bath.'

Coral stooped and pressed her face to the bag to see inside. Her skin shimmered, scales rippling against skin and hinting at impending transformation. Jenny pulled her up the stairs.

'I'll show you,' Jenny said, hoping politeness would stop Adam following them.

Behind them, the stairs creaked. His steps slower than theirs, cautious. Coral flopped to the bathroom floor, her fish-*self* buried within the dress. Jenny gathered it and dropped it into the bath. The landing floorboards groaned. The Coral fish swam from the neckline. Jenny gathered the dress and dropped the sodden fabric into the laundry basket just as Adam entered the bathroom.

'Where's your friend?' he asked.

'Why in the plastic bag you're carrying,' Jenny said.

'I meant your human friend.'

'She's lying down. Tough day.'

Adam sat on the edge of the bath and placed the plastic bag inside the bathwater. He didn't open it. 'I would have come to the funeral but I figured, considering the circumstances of Lou's death, it might seem odd and perhaps callous that I brought a fish instead of flowers.'

The box containing the fish food, which perched on the corner of the bath, wobbled behind him. The key protruded from the lock.

'It's a lovely thought. Would you like a drink?'

As they left the bathroom, something heavy splashed into the bath. The box. Jenny bit her lip and blinked against tears. *Let it have fallen closed. Let it be watertight.* The box contained her only supply of the magical fish food and Aunt Lou had left no instructions as to where she could purchase more. As they headed downstairs, Adam pressed his hand to her lower back. She supposed he thought her tears for her aunt and not for the girl who this moment thrashed into life for the final time.

'My aunt didn't happen to buy her fish food from you?' Jenny asked.

Water splashed, sounded more tidal wave, in the bathroom.

'No, but I'm sure our brand is as good. What's that' – Adam turned – 'noise?'

Coral would need reminding who she was, who she would never be again. Perhaps if she'd gobbled the entire contents of the box she would last a lifetime.

Adam reached the bathroom before Jenny. As he dragged Coral out of the bath, her foot caught around the plug, releasing the water. Playing double the hero, Adam scooped the plastic bag containing his gift fish out of the water, while Jenny wrapped a towelling gown around Coral.

'Your fish must have gone down the plughole. I'm sorry,' Adam said, as if this was his fault. 'Are you okay?'

The plughole was too small for a fish to swim down, but she hoped he didn't notice or question that. Jenny rubbed Coral's skin within the towelling robe. Psoriasis flaked from Jenny's skin and clung to the scum that circled the bath. Her hands shook. The flakes resembled the fish food. She scratched her skin, fingernails digging into scabs. *No, Aunt Lou wouldn't...*

But, of course, Aunt Lou would. If her psoriasis was the food, then every time Aunt Lou took a medicinal brush to her skin and left her inflamed, she was gathering food for her fish.

'Leave the bathroom,' Jenny said.

'Me?' Coral whispered.

'No, not you. Please, Adam. I'll only be a moment.'

'I should leave.'

He should and yet, she said, 'I'll only be a moment. Please stay.'

Adam left the fish in the sink. Jenny placed the plug in the hole and ran the tap. She opened the plastic bag and allowed the fish to swim out, not worrying that it hadn't acclimatised. Coral held her hands to her face, examining her knuckles and her thumb, marvelling at them. *She does remember.* Jenny scratched her arm until several flakes dropped into the water. The fish, another Veiltail, gobbled them. Its features stretched and bulged and flapped until a man fell from the sink, cracking his elbow against the bathtub.

Coral screamed.

Jenny pressed her hand to her arm, to her skin, to evidence that her aunt had betrayed her. The doorknob dug into her lower back. It rattled. Adam.

'Are you okay? What's going on?'

'Everything's fine,' Jenny said.

The fish-man's scream added to the chorus. He rocked back, clutching his elbow, and she could think of no name to offer him, no comfort. Coral sucked in air, calmed her scream.

'I'm not. I'm not. I'm not,' Coral said.

You are, you are, you are. Jenny wrapped her arms about herself. As the door pushed open, she fell forward.

'What's. . .?' When Adam noted the naked man, his mouth flapped open.

'Who am I?' the man-fish asked.

'Indeed,' Jenny stood between them. 'Adam, this is my cousin. . . David.'

'No. No, he's not. He's the fish,' Coral said.

'What's going on?' Adam asked.

Jenny wiped away a tear. 'I just found out my aunt wasn't who I thought she was and I'm left wondering if I'm who I thought I was. What if I'm like them? What if I'm. . .barely breathing?'

Jenny turned for the door and raced down the stairs, slipping on the final step. Who would scoop *her* up if she turned into a fish? Who would place her in the bathtub or an aquarium or, god forbid, a fishbowl? She skidded across the kitchen tiles, following the path the dead goldfish had marked out a week before. Her skin screamed as she dropped into the chlorinated pool.

Let me remember who I was.

She sank to the bottom, arms and legs flapping but gaining no purchase. A week's worth of autumn leaves clung to her skin and affixed to the tiled floor. A final leaf pressed against her lips and mouth. She sucked the leaf in, choking against it and the wall of water that filled her lungs.

Remember . . . Remember . . . Re . . .

IMOGEN

IMOGEN HAD BEEN blatant that night. She wanted Michael to know how she felt, wanted to share her love, her sex, her emotions, before they bubbled out unchecked for everyone to see. Day after day she was holding it together but the nights were the worst. She wanted him even though she knew it was a sin and no number of Hail Marys was ever going to change that.

Imogen sat in the dark waiting for Michael to return. It was late. He was often home by two, but that night he still hadn't arrived by four. She was worried. She rubbed her eyes, reached for the cold cup of coffee beside her chair and glanced down at the bare flesh that showed through the slit in her nightdress. Her hand slid over her thigh and her fingers slipped under the fabric until they stroked the bare skin there. She imagined it was *his* hand, skin slightly roughened from his job as a carpenter that touched the intimate and soft area between her legs.

At some point in the night she had dozed in the chair. It helped to ease the long hours, and it meant she didn't see the painful bleakness of dawn struggling through the wintery clouds. Sleeping on the job, so they say, was a dangerous game she sometimes played. What would he think if he came home and found her in *his* chair, with so little clothing on? Nothing probably. That was the thing: he wouldn't even notice. All he saw when he looked at her was his little sister. But then, how could she possibly expect him to think of her in any other way?

Imogen stood and stretched, the thin shoulder strap of her nightdress fell and the fabric slipped down, revealing one of her pert small breasts. She looked down at it. If only Michael would come home now. She was so ready to show him how she felt. Her hand slipped over the fabric, briefly cupped her breast and then she pulled up the strap, covering herself.

Headlights illuminated the room as a car pulled into the drive and Imogen's heart jumped in her chest. Her resolve diminished instantly and she ran for the stairs taking them two at a time. At the top she glanced back down before turning and heading straight to her room at the front of the house. She didn't look out as the engine switched off, but instead slipped into her bed and lay there, heart pounding.

She heard the front door open: although as always, Michael was trying to be quiet. A dull scraping noise told her that the chain was now in place. She lay in the bed, her legs apart, hoping he would come in, but knowing he wouldn't. For a while longer she could make out the muted sounds of Michael moving around the house.

Work clothing in the washing machine, she thought. *Glass of juice from the fridge.*

Imogen knew her brother's routine so well she barely heard the noises but recognised them anyway. Michael was very fastidious about hygiene. He would be in the bathroom shortly brushing his teeth. *There!* Water ran into the sink. The shower switched on.

Oh Michael! She imagined his rough hands running over his own body, washing away the day's grime. She imagined him naked and hard and eager.

The shower switched off. Imogen's hand rested on her pubis

as she listened. Then she heard Michael open his bedroom door. It wasn't long before his soft snores filtered through the wall.

She brought herself to a guilty orgasm. Then lay panting softly. Wishing again that she wasn't his sister. It all seemed so unfair.

In the morning she ate breakfast alone, Michael was still in bed. She hated the late shifts he worked. They barely spent any time together at all. Since their mother died, Michael had taken extra hours, worked harder, all in the name of supporting them both.

At lunchtime Imogen heard the shower again and soon Michael came downstairs.

'Hi,' she said.

'Morning.'

Michael looked tired but relaxed. His blond hair was washed and combed back wet from his face. His blue eyes were bright as he smiled at her. His colouring was so different from hers. Imogen brushed back her dark hair and scrutinised Michael with her hazel eyes. Sometimes she daydreamed that they weren't related at all. Their colouring was so different that this wasn't so hard to imagine. They were in fact opposites.

'How was your day, Gen?' he asked.

'A little dull. I missed you.'

Michael nodded his head but said nothing as he sat down at the kitchen table. Imogen put a cup of coffee – white, two sugars, just as he liked it – down on the table before him. Then she sat down opposite him.

'I thought I might go down to the job centre today,' Imogen said. 'It's not fair that you have to work so hard all the time when I'm more than cap-'

'No,' Michael said firmly. 'You need to stay home, Gen. *That* is your job.'

Imogen felt that knot of anxiety she sometimes felt when

she wanted to disagree with Michael. He was pretty stubborn. He took after their mother that way. His ego would cause him no end of trouble one day, but it was impossible to argue with him.

Michael placed his hand on hers and looked at her over the table.

'I promised Mum that I'd look after you. And I will. Always.'

Imogen's face lit up as Michael looked into her eyes, but her brother suddenly blushed and pulled back his hand.

The guilt came again. She shouldn't love him this way. She had to be careful. Surely he knew how she felt? She couldn't help reading into his reaction though, always giving herself false hope. *What if the blush means he feels the same?*

Imogen stood up and went to the dishwasher. Her hands were trembling, her heart pounding in her chest. All the thoughts and feelings she carried inside her rumbled around and yelled 'sinner' inside her head. She began to fill the machine with the breakfast dishes and dirty mugs, but her fingers were clumsy and one of the glasses fell from her hand and smashed down on the tiled floor.

'What the fuck . . .?'

Michael stood but Imogen was already cleaning up the mess. She knew how he hated chaos. She had to keep the house clean for him. *That* was her job.

'Mind you don't cut your –' Michael said calmly.

'It's fine. I'm fine,' she answered. 'Sorry.'

She made him chicken salad for lunch. He ate it silently while sipping orange juice.

'Must get back to work,' he said pushing back his chair. 'Cupboards don't build themselves.'

Imogen said nothing but she watched him pick up his tool bag. Inside she knew were all the things he needed to work. She remembered watching him build a cupboard recently. It might even have been a wardrobe. He had caressed the wood, smoothed and shaped it: worked with so much love and care that she couldn't help admiring his hands as they moved. Perhaps that was even the moment when she realised she loved him more than she should.

'Will you be late tonight?' she asked as he pulled his jacket from the coat rack by the door.

'No. This job is almost finished. Should be back early. About six.'

'I'll make dinner then,' Imogen said.

After he left, the house felt empty. Imogen cleaned and tidied and emptied the washing machine. She shook out Michael's overalls and examined the stains. Brown smears marred the cloth. Imogen knew it was wood stain but the splatter made her feel uneasy. It never came out fully, and to Michael it probably didn't matter at all. After all next time he wore them more stain would find its way onto his cloth. Imogen wanted them cleaner though and so she put the wash back on and ran the cycle twice more before switching the load over to the drier.

Then she chopped some vegetables and made a beef casserole.

'Gen? Are you home?'

Imogen jerked awake. She had dozed off in the chair in the lounge again and the hours had passed as though she didn't exist. There had been no dream but the sleep had been deep and sound.

'Must have fallen asleep,' she said as Michael entered the room.

His eyes skittered over her and Imogen realised that she was still in her nightclothes and her robe was lying open exposing her leg.

'It's six,' he said.

'Oh good. Dinner should be perfect now.'

They went into the kitchen and Michael sat once more at the table as Imogen passed him a bowl and a plate with a crusty roll on. Then she placed a bottle of red wine and two glasses down. They sat together talking about the day, but Imogen could barely make conversation as hers had been so dull. She listened to Michael talk though. He loved his work and his affinity with his craft was evident in his words.

'I might have to go out again tonight,' Michael said. 'There is one last thing that needs to be finished on this job and there seems little point in leaving it undone when it would only take me an hour or so.'

'Oh that's a shame. I thought we would watch something on TV together. Michael I hardly see you. I'm alone so much.'

Michael looked down at his plate and took a sharp breath. He seemed on the verge of saying something but instead he stood up, bumped the table and knocked his glass over. The wine splashed over the table and onto Imogen's robe. She looked down, watched the wine seep into the cloth like a bloodstain on her abdomen.

Michael stared at her, then backed away.

'I can't do this Gen. Not again!'

Imogen heard the front door slam and she stared at the spilt wine and the stain and her empty bowl. Nothing made sense. She had upset him, but didn't know how. She removed the robe and placed it in the washer.

At two she heard him return. She waited downstairs as always, saw the headlights, hurried to her room. It was a cycle that repeated night after night. Sometimes she lingered outside of his door while he slept. She knew that entering his room would be bad but she couldn't help toying with the idea. She would pace silently, waiting for him to wake and find her there. She wished again and again that they weren't related. That she was just some girl that lived in the same house as him. Not his sister, but his lover.

It was as though she only lived when he came home. Each day was the same. She cooked, she cleaned, she washed his overalls and then he would return and fall asleep leaving her lonely.

'Something weird happened today,' she said. 'I waved at the neighbour when she was in her garden. She was looking straight at me but completely ignored me. She used to be so friendly. I think I must have upset her somehow?'

'I'll speak to her,' Michael said.

'It was odd wasn't it?'

'Yes.'

'If I have offended her will you apologise? I didn't mean it. But I might have said something without realising.'

'I'm sure it's nothing . . .'

That night Michael didn't go out. They sat watching the television and he nursed the remote control as he always did. Imogen didn't mind. She felt alive and calm and happy. She always felt more vital when Michael was around.

At bedtime she followed him upstairs. She waited while he used the bathroom, then stood awkwardly at the top of the stairs as he opened his bedroom door.

'Michael?'

'I'm tired, Imogen.'

'Can I . . .?'

'Goodnight,' he said closing his door firmly shut.

Imogen jumped awake as she heard the phone ringing beside her. She had fallen asleep in the chair again. Her hand took the receiver and she pressed it against her ear before she realised that Michael had already answered.

'Good morning gorgeous,' said a female voice. 'I missed you last night.'

Imogen was too surprised to speak.

'Stacey . . .' Michael's voice sounded sleepy and soft.

'So . . . I was thinking I might come over to your place tonight instead.'

'No. I'll come to you. Things are a bit messy here at the moment.'

Imogen listened as Michael talked about the chaos at home. She looked around the immaculate lounge and wondered what it was that she wasn't doing properly. She placed the receiver down quietly as Michael finished his conversation, and then she sneaked upstairs and back into her room before he discovered that she was awake.

She felt hurt that he hadn't mentioned his new girlfriend and that he had lied to her about where he was all of those evenings. Clearly he wasn't working so late all the time. He was sleeping with his new whore instead.

Imogen felt a terrible rage. Her ears burst with noise as her heart leapt in her chest. *There was someone else!* But then, what did she expect? She couldn't have him. Ever. She had to accept that and move on.

'Michael, why didn't you tell me you had a girlfriend?' she asked as she poured tea from the pot into his cup.

'What?'

'I heard you talking to her. Stacey isn't it?'

Michael flushed with guilt.

'Gen, we've been through this before. I don't like to talk about these things with you.'

'Why?'

'Because . . . because you don't take it well. But there's nothing to fear. I will look after you. Like I promised.'

'I'm lonely. I'd like a boyfriend.'

'Don't Imogen,' Michael warned. His face was flushed and he appeared on the edge of anger.

'Maybe I'll go out today and find myself someone. Bring him back here and fuck him. How about *that* Michael?'

'Stop it, Imogen. You know I don't like you to talk that way,' Michael was so angry now, he gripped the table. 'I won't hear any more about this. I'm entitled to have some life.'

Imogen was angry too and she was suddenly not afraid to show it.

'I want a life too. I'm entitled to have life and love and sex, just the same as anyone else is.'

Michael jumped up throwing his chair back. 'You want sex do you? You dirty little whore. You want to tempt me again and again. Don't you remember where that led last time?'

He brought his open palm down across her face, hard, and the stinging slap rang through the kitchen and echoed out into the hallway.

Imogen fell against the sink but Michael wouldn't leave it there. She hadn't been chastised enough. He grabbed her hair, pulling her backwards until she fell down at his feet. He pulled open her robe, ripping at the nightdress.

'You fucking slut. Always lying around half dressed, always flaunting yourself. What do you expect me to do?'

Imogen felt his carpenter's hands roughly squeezing her bare breasts. But it wasn't sensual, or nice. Not at all as she had hoped. It hurt and she was scared.

'Do you know how hard it's been for me? Ever since that day? And it's all your fault Imogen. All because you found those papers . . .'

Imogen couldn't understand what he was saying, she could feel his hands on her, and that was all that mattered. Even though there was no love in his touch at all. Everything that happened had been leading to this moment. She wanted him, was he finally taking care of everything.

She felt the knife penetrate her stomach and when she coughed, a gout of blood gushed from her mouth. But Michael didn't stop. He plunged the knife into her over and over again, like a parody of the sex act that could never happen between them.

'It's a sin. You dirty fucking tramp. Even if mother did adopt you. So what if we aren't really brother and sister? We were brought up that way and I can't want you. You're better off dead.'

Blood poured on the floor. Something she would have to clean up when Michael had finished murdering her.

She lay still while he enjoyed himself: twisting and turning the knife while the red stuff spread over them both. His overalls were covered in stains by the time he discarded them, pushing them straight into the washing machine. The walls and cupboards were splattered in her blood

'Get up,' he said finally. 'Clean this mess you made.'

Imogen grimaced and pushed her intestines back inside her stomach. The hole closed. She staggered to her feet, sore and barely able to stand but still she hobbled over to the cupboard to find the mop and bucket. Then she cleaned up the blood while Michael sat at the table with a fresh pot of tea.

'I'm going out,' he said.

'Will you be late?' she asked.

'Yes. Don't wait up for me.'

Imogen slipped into oblivion again for a few hours. When she woke she found herself sitting once more in the chair. Her eyes were stinging. She sat in the dark waiting for Michael to return. It was late and she couldn't remember how she got there.

Her robe lay over the back of the chair and she was wearing her favourite nightdress. It was made of a pure white satin. She glanced down at her bare thigh and then back at the window. She was waiting for Michael. She was always waiting for Michael.

A car turned into the street and for a moment the headlights lit up the room. Imogen ran upstairs and went into her room. She lay down pulling the sheet over her.

Michael woke. He pushed aside the covers and sat up. The room was in darkness, but he could see the light peeking around the corners of the curtain. He smelt frying bacon, heard the kettle boil and he knew his sister would be making breakfast.

He shook away the horrible dream that still lurked in the back of his head. Imogen. A knife. Blood. It was all too awful to even consider.

He showered, washed his hair, and combed it back and away from his face. Then he shaved away the bristle. When he came out of the bathroom, he glanced at Imogen's room. The door was closed and he didn't like to go in, but she had left her robe over the edge of the bath.

He quietly entered her room and placed the robe on the chair at the bottom of the coffin. Then glanced through the glass panel to see the rotting face of his sister looking impassionately back at him. His hand stroked the smooth lid of the coffin. It had been his finest work and no one but him would ever see it.

Downstairs Imogen placed a cup of coffee before him. Then a plate containing eggs and bacon, with toast that was slightly burnt.

She was wearing her favourite nightdress just to taunt him, but Michael chose to ignore it. Today he would be kind. Today he would pretend nothing was wrong. He hated to argue with her. Today things would end differently.

Michael sat and began to eat his breakfast.

Imogen sat opposite. The strap of her nightgown had fallen off one shoulder and she was wearing red lipstick. He could see her pale pink nipples showing through the sheer satin fabric.

'I thought I might look for work,' she said. 'It's not fair that you have to work so hard to support us.'

'No,' he said a little too sharply. 'I promised Mum I'd look after you.'

'Michael I found something today. Haven't you ever wondered why we look so different?'

'Don't, Gen. Let's not do this . . .' he pleaded. His stomach heaved against the bacon.

'We're not related. I was adopted,' Imogen said.

Michael turned away as she slipped the nightdress down revealing her breasts.

'I'm not your sister.'

'Stop it. I don't want to do this.'

The satin fabric fell to the ground. Imogen was naked underneath and he could see the pink nipples that haunted his dreams and the fine black down between her legs.

'What are you?' he cried dropping his face into his hands. 'Damn you. Can't you leave me alone?'

'I love you Michael. I want to be your wife.'

Michael felt Imogen's hand stroke his hair. He wanted to die but didn't feel brave enough to take his life.

'I'm sorry. I'm sorry. I didn't mean to hurt you.'

'Death do us part,' she said.

'You're dead . . . Can't you leave me in peace?'

'I want to be yours, Michael. Can't you see that?' Imogen smiled. 'This time I'm giving you permission.'

Michael pushed away from the table and backed up to the door but Imogen came forward holding out the knife.

'Kill me, Michael. Make me yours.'

Michael took the knife. Maybe this time she would stay dead. He slashed and stabbed, twisted and turned. Blood covered the floor, the cupboards, the walls. Imogen was still.

Then she turned her head and met his gaze with that cold, dead smile pasted on her painted lips.

'I had better clean up this mess,' she said.

Michael stood. Removed his overalls and placed them in the washer.

Then he cried.

ALISON LITTLEWOOD

IN THE QUIET AND
IN THE DARK

THE STREET WAS dead. Steph looked up and down it and saw honey-coloured houses, a quiet church, and behind everything, sleeping fields. She wrinkled her nose. 'Street' didn't seem the right word for it, not really; she didn't know what was. 'Lane' was too small – this was the centre of Long Compton – and 'road' implied it was going somewhere. Anywhere.

She thought again of the way her mother had said goodbye, walking down the platform after the train as if she hadn't wanted Steph to go. Then she'd turned before she was quite out of sight, taken her new husband's arm and walked away, a spring to her step, off to live in some cheap bar on an unfashionable stretch of Italian coastline. Steph scowled. She had asked if she could go too – just once – and she didn't really remember the words her mother had used, but she remembered the look in her eyes. Steph knew, when she saw that look, that it wasn't any use. The flat in London was already sold – the one that lay on a street, a proper street – and now she was here in the Cotswolds with her dad, nowhere to go and nothing to do, in the far reaches of the back of beyond.

But it's beautiful, a voice said in the back of her mind,

and Steph shook the thought away. She didn't want it to be beautiful, didn't want the sun to be pressing down insistently on the top of her head, shining on the mellow stone of the church. It was late summer, nearly time for school, and that meant everything starting, her life here; everything beginning again.

A bell rang behind her, tinny and shrill, and Steph jumped. A bicycle flew past, its tyres whizzing against hot tarmac. 'Watch it,' a voice said, and there was a flash of yellow hair. The girl braked, set down her feet, wheeled the bike around. 'You moved into Willow Cottage,' she said to Steph. She made it sound like an accusation.

Steph nodded.

'We're off to the Rollrights,' the girl said. Her hair was pale, her skin tanned to honey, a tone darker than the buildings behind her. 'You want to see the Rollrights?'

Steph shrugged. She didn't know what the Rollrights were, whether they were things or people, and didn't much care either way.

'You got a bike?'

Steph shook her head. She hadn't needed a bike, had always used the bus or the tube.

'You should have borrowed one, like me.' The girl grinned. 'Well, get on then.'

Steph got onto the back, found herself reluctant to hold on but didn't have much choice; she put her hands around the girl's waist as they headed away, strangely intimate, the shadow of their wheels churning on the pavement, and realised that she didn't even know her name.

The girl was called Holly, and the other part of the 'we' was Anne. They were Steph's age – fourteen – and would be in her class in school. The three of them walked up a path from the warden's hut, where an information sign informed Steph that the Rollright Stones were a thing, not a family; but the place was green and empty and she wondered why they had come here, where there was nothing. They passed a few walkers on their way, and all of them were Steph's father's age, and they didn't seem particularly excited about anything much.

'Race you,' said Holly, and they charged up the rest of the slope under the late summer sun until they doubled over, laughing, and Steph looked up to see a stone circle at the top of the hillside.

She pulled a face. It was smaller than she'd imagined when she'd seen the sign at the bottom. The circle was wide, but the stones were nothing but a jumble of worn-down teeth. She had imagined something like Stonehenge, towering, formed into rough arches.

'The King's Men,' said Anne, and she ran to the nearest stone and slapped it before weaving in and out of the next.

'They're supposed to be soldiers, turned to stone by a witch,' Holly said. 'Stupid, really. But it's pretty cool up here. You can see for miles.'

Steph looked out over the landscape. It was green and rolling and went on and on. A few small villages nestled into it, calm and cosy and safe. She couldn't see her old home at all. She wondered if her mother was out there somewhere, looking back towards her, and felt a pang of homesickness.

'Witches come here,' said Holly.

'They're not witches, idiot,' said Anne. 'They're druids, or pagans or something. They have rites.'

Steph thought she'd said *rights*, frowned as Anne mimed pulling a knife from her jeans and cut her own throat. Then she got it.

'They *don't* do that,' laughed Holly. 'They just – I don't know, greet the dawn or something.'

'Freaks.'

'Weirdos.'

Steph grinned at the pair as they joined hands and spun each other around, moving towards the centre of the circle. Then they stopped.

'You can't count the stones,' said Anne. 'If you count them three times and get the same number, you get a wish.'

Holly snorted. 'I thought it was 'the man will never live' who can do that,' she said. 'I always thought that meant, if someone managed it, it means they'll die.'

Steph laughed, but she wasn't really looking at the girls any more. She was looking around at the circle, the whole empty place, nothing to do, nothing to see, but it didn't feel like that, not really; she had a sudden sense of people coming here, century upon century, because there was something here after all: something important. She wondered for a moment if maybe they *had* killed people here, put them to death while they sang and the stars wheeled overhead, but then she shook the thought away. It was a pile of rocks and empty fields and nothing more. If she was in Italy, there'd be the sea. She could swim. There would be shops and things to do and people, lots of people. She looked back at Holly and Anne and found they were staring at her.

Holly shrugged, as if Steph had asked her a question she couldn't answer. 'Come on,' she said. 'Let's go and see the Knights.'

The Whispering Knights were a collection of tall stones, four or five of them together a distance away from the main circle, and they didn't look like knights to Steph. There was a fence around them, each black strut ending in a blunted arrow.

Holly and Anne walked together, talking about what their friends had been doing, Janey and Finch and Tom, names Steph didn't know. She cut away and went towards the stones.

They were taller than she had thought, broad and powerful but rough, their skin pocked and pitted.

Their skin, she thought, and smiled at herself. They weren't knights; the name was more exciting than the place.

'They can tell your fortune,' Holly said close to her ear, and Steph jumped. 'They see the future. If you sit and listen, they'll tell you who you're going to marry.'

Anne, behind her, laughed. 'Jason Dereham,' she said. 'That's who Holly's going to marry.'

Holly hit out at her friend, and judging by the face she pulled Steph gathered that Jason Dereham would have been her last choice on the planet.

'I wonder who you'll get?' Holly said. 'Hmm, Cal Parker might do.'

'Get real,' said Anne. 'Maybe Ben Hodson.'

'Or *Marcus.*'

The two joined hands, laughing, and Steph pulled an uncertain smile, unsure if they were mocking her or if the boys they named might actually be someone she could like. Then she shook her head. She wasn't going to fall for some local kid, *marry* some local kid; she wasn't going to stay here at all.

'You should try it,' said Holly.

Steph shook her head. 'I'm not getting married.'

Holly shrugged. 'Maybe you will, maybe you won't. It's fate. It's up to the stones to decide.'

Steph snorted.

'Let the stones decide!' chanted Anne. 'Let – the – stones – '

'Fate,' said Holly. 'Come on, we'll all do it, won't we, Anne.'

'I don't believe in fate,' said Steph, 'or any of that. I don't believe there's one person we're supposed to be with. It's all bullshit.'

Holly pulled a face, half-shocked, half-amused. 'Don't

insult the stones,' she said, 'or *you'll* have to marry Jason Dereham. And you don't know how bad that is, but take my word for it, it's pretty bad.'

'I don't believe my mum was *supposed* to marry my dad. Look how that turned out.'

'But then you'd never have been born. Everything was *supposed* to happen,' said Anne. 'Come on. It's only a laugh, anyway.'

Steph tried to smile. Anne was right, it was only a bit of fun, and she wanted to be friends, didn't want to be labelled the boring one or the miserable one before school even begun. The three of them sat with their backs to the railing, sinking into the long grass that grew around its base.

'Close your eyes,' Holly said. 'Close your eyes and be quiet and wait until you hear a name.'

Steph's nose itched, and she scratched it. She heard a soft titter at her side: Anne. She wondered if the others still had their eyes closed or if it was all some stupid trick, whether they were making fun of her. Then she heard a voice: Holly's voice but deeper, full of barely suppressed laughter. *'Jason Dereham . . .'*

Anne giggled. 'Stop it.' And they fell quiet again. Steph felt the sun warm on her face, the soft breeze a cooler note. She could smell green things, sap rising through the grass, a sourer tang from the fields. It was different, here. There was no sense of presence, of layers of things past just beneath the surface. There was nothing at all, and it wasn't home, and she didn't know any boys and didn't have to and it was all right because she didn't have to stay.

The sunlight stopped shining on her skin. She opened her eyes and there was a figure standing over her, someone tall, silhouetted by the sun. She felt Holly's hand on her arm.

'So,' said the voice. It was a boy's voice, full of amusement. 'Who's it going to be?'

The boy gave his name as Kix, short-for-something-boring, and he sat next to Anne and pulled a packet of cigarettes from his pocket. He was good looking in a thin, bony kind of way, and had pale hair that hung over his eyes. From the way Holly and Anne hung on his every word, Steph gathered that he was the popular kid in school, the cool kid. Then he flicked his hair and held out a cigarette. She didn't take it; didn't like the smell, never had. He shrugged and passed it to Holly and she took it, breathed in deep, and from the way she tensed, Steph could tell she was trying not to cough.

'So, you were asking the stones a question. Don't let me stop you.' Kix smiled a sardonic smile.

'She's going to marry Jason Dereham,' Holly said and laughed, the forcefulness in her voice almost trying to make it true.

The boy breathed a plume of faint smoke that vanished into the air. 'No,' he said after a while, drawing the word out slow; 'no, I don't think so. I don't think Jason Dereham would do at all.'

Steph found her cheeks colouring. 'I'm not getting married,' she said. 'Marriage is a joke. It's all a joke. I'm going to travel; I'm going to see the world.'

'The world, eh?' he leaned forward, peering at her from under his hair, so that she wondered why he didn't brush it aside; that way, she could have seen his eyes. 'Maybe. Maybe not. It depends what fate has in store for you, doesn't it.'

Steph pushed herself up from the grass. 'This is crap,' she said, knowing as she said it that she was burning her bridges, marking herself out as no fun and no use before she'd even started her new school, but she couldn't help herself. 'It's all crap. If you think it's fate – why did my mum leave my dad? Why did he even let her go?' And she was walking away, fast

172

as she could, knowing she'd have to walk all the way back into town on her own, and she didn't care about that either; she had nowhere else to go, nowhere else to be. Only the quiet, sleeping village, where nothing seemed to happen and she knew no one.

She looked at the King's Men as she left the site, still in the places they had been for centuries, but looking more like people now that the sun was lower; motionless people looking back at her, their expressions nothing she could read.

Holly caught her as she walked along the lane, chinging her bicycle bell as she stopped. Anne was nowhere to be seen.

'Wait up,' she said. 'What'd you go chasing off for?'

'Sorry,' said Steph. 'It's just – '

'I got what it was. I gather things aren't all contentment in Willow Cottage.'

'Not exactly.' Steph thought of the quiet house her father had bought after the divorce, its small rooms, the quaint thatched roof. It was the image of contentment; her father, indeed, seemed more than resigned to it. It was Steph who was angry, who had brought a note of discord into the house. *But it's their fault.*

'Kix really likes you,' Holly's voice took on a more teasing note, and something else – jealousy? Steph wasn't sure.

She shook her head. She remembered the way he'd looked at her through his hair, his eyes nothing but two bright points. She didn't think he'd looked as though he liked her, wasn't really sure if she liked him.

'He said so,' said Holly. She moved aside on the bike, making room for Steph. 'He's gorgeous, isn't he. Maybe it's *him* you're going to marry.' She looked mock-startled at Steph's expression. 'Just kidding.'

Steph slipped onto the bike. 'What's his name anyway?' she asked as she took hold of Holly's waist. 'Kix isn't a name.'

'No idea,' Holly said, giving a quick chirr-chirr of her bicycle bell. 'I never met him before in my life.'

The tallest of the King's Men was bony against Steph's back as she closed her eyes and listened to the tour guide. She wasn't with the tour guide, wasn't really with anyone – she'd walked to the Rollrights this time, just for somewhere to go. She didn't have any money but the warden hadn't been there so she'd come in anyway, was now sitting out of sight of the guided tour while they went on about megalithic structures and burial chambers and thousands and thousands of years.

Then she heard familiar words, and opened her eyes, startled. 'The man will never live who can count the stones three times and arrive at the same number,' the voice said. 'Either that, or they'll get their heart's desire. Do you want to try it?'

Steph heard murmurs of assent and footsteps edging around the stones, and caught her breath. Would they know she hadn't paid? And then someone was close, really close, and so she stood and pointed to the nearest stone and the next, counting them herself, just another one of the group.

She glanced around and started. It was Kix standing there, watching her with an amused expression. 'Three, four, five,' he prompted, and grinned.

'What are you doing here? I thought you were – '

'Not me.'

'How'd you know what I was going to say?'

He tilted his head, and she got the distinct impression that he'd winked at her, though couldn't really see his eyes.

'So let's do it,' he said. 'Let's count them. You go that way, I'll go the other.'

Steph let out a splutter of a laugh, and nodded. She turned her back on Kix, continued around the circle, counting each pillar and boulder and stub, stepping out of the way as she crossed paths with various tourists. When she was halfway round she glanced up and looked for Kix; saw only the tour guide looking at her with narrowed eyes. She put her head down, kept going. Thirty-three, thirty-four. On around the circle, focusing on the ground so that she began to feel dizzy. When she looked up she was almost back at the tallest stone and she found that Kix was waiting for her, grinning that broad grin.

'Seventy-four,' she said, triumphantly.

'If you say so,' he said. 'Now, the other way. Come on!'

Steph doubled back, already growing tired of this. It was getting boring, counting the stones. But still – twenty-six, twenty-seven. It wasn't difficult, wouldn't take long.

She finished the circle and once more Kix was there ahead of her. Steph smiled at him, ready to count the last few stones before the tallest – she'd counted that already, hadn't she? And she drew alongside, and looked puzzled.

'Problem?'

'Seventy-six,' she said. 'No, that can't be right. I must have missed – when – '

'Never mind. Once more, back the other way.'

And so she did, she made her way around the circle, making sure to count each stone. And she'd counted the tallest already: definitely. This time there could be no mistake. When she reached the starting point, she wasn't surprised to see that Kix had beaten her to it; she had taken her time. She counted the last couple of stones and her smile faded.

'Seventy – but – '

He grinned again, that knowing grin she wasn't sure she liked.

'So it's true,' he said. 'And no heart's desire for you, young lady.'

'Or you.'

'What makes you say that?'

'You got the same number? Three times?'

He tapped his finger on the side of his nose. 'That'd be telling.'

'So what did you wish for?'

'I have no need for wishes, Stephanie. I have everything I need. And the things I want, I can take.'

She looked at him uncertainly. 'What do you mean?'

He tilted his head on one side, as though he was listening. 'I have to go. See you later, Stephanie who wants to see the world.'

'It's *Steph*. What did you mean?'

But he just did that quick gesture again over his shoulder, the slight bob of his head that could have been a wink, could have been anything at all. And his words floated back, so faint she could hardly tell what he said: 'Which world did you want to see?'

Steph stared after him. She'd meant to ask who he was, whether he lived here or was just holidaying, whether he would be in school come the autumn. Instead she'd let him walk away, having discovered nothing at all.

'He was weird,' Steph said, her voice rising. 'He said if he wanted something he'd just take it. What do you think he meant? I don't know what he meant.' She had found Holly and Anna sitting by the church, drinking cans of coke and tapping their feet against the wall.

Holly frowned. 'Probably just confident,' she said. 'I like that in a man, don't you, Anne?'

'He was *weird*.'

'Why? What else did he say?'

'He said – he asked – I dunno.' Steph subsided. Maybe Holly was right, maybe she *had* overreacted. She wasn't really sure Kix had said anything all that odd. And it was nice having someone like that, cool, confident – yes, *confident* – choosing to spend time with her. Not that he'd spent much of it. She remembered how he'd walked away, and wondered if, after all, she'd been a little disappointed.

'You like him,' Holly said, and Steph met her eye, startled.

'No, I don't. I – I don't think I do.'

Holly giggled. 'Steph and Kix, sitting in a tree . . .'

'Don't.' Steph laughed, caught Holly's eye and laughed harder. 'Really, I *don't*. Let's talk about something else. Tell me about the stones.'

'What, the Rollrights?'

'There are legends about them, aren't there? What are they?'

Holly pouted. 'Not much to tell. It's boring, really. They're king's men, invading England, only a witch stopped them and turned them to stone. There's some story about them all going off to a stream to drink when the church clock strikes midnight, but it's all rubbish.'

'And there's the one about how they can't be moved,' said Anne, 'or misfortune will strike.'

'And the one about fairy-folk living under them, waiting to drag you beneath the stones and turn you into some sort of slave.'

'Plus the one about the knights telling your fortune,' said Anne. 'That's about it.' She shrugged. 'We told you. Boring.'

Steph thought of the circle and wondered what it would look like now the daylight was fading. She imagined they would look more like people than ever, huddled in the half-light. But the others were right, it *was* boring. The fact that she had ever felt interested – it was a sign of her horizons shrinking, of having nothing else to do. She should remember she was leaving this place as soon as she could. She could go to university or get a job, or do as she'd boasted to Kix and travel the world. And then she remembered the thing she'd almost thought she'd heard, as he walked away: *Which world did you want to see?*

'Course,' said Anne, 'It wouldn't be so boring if we went up there at night.'

Steph stirred. Holly was staring at her friend. 'Yes! We could sneak out, take candles, and dance round the stones in the dark, like the nutty witches.'

'Pagans.'

'Whatever.' Holly turned to Steph. 'And we can ask the knights to tell our fortunes.' She laughed. 'We'll know for sure if you're going to get married then.'

Steph sat on the wall and waited, watching for Holly, but she jumped anyway when the shadow of a bike appeared in the road. The moon was fat, almost full, and Holly's face was a pallid oval in the dark. They didn't say anything, just headed away. As they went, Steph stretched out her legs to either side of the bike, feeling an unaccustomed sense of freedom; as though she was leaving Long Compton and her father and everything behind, nothing to think about, nothing holding her back.

The warden's hut was locked up but they crept by it anyway, and waited for Anne at the top of the path. She arrived at last, out of breath. 'I nearly got spotted,' she said. Her voice sounded loud on the hillside. Above them, the sky sparkled with stars. The breeze was cold but felt good on Steph's face.

'Come on,' whispered Holly. 'The King's Men, first.'

They stood in the centre of the circle. Stones stood out eerily in the dark, their paleness catching the moonlight. Holly pulled a candle from her bag but it was cold, and she found she hadn't brought any matches, and she started to shiver. 'Sod this,' she said. 'Let's go to the Knights.'

They headed down the hillside. Steph felt the circle of stones like a presence at her back, and she turned and saw them, still there as they had been for centuries. She remembered the story of them going down to a stream to drink, and her lip twitched. When she turned back she could see the Knights and found she had been right: they *did* look like human figures leaning towards each other, whispering their secrets. Seeing them now, in the quiet and in the dark, she didn't find it surprising that the story had been told.

'Sit down,' said Holly, 'like before. We can close our eyes and chant or something.'

'No,' said Anne. 'Be quiet: if we're quiet, we might hear them.'

They sat as they had before, Steph sinking into the long grass. She immediately felt chilled through, the ground cold beneath her. *So* cold. It had been a warm day, the sun shining, and it surprised her it should be so cold.

'Right,' said Holly. From the sound of her voice, she wasn't finding this so much fun as she'd expected either. 'Shut it.'

They did, and Steph leaned back against the railings. It wasn't comfortable and it didn't help with the cold, but she didn't want to change position and annoy Holly. Somewhere, out over the hillside, an owl hooted. Someone – Anne – let out a spurt of air.

'*Shh,*' Holly said.

Steph let her mind drift. She told herself she could be anywhere: France or Spain or Italy. Anywhere.

There was a sound at her back. Steph started, tried to turn. The others still had their eyes closed. After a moment, she settled back down. It hadn't sounded like Anne, messing about. It had sounded like someone whispering behind her back. She didn't like sitting here like this, not any more. She would have preferred it if the stones had been in front of her.

She felt a sharp elbow in her ribs and forced her eyes closed.

It was a short while before it came again, a soft sound gradually getting louder. There was a strange feeling too, a numbing feeling that rose from the ground. It must have been the cold, but it didn't quite feel like that.

'Sssss . . .'

Steph started up again, spun around. There was only rock and nothing more.

'*Steph.*'

But Steph no longer cared if Holly was annoyed. She jumped to her feet and walked around the stones, checking if someone was hiding behind them. There was nothing. No one.

'What is it?' Holly was standing now too. 'Did you hear something?'

'No,' said Steph. 'Just a bird, maybe.' She went back to her place and sank down. This time, when she closed her eyes, the voice was there. She knew it wasn't Holly. It didn't sound like anyone she knew, wasn't the *kind* of voice she knew. This was something else. It sounded at once deep and sibilant and close and distant, and older than any voice had a right to be. 'Kixxsss . . .'

'Jesus,' said Steph, jumping to her feet.

Holly's eyes snapped open. 'What's up?'

'I heard it. Didn't you hear it?'

'Seriously – you heard something? What did it say?'

Steph didn't answer.

'Tell us,' said Anne.

'She's fooling about.'

'She's not. Look at her face.'

Steph put a hand to her cheek. She didn't know what Anne meant, but she felt pale; very pale. 'It said 'Kix,'' she stammered, 'but it wasn't real. I must have fallen asleep or something.'

'No, you didn't.' Holly stood. 'You really heard something, didn't you? And – Kix!' Something about her voice changed. 'Score.'

'No – I mean, it isn't real. Or it isn't *right*. Something isn't right.' Steph wanted to explain, but didn't know how: none of this made any sense. 'I don't even like him,' she finished.

But then they fell silent, because they heard a new sound; footsteps swishing through grass. Someone was coming towards them. 'Shit,' hissed Holly, but it was too late, they had nowhere to go. A dark figure stalked down the hillside. After a moment it started to whistle, and then pale hair caught the moonlight. It was Kix.

'Speak of the devil,' said Holly admiringly.

'But – but how – '

'Kix!' Anne cut in. 'You'll never believe what – '

'*Anne.*'

But Kix didn't seem interested in what Anne was going to say. He stopped in front of them and looked at Steph. 'Hey,' he said. 'I saw a bike at the bottom. Thought you rebels must be up here somewhere.'

'Well, you found us,' said Holly, her voice full of smiles.

Kix kept his eyes fixed on Steph. 'I was wondering if I could talk to you,' he said, and reached out a hand; let it fall again before touching her. 'I wanted to apologise for something I said earlier.'

Steph shook her head. 'Sorry, but it's late, and it's dark. I need to be getting back. Holly, we should go.'

Holly spluttered. 'Already? You've got to be kidding.' She took Anne's arm. 'Come on. We'll wait for you at the circle, Steph.'

'No, but – '

It was too late. They were already heading away, and Steph was left alone with Kix.

'Walk with me,' he said, and his voice was soft; he made it sound like a question, and Steph nodded.

They headed down the hillside, away from the Knights and further from the circle, and soon Steph could hear a stream. She remembered the story about how the King's Men would come and drink, and it made her smile.

'The things I want, I can take,' said Kix, and sighed. 'I said that, and I wanted to say I'm sorry.'

'I – it's okay.'

'It's true, of course. But I prefer them to come willingly.'

'What?'

He smiled. 'Willingly,' he said. 'Please do come willingly, Stephanie.' He put a hand to his brow, pushed back his hair. She stared at him.

'I asked you a question, once,' he said.

Which world did you want to see? Steph heard the words, though his lips didn't move. She didn't move either. She felt she could never move again, as if she was rooted to the spot. Her legs were heavy, lifeless. She couldn't look away from his eyes.

'We were both right,' he said softly. 'You and I – we'll always be together. But you're never getting married, Stephanie.'

His eyes were gold. *Gold.*

'You're mad,' she said, but her voice faltered. 'Let me go.'

He held up his hands, the palms turned outward.

'Please.' Steph could feel coldness rising from the ground, creeping up her legs, penetrating deep into her knees, wrapping itself around her thighs. It rose higher and she gasped, felt its tendrils easing under her clothes, finding her spine. Soon she wouldn't be able to move at all. She looked down and saw a peculiar thing; her clothes were glowing in the moonlight, the same pale sheen as the stones. She blinked. *Like* the stones. 'No,' she whispered. 'Kix, don't.' She looked at his face and his eyes shone and there was no mercy in them, only amusement, and understanding, and age-old knowledge.

He mouthed something: *Be with me.*

It was rising higher, freezing her; it was killing her. Soon the cold would reach her heart and it would stop, just *stop,* while all around her the years would pass and she would still be there, just as now, except she wouldn't be able to move or breathe or speak. *Speak.*

'Please,' she said, her thoughts running wildly. Let me go. I'll give you anything.'

He smiled, as if at the antics of a child.

'I'll count the stones,' she said. 'Just give me a chance. Let me count the stones, and if I get it right – three times – you'll let me go.'

He laughed, loud and sharp, and suddenly she could move again. 'Done,' he said. 'I knew there was a reason I chose you, Stephanie. I knew, if nothing else, you'd make this interesting.'

When they reached the King's Men Steph looked around for Holly and Anne. They weren't there. She scanned the site, back and forth, but she couldn't see them. They must have decided to wait by the entrance, or left her alone, thinking it a fine joke to leave her with Kix. 'Holly!' she shouted, starting to run, and suddenly Kix was in front of her, and he was laughing. When she heard that laughter, she knew it wasn't any use. Tears sprang to her eyes. Kix put both hands to her shoulders, not holding tightly but steadying her. 'There, there,' he said. His voice was kind, but those eyes were hard. He indicated the stones. 'Count,' he said. 'That's all you have to do. Count them.'

Steph took a deep breath. He was taller than her, and she knew he would be faster; there was no use in running. She looked around, found the tallest stone, and began to count.

She had thought it would be harder in the dark, but somehow it was easier. Each stone shone in the moonlight, standing out clearly against the dark grass. Kix stayed in the middle of the circle, turning slowly like the hand of a clock. She glanced towards him, almost lost her place; but no, she'd counted the small one, was on to the next. She went slowly, carefully. Then she was back at the starting point and she opened her mouth, but Kix spoke first.

'I'll give you a clue, little Stephanie,' he said. 'There are seventy-seven. Have you counted them all? I'll know if you're lying.'

She met his glance. 'You're the liar,' she said. 'There are seventy-six.'

He made a slight bow. 'Again,' he said.

Steph's heart beat faster as she made her way around the circle for the second time. When she reached the end, she let out a long breath. 'Seventy-six,' she said.

'Again.'

And she began. This time, as she went, she started to remember the things Holly and Anne had told her: that the stones could tell fortunes. That they were soldiers turned to stone. That fairy-folk lived beneath them, waiting to drag prisoners down under the ground. *Which world did you want to see?*

She shook her head, terrified she would lose count. No: she was up to that one, the reddish stone that stood a little apart from the others. She forced herself to concentrate, knew she was reaching the end when she started to count into the seventies. *Seventy-three. Seventy-four. Seventy-five* ... no, that wasn't right. The seventy-fifth stone was the tallest, the starting point: she had counted it already. *Seventy-four.*

'Well?' Kix was there.

She stared at him. *I'll know if you're lying.*

'Seventy-six,' she said.

He reached out, quicker than she could see, and grabbed her arm. His fingers were long and narrow and hard as steel. 'Liar.'

She tried to pull away.

'How many?'

Steph was crying now, crying and struggling. 'Seventy-four. Seventy-four.'

His grip on her arm relaxed and he started to laugh. Steph pulled back, hard, almost fell; and suddenly she was free, she could *move*, and she was running, careering down the hillside as fast as she could.

Two figures rose in front of her. They didn't look like the figures she knew. They were taller somehow, and their shapes were wrong, too thin; they were blocking her path, and their eyes were cold.

Steph stopped in front of them, gasping for breath. It *was* Holly and Anne, but they were different: different in a way that reminded her of Kix.

'Bring her back,' came a commanding voice from the stones: and they did.

Holly and Anne held onto Steph and she couldn't shake them off. Kix stood in front of her, peering into her eyes as if he could see through her. He smiled. 'Do you see?' he asked. 'Do you see now?'

Those eyes bored into her and she couldn't look into them. She looked away, saw instead the stones; motionless, silent stones.

'How many are there, Stephanie?'

'Seventy-seven,' she whispered. 'I get it now. But one of them was you, and you weren't in the circle: and then two more were gone. But there were always seventy-seven.'

He smiled that knowing smile. 'Wrong again,' he said, and he stepped forward and breathed on her, and he put the cold inside her, and it grew; and Steph only heard him faintly as everything began to dim.

'Seventy-eight,' he said.

The days passed, and then the seasons. Autumn came, and it felt like everything was dying: and then winter with its hollow slowness, and the struggle began to sap from Stephanie's being. Not that she had struggled, not really; not only because she couldn't move, didn't move, but because struggle was no longer part of her make-up. And then winter melted away and spring came, and summer, and after a time the seasons flickered by like days; one after the next as the world turned, and she turned with it, her roots sinking deeper into the earth and becoming one with it, as a tree might.

There was no hunger, no thirst. Only the endless cold.

She saw people, too. They came and went, momentary darting things like dragonflies settling for a moment before moving on. Sometimes they stayed by the stones; they came and lit candles, or sat in a ring with their eyes closed, or sang, or dressed the stones with flowers. She wondered if her mother missed her; if her father did. And then she noticed, somewhere in the back of her consciousness, that the visitors began to appear different as their styles and modes of dress began to change.

Which world did you want to see?

Always, she felt Kix's presence. She dimly remembered a time when she had railed against it, but as the days passed, she found she couldn't remember why; and after a time, it became a comfort.

On some occasions, when visitors came and walked the circle, she would feel Kix leave her side and he would walk among them. Sometimes they saw him and sometimes they didn't; sometimes he was older and sometimes younger, but Steph always knew it was him.

Sometimes Holly and Anne left the circle and spoke with some wanderer they found there. At those times Steph would remember how it had felt to ride on the back of a bicycle, her legs outstretched to feel the rush of freedom: to talk about the future, to plan, to laugh.

Sometimes, in the quiet and in the dark, the stones moved. Sometimes, they danced.

She wondered if, one day, she would learn the trick of it.

MARK MORRIS

THE SCARIEST PLACE IN THE WORLD

HOLLY RESENTED DAYTIME callers. Most of them weren't to know that she worked at home, but even so, her first response when someone rang the bell or banged on the door was to grit her teeth and ball her hands into fists, as if in imitation of the tight knot of resentment she felt clenching in her belly. It had been several weeks after moving in before the old lady who lived next door had got the message. The first time she turned up she'd been clutching a dented biscuit tin containing one of those old-fashioned sponge cakes, the ones with jam and cream in the middle and a light dusting of icing sugar on top.

'Hello, dear,' she'd said, her thin shoulders hunched like vestigial wings within her pale green cardigan and her grey hair drifting like a wind-stirred mass of cobwebs. 'I'm Mrs. Bartholomew. I'm your new neighbour – or rather, I suppose you're mine, as I've been here for donkey's years. I just thought I'd pop round to see how you're settling in.'

Holly had kept the door half-closed, and positioned herself firmly behind it, as if wary the old lady might try to force her way inside. When Mrs. Bartholomew smiled, her face crumpled like a brown paper bag and her beige-yellow teeth sprang forward, reminding Holly of a row of clothes pegs on a washing line.

'We're fine, thanks,' Holly had replied, responding to her neighbour's grin with a half-hearted grimace. 'We're a bit busy just now. Lots to do.'

She'd begun to push the door shut. Quickly the old woman said, 'Just the two of you are there?'

Holly had hesitated, then nodded. 'Yes, me and my husband, Mike.'

'No children?'

'No.'

'Ah.' The old woman looked thoughtful. 'Well, it'll be a lovely house to bring up little ones. When the time comes.'

'Yes.' Holly inched the door further closed. 'Well, thanks for coming round, but we really are busy.'

'Oh, I brought you this.' Mrs. Bartholomew raised the biscuit tin as though making an offering to an arcane god. 'A little house warming present. Home-made.'

Holly had thought of the old woman's bird's-claw, liver-spotted hands buried in cake mix, perhaps even scraping it from under her yellowing fingernails, and her stomach turned over. Mustering a smile she'd said, 'That's very kind of you, but Mike and I don't really eat cake.'

'Oh.' Mrs. Bartholomew looked crest-fallen.

'Sorry,' said Holly. 'Well, goodbye.'

She'd pushed the door shut, and then tensed as, from the other side, she heard the old woman call, 'Goodbye for now, dear. Perhaps I'll pop round again when you're less busy.'

She *had* popped round again. In fact, she had 'popped round' on at least half a dozen occasions over the next few weeks, though Holly had never allowed her over the thresh-old. In the end Holly had had to tell her that she worked from home, that her time was precious, that she had deadlines to meet, that she couldn't afford to just break off whenever she felt like it. Her voice, when she'd said this, had been a little snappier than she'd intended, and she'd felt bad about it afterwards, thinking that the old woman was probably just lonely and wanted a bit of company. But still . . . her neighbour had to respect the fact that Holly needed to make a living. She had to understand that just because Holly was at home all day it didn't mean that her time was her own to squander on coffee and local gossip. And when Holly *did* get time to herself, in the evenings, she wanted to spend it with Mike – which was natural, wasn't it? They had things to do on the house, after all, plans to discuss.

She soothed her conscience by promising herself that at some point, when things had settled down and they were more on top of the situation, she *would* call on Mrs. Bartholomew and say hello properly. She *would*. But just now she was too busy, too preoccupied. And besides, if the old lady *had* lived on the street for donkey's years, then surely she had other friends to call on? It wasn't as if Holly and Mike ought to feel responsible for her in any way.

Which was why, when the knock came on the front door one Tuesday morning, just as Holly was dropping a camomile teabag into the flip top bin in the kitchen and trying to structure the next sentence of her latest article in her head, she felt that familiar knot in her belly tightening once more. Who was this *now?* Surely not Mrs. Bartholomew *again?* Perhaps it was one of those ex-prisoners selling shoddy and over-priced household wares from a leather holdall – the ones who always made her feel nervous. Or just someone delivering a parcel. Mike was always ordering himself the latest gadgets online. She'd told him to have them delivered to his work address so that she wouldn't be disturbed during the day, but sometimes he forgot.

Pushing open the kitchen door, steaming mug held before her like a weapon, she looked to her right, moving her head slowly, a little fearful of making a sudden move and drawing attention to herself. She didn't *think* whoever was standing outside would be able to see her, but you never knew. After all, she could see the caller through the stippled glass panel of the front door – or at least, she could see a vague dark shape with a pinkish blob on top.

She hovered a moment, willing the caller to go away. If it was someone with a parcel he'd put an attempted delivery slip through the letterbox, whereupon she could rush up to the door and open it before he'd reached the end of the drive, claim she'd been preoccupied with some household chore and hadn't been able to get to the door in time.

But the caller didn't put a note through the door. Instead he knocked again. Three quick taps, timid but insistent. If she'd been upstairs, sitting at her desk, she might have ignored it, but she was damned if she was going to stand in her hallway all day, feeling trapped.

With a grunt of exasperation she marched up to the front door and opened it. Standing outside was a thin young man in a dark jacket, jeans and a white T-shirt with some sort of fuzzy, black-lettered slogan on it that Holly could neither read nor identify. He looked like a student – bony wrists, thick mop of fashionably tousled hair, insipid expression.

'Yes?' she said sharply.

'Hi,' he said with a vague smile.

Holly didn't smile back. 'Can I help you?'

'Er . . .' The young man looked ill at ease. He wafted a hand vaguely. 'This is a bit weird, but . . . I used to live here. A long time ago. I was in the area, so I thought. . . well, it was just a whim really. I just got an urge to see the old place. The house where I grew up.' He grimaced. 'I haven't been back in . . . I dunno . . . nearly twenty years? My name's Rob, by the way. Rob Norton.' He nodded at the side wall of the house next door. 'Is Mrs. Bartholomew still there?'

'Yes,' Holly said.

Rob Norton smiled. 'That's good. It's nice to know that some things never change.'

Holly narrowed her eyes. '*When* did you say you lived here?'

'I didn't. The 70s. I was born in '78. We lived here till I was eighteen.' Nodding at the expression on Holly's face, he said, 'I know what you're thinking. I get it a lot. But I'm older than I look.' He gestured vaguely at the house. 'Any chance I could have a quick look round?'

'I don't think so,' said Holly quickly. 'I'm very busy. I've got a deadline to meet. I'm a journalist.'

He pressed the palms of his hands together, as if in prayer. 'Please. Just five minutes. Two even. It's been such a long time since I've been back, and I don't know when I'll be in the area again.'

'How do I know you're who you say you are?' Holly asked.

Rob Norton flourished a hand almost triumphantly at the house next door, like a stage compere introducing a popular act. 'You can ask Mrs. B. She'll vouch for me. She knew me from when I was a baby.'

Holly pictured it all in an instant, saw immediately how protracted and awkward the situation would become. They would knock on Mrs. Bartholomew's door, and the old lady would answer it. And when she clapped eyes on her old neighbour her face would light up with incredulity and delight. No doubt there'd be a joyous reunion, a babble of questions. Mrs. Bartholomew would invite them in for a cup of tea, and Holly would have to play the killjoy, the party pooper, would – as usual – have to plead the pressure of work and deadlines. So she'd come home, and Rob would probably stay at Mrs. Bartholomew's for a bit. And even though Holly wasn't with them, she'd be unable to settle to her work, because she'd be on edge, waiting for Rob to come back, knowing not only that at some point she'd be disturbed by him again, but also that next door they'd probably be talking about her – Mrs. B telling Rob how unfriendly she was, how un-neighbourly, how she wished things were back to how they used to be, when he and his family lived next door.

Holly didn't think she could stand all that – the time wasted, the disruption to her schedule, the uncomfortable knowledge that she'd be painted as the villain of the piece. And so she heard herself saying, 'Oh, it's okay, there's no need for that. You can have a look round. But it *will* have to be quick. I *do* have a deadline.'

'Of course,' Rob said, nodding. 'Thanks so much. I really appreciate it.'

Holly stepped back, tugging the door open reluctantly so that he could enter. He came in, looking around eagerly, peering up the hallway, towards the kitchen, his dark eyes gleaming, the light slithering across them.

Holly took another step back as he closed the door behind him, trapping the shadows and the silence in with them. Outside he'd seemed harmless, skinny, almost frail, but here, inside, right next to her, he seemed taller, rangier, lithe rather than skinny, possessed perhaps of a deceptive strength, a tensile vigour.

What am I doing? she thought. If Mike knew he'd be furious. She wondered if she'd tell him. She knew what he'd say, could almost hear him saying it:

'How could you have been so gullible? Anything might have happened.'

You read about these things, don't you? she thought. Strangers wheedling their way into people's homes. And you think: serves them right for being so stupid. But it's different when it's you. After all, *you're* not a newspaper headline; other people are. You're too smart, too careful.

'Where do you want to start?' she asked.

Her voice was a little abrasive. *Too* abrasive? She didn't

MARK MORRIS – *The Scariest Place in the World*

want to antagonise him. Better to be business-like, though, rather than demure, defensive. The worst thing would be to appear vulnerable, to show any nervousness, any fear.

'This was all wood-panelled when I was a kid,' he said, his eyes sparkling. 'Well, not wood-panelled . . . you know that cheap stuff? Thin. It came in sheets and you just stuck it on the wall.' He gave a sudden laugh, little more than a hitch of breath. 'Pretty tacky, I suppose. But people thought it was sophisticated back then.'

He sidled past her, away from her, towards the door on the left that led into the front room. 'Is it okay if I . . .?'

She nodded, and he opened the door, pausing before he did so and taking a deep breath as he turned the handle – relishing the moment, or perhaps bracing himself for what he might see.

She guessed that the room must have changed a lot since he had lived here, been redecorated and refurnished several times over. Perhaps even rewired, the light fittings repositioned, the windows replaced. Yet he stood there looking around with a kind of wonder. She saw that he was trembling slightly.

'Are you all right?' she asked to break the silence.

His eyelids fluttered, as if he was about to pass out. He turned his head so slowly towards her she almost expected to hear the bones creak in his neck.

He licked his lips. 'I can't tell you how strange this is,' he said. 'It's like . . . somewhere I've seen in a recurring dream. Or like I've been asleep for a long time and I've just woken up.' He shook his head suddenly. 'Sorry. You must think I'm a total weirdo. It's just . . . it's hard to explain. Everything is so familiar . . . intensely familiar. And yet at the same time it's different. Like a new reality has been laid over the top . . . Does any of this make sense?'

Holly was a forward-looking person. She was not nostalgic.

She had never had any desire to revisit the past, to explore old haunts. Last year she had been invited to a school reunion, but she had declined; the very idea of it made her shudder. Yet she found herself nodding now, to humour him. 'It must be very odd coming back,' she said.

'It is.' He swayed a little on his feet. 'Sorry, could I have some water?'

'Sure.' He wasn't the only one who found the atmosphere stifling; she was glad of the opportunity to step away from it for a moment. 'Sit down. I'll get you some.'

She exited the room, hurried to the kitchen, opened the cupboard above the sink and reached instinctively for a glass. Then she thought better of it and took down a plastic beaker instead.

It was becoming heavier in her hand as she filled it with water when a shadow crept across the wall and the cupboard door in front of her. She turned with a gasp, water splashing over her hand.

He was standing right behind her.

'What are you doing?' she cried, immediately appalled at how shrill she sounded.

He backed off, raising a hand. 'Sorry, I didn't mean to make you jump.' His attention seemed suddenly caught by the room, his eyes flickering from wall to wall, floor to ceiling.

'Strange how small this room seems now,' he said. 'How narrow.'

She felt oddly insulted. 'It's plenty big enough for us,' she said.

He smiled crookedly. 'I just meant . . . when I was a kid this seemed . . . not vast, but . . . bigger, you know? Everything seems bigger when you're a kid, doesn't it? More formidable.' He looked out of the narrow window beside the cooker. 'I used to think that field out there was massive. But it's not, is it?'

'You sound disappointed.' Holly was still holding the

beaker. Water was dripping from her hand, forming dark coins on the slate-coloured tiles at her feet.

'Not disappointed,' said Rob. 'Just . . .' he looked thoughtful, even sad. 'The older you get, the more the world closes in on you. Stifles you.'

Holly didn't agree. She thought the opposite was true. But she didn't argue. She held out the beaker. 'Do you want your water?'

'Thanks.' He took the beaker, but he didn't drink. 'Is it okay to look upstairs? My old bedroom.'

'Sure,' she said, and raised a hand. 'After you.' She hoped her reason for inviting him to go first – because she didn't want to feel trapped with him; because she knew that if he stayed ahead of her she would always have an escape route – wasn't as evident to him as it seemed to herself.

He turned obediently enough, and as he did so he put the beaker down on the breakfast bar that ran along the left-hand wall of the kitchen. She looked at it, thought about saying something. But why make it an issue? Was it *really* such a big deal that he hadn't drunk the water he'd asked for? Maybe he'd changed his mind. People were entitled to do that. Maybe his feeling of faintness had passed.

She followed him up the stairs, though remained a good few steps behind him. She didn't want to get close enough that he could thrust out an arm and give her a shove. He moved slowly, deliberately, as if wary of disturbing a sleeping incumbent on the floor above. Two steps from the top he halted and turned. When he spoke his voice was sombre, hushed.

'That first door was my bedroom. Is it okay if I . . .?'

'Be my guest.'

He ascended the last two steps, crossed the landing, pushed the door open. It was her study, so the door was already ajar. Pearly light spilled out of it as he stepped forward, softening his outline. When she entered the room behind him he had already crossed to the window beside her desk and was looking at the paved yard below.

'I thought you might have turned it into a garden again,' he said. He sounded wistful, disappointed.

'Again?'

He turned to her. His eyes were wide and soft. He looked ... haunted? Was that too strong a word to describe the expression on his face?

'When we came here it was a garden. Lawn. Flowerbeds. Then my parents ... my dad really ... began to breed dogs. Alsatians. And he had the lawn ripped out, paved over. I thought ... I hoped ... it might be green again by now.'

'It was like that when we moved in,' Holly said defensively. 'We haven't been here long.'

Rob seemed not to hear her. His gaze swept the poky, square room, little more than a cell really. 'This was my room.'

'Yes, you said.'

His eyes fixed on her. They were dark, almost black. And seemed suddenly flat. 'You know what a little boy's bedroom is, don't you?'

She shrugged, discomfited. 'What?'

'It's the scariest place in the world.'

A beat. A silence in which meaning thrummed and throbbed, like the air beneath an electricity pylon.

'Is it?' she said at last, and to her own ears her voice sounded hollow, on the verge of cracking.

He nodded. 'He dominated us ... my dad, I mean. He never touched us, my mum and me, but we were scared of him all the same. He had a way about him ... a way of grinding us down ...'

His eyes drifted away from hers, becoming unfocused. She knew he was looking into his past. 'Some people do. There's a force about them ... a sense that ... that something terrible could happen at any moment ... do you know what I mean?'

Holly wasn't sure what to say. Yet she felt compelled to say something. In the end she muttered, 'You felt threatened?'

'More than that. I was scared ... terrified ... every minute of every day of my life.'

His voice had dropped to a whisper. Suddenly he shook himself, like a dog. His head jerked up and his eyes were bright and black again.

'Have you seen him?'

'What?'

'Have you seen *anything*? Since you moved in? Anything ... unusual?'

'No.' She shook her head angrily. 'What do you expect me to have seen?'

He half-smiled. 'I used to see ... even after he died ...'

'He died?' said Holly. 'Your dad, you mean?'

He nodded. 'His car was hit by a lorry on the motorway. I was eleven. I cried, and Mum cried, but secretly ... I was glad. Relieved. I think she was too, but she didn't say so. But then ...' His eyes drifted, not to the window, but to the corner of the room *beyond* the window, the one where Holly kept her exercise bike when she wasn't using it. His voice had dropped to a whisper again, and his eyes were full of fear now. 'Then he came back. I'd see him at night. I'd wake up and he'd be standing there. A dark shape in the corner. Watching me.'

'It was just your imagination,' said Holly carefully. 'You felt guilty, and afraid.'

He looked bewildered. 'So you haven't seen him?'

'Of course not.'

He nodded slowly. 'I couldn't wait to get away. When I did, when I moved out, I thought it'd be over, that I'd never see him again.' He gave a sort of sob, and his face twisted for a moment, an expression of fearful anguish. 'But it was no good. He followed me. Wherever I went, wherever I lived, I'd wake in the night, and he'd be there, standing in the corner, watching me . . .'

He swayed, as though about to collapse. Standing beside the window, framed by the light, he looked ethereal, as though the blaze of his own fear was corroding him, devouring him.

Against her better judgement, Holly stepped forward, raising her hands as though to grip his elbows, hold him upright.

'He's not real, Rob, don't you see?' she said. 'You only think you saw him because he was such a presence in your life, because he frightened you, and because you felt guilty for being relieved when he died. But you mustn't let him haunt you any more. He's gone. You're free of him.'

Rob shook his head. 'I thought if I came back, I might be able to bring him with me, leave him here, lay him to rest.'

'Do that,' said Holly decisively. 'Leave him here. He has no power over me. I don't believe in him.'

Rob barely seemed to hear her. His eyes were wild, distracted. 'But it's no good,' he said. 'He'll always be with me. I see that now.'

'No he won't,' said Holly. 'You just have to -'

Her words dried in her throat, her body jerking in horror. Rob had produced a black-handled kitchen knife from his pocket and was now holding it uncertainly in front of him.

Holly's voice, when she rediscovered it, was eerily calm, far calmer than she felt. 'Rob,' she said, 'put that away. You don't need it.'

'He won't leave me alone,' he said miserably.

'But that won't solve anything, will it? By . . . by using that . . . you'd be letting him win.'

Though she said it, she had no idea how he intended to

use it. On her? On himself? On his non-existent father? She backed towards the door, not deliberately, almost subconsciously.

He looked at her and his face was wretched. 'I'm sorry,' he said.

Then he rammed the blade of the knife in his own throat and jerked it sideways.

It was like puncturing a high-pressure hose. There was a hiss and a fan of blood spurted from him, rising high in the air and coming down with a spatter like falling raindrops. He reeled and tumbled sideways, his legs simply folding beneath him. Blood continued to gush and jet from his neck as his body bucked, staining everything – the sand-coloured carpet, the walls, the bookcases, the laptop on the desk, even the ceiling – with streaks and spatters.

Holly crammed her fists to her mouth and screamed. She felt a wrench and a wave of dizziness, as though some instinctive, essential part of her was so appalled by what it was witnessing that it was trying to flee, to tear itself from the unresponsive lump of flesh in which it was housed. Barely aware of what she was doing, she turned and stumbled, almost fell, down the stairs. The air felt thick and heavy as soup, and yet at the same time vibrant and piercing, as if filled with a thousand screeching alarms.

'Ohmygod,' she whispered, barely aware that she was doing it. 'Ohmygodohmygodohmygodohmygod.'

She couldn't think straight. Her only thought was to get away, to put as much distance as possible between herself and the terrible thing that had happened upstairs. She felt contaminated, poisoned by it. She rubbed and clawed at her arms, at her clothes, as if she was covered with crawling things that were biting her, trying to burrow under her skin.

At the bottom of the stairs she made instinctively for the light falling in fractured waves through the stippled glass of the front door. Her hand felt large and clumsy as she grasped the door handle, but somehow she managed to twist it, tug it open. She staggered outside, and the light hit her like a slap, causing her to spin around – or perhaps it was the world that was spinning. Next thing she knew her feet somehow became tangled together, and suddenly she was on the ground. She lay there sobbing.

When hands began to tug at her she screamed, but the voice that accompanied them was soft, soothing.

'Now, now, dear, it's all right. You're perfectly safe.'

Holly looked up. Mrs. Bartholomew was crouching beside her, the sun turning her feathery grey hair into a halo of white fire.

'You've got to . . . need an ambulance,' Holly spluttered.

'An ambulance?' Mrs. Bartholomew looked her over quickly. 'Are you hurt? What happened?'

'Not me – him,' Holly wailed.

'Who, dear?' asked Mrs. Bartholomew.

Holly's thoughts were racing, hurtling through her head at such a speed she could barely communicate. Forcing herself to think, to concentrate, she said, 'You know him. His name's . . . Rob Norton. He used to . . . used to live here.'

A strange look came over Mrs. Bartholomew's face. 'Rob,' she said. 'So he's come back, has he?'

'Yes, but he's . . . hurt. Maybe dead. He had a knife and he. . .' unable to say the words she mimed stabbing herself in the throat.

Slowly Mrs. Bartholomew rose to her feet, wincing as her knees cracked. She took hold of Holly's hand, and with a tug she encouraged her to stand.

'Come with me, dear.'

'Where?'

'I want to show you something.'

Holly stood shakily, but resisted when Mrs. Bartholomew

started to pull her back towards the open front door that Holly had just tumbled out of.

'No,' she said, 'I can't. He's in there. I don't want to see.'

'It's quite all right,' Mrs. Bartholomew said. 'Come on, dear.'

Such was the gentle authority in her voice that Holly allowed herself to be led. Inside, though, when Mrs. Bartholomew tried to persuade her to go upstairs, she shrank back again.

'No, I can't,' she said again.

'All right, dear,' Mrs. Bartholomew said gently. 'All right, I'll go. You wait here.'

She went upstairs. Holly waited, slumped against the wall – the one that Rob had told her used to be covered in sheets of chipboard made to look like real wood – panting as though she had just run a five-miler.

Eventually Mrs. Bartholomew appeared at the top of the stairs. 'Come up, dear,' she said.

Holly shook her head. 'No.'

'There's nothing to see,' Mrs. Bartholomew said. 'Trust me.'

Such was the conviction in her tone, combined with a note of reassurance, that Holly sidled across to the foot of the stairs and crept up them like a timid child ready to bolt at the slightest sign of threat. When she reached the top Mrs. Bartholomew took her hand.

'It's all right,' she said gently.

The door to the room in which Rob Norton had cut his own throat was ajar. Holly flinched, and almost cried out, as Mrs. Bartholomew stepped towards it, holding her at arm's length, and pushed it open.

The door swung back. The room was empty. Holly stared. There was no blood, no body. Everything was as it should be.

She felt her mind *flex*. That was honestly how it felt.

'I'm going mad,' she whispered.

Mrs. Bartholomew shook her head. 'No, dear, you're not.'

'But he was *there*. I saw him. I spoke to him.'

'I'm sure you did. But he died a long time ago. 1997 to be exact. He never got over his father's death, and he came back and killed himself in his childhood bedroom. I expect it was the only place where he felt safe.'

'No.' Holly shook her head. 'He didn't feel safe here. He said it was the scariest place in the world.'

Mrs. Bartholomew looked sad. 'He's been back several times. Everyone who's lived here since Kath Norton moved out has seen him – spoken to him too. Only once, mind,' she added hastily. 'He never visits the same person twice.'

Holly looked round the room. The pristine laptop, its cursor blinking languidly on the last word she had written. The sand-coloured carpet. The white ceiling, fresh and newly painted. Her eyes moved past the window to the corner, where her exercise bike stood at an angle.

Who will *I* see at night, she thought. Who will *I* see standing there?

She didn't believe in that sort of thing. She didn't believe in ghosts. But from now on, whenever she came in here in the dark, she would see someone. She felt certain of it. She would see a tall, dark shape, standing there, watching her.

She knew that she would never be alone again.

SIMON KURT UNSWORTH

QIQIRN

BECKER WASN'T WHAT Pollard expected. He was younger
for one thing, baby-faced and clean-shaven and without a tie,
and there was no desk or drawers in the room, just the chairs
and a small table that held a jug of water, a box of tissues
and a small vase containing a single flower. Becker sat in an
easy chair in front of the window and indicated that Pollard
should sit in the chair on the other side of the room, a leather
wingback that looked old and proved comfortable. He made
no notes as they spoke and referred to no paperwork, simply
steepling his fingers and looking at Pollard over the spires he
had created, listening as Pollard talked.

It took a while, because at first Pollard found it hard. His
voice had dried, to catch like dust in his throat, and he drank
three glasses of water from the jug as he told Becker about
what had happened, about the panic and the running and
the cold. About the fear, and the thing that had taken up residence in his home. Becker kept nodding, not interrupting,
not moving apart from those little bobs of his head, and when
Pollard had finished, he said, 'So this has been happening for
a few weeks?'

'Months, really,' said Pollard. 'Building up. The last few
weeks have been the worst.'

'Tell about the first one again.'

Pollard had been coming down his stairs when he first felt it, a prickle across his skin as though something had exhaled along the hallways of the house. Gooseflesh rose on his arms despite the warmth of the day and he shivered, suddenly cold. A quick, reassuring glance told him that the front door was still closed, things were in their places; nothing appeared amiss. So, why was his heartbeat increasing? Getting faster, harder, more urgent? Why was the hair across his body refusing to lie back down, the follicles tightening further so that his skin felt covered by hard little nodules like scales? Why did he feel cold? He took another step, down off the stairs and onto the carpeted floor, uncomfortably aware of the rub of his flesh inside his clothes, of the accelerating movement of his heart, of the way his hand, holding his empty cup, was shaking. What was this? The hallway was empty, the sunlight dropping into it through the open doorway from the kitchen, the house as silent as it had been these last months.

There was something in the kitchen.

As soon as he thought it, Pollard knew it was true. Something was in the kitchen, something awful, hiding just on the other side of the doorway, out of sight and waiting for him. He gasped, unable to help himself, his hand flexing sharply, opening and closing so that he dropped his cup. It bounced on the thick carpet, unharmed, knocking against his foot, and the cold porcelain bite made him scream and the next thing was, he was running.

'And you stopped where?' asked Becker.

'At the end of my path. I was barefoot and I must have trodden on something. It, I don't know, startled me back into myself or something because suddenly I wasn't scared or cold anymore, and I couldn't remember quite why I'd felt the way I had.'

'How did you feel?'

'Embarrassed, mostly, in case any of the neighbours saw me; I was only dressed in my pyjamas. They all pity me anyway, and I don't want to give them other reasons to talk about me. The sympathetic looks and little nods of concern are bad enough.'

'And when you went back in the house?'

'It was fine. The feeling that something was in the kitchen was gone. Everything was normal.' Pollard paused before saying the word *normal*, and then wondered if Becker had noticed. *What's normal any more*, he thought? *There's no such thing.*

'Good. Mr Pollard, what you're experiencing isn't pleasant, but I can tell you, it is entirely typical. The feelings and reactions you describe are symptomatic of panic attacks and phobic reactions; in your case, although it's unusual, I'd be inclined to treat this as a phobia. Your panic is related to a specific thing, to a fixed point, yes?'

'Yes.'

'Each time?'

'Yes. Every time, there's something that frightens me, terrifies me, and it's specific. It's in the kitchen, or the lounge, or the hallway or landing, just out of my sight. I just don't know what it is.'

'Then, for all intents and purposes it's a phobia, and we'll deal with it as such. There are two main ways for dealing with phobias: flooding and graduated hierarchies. Flooding involves, essentially, placing you somewhere with the thing causing your phobia and not letting you leave until you simply can't sustain the panic any more and you calm down. Quite apart from the fact it's not at all pleasant, it'd be hard to achieve with you because we don't know what specific thing the phobia is focused upon, so that leaves graduated hierarchies. We approach the thing that's causing the feelings small step by small step until you have the ability to deal with it, to not panic any more.'

'That'd be good,' said Pollard, remembering the fear he had felt, the sheer *terror*. 'I'd like to not be frightened any more.'

'There'll be homework each week, a new step to take' said Becker, 'things for you to think about and come prepared to talk about. This process will only work if you're honest, you understand?'

'Yes.'

'Good. I'll see you next week, and we'll talk a bit more about how these phobic attacks make you feel, what happens to you when they're occurring.'

Pollard had risen, was at the door, when Becker said, 'And Mr Pollard? I know we've not talked about your wife at all, but we will. Next week, Mr Pollard.'

'So, how have things been?'

'Awful,' said Pollard, 'much worse. I've had three attacks, each worse than before.' The office was warm and bright again, Becker in the same place and the same position, everything the same except for the addition of a piece of folded paper on the occasional table, held down by a small glass paperweight. Becker made no mention of the paper.

The worst of the attacks had been the previous evening. Pollard had been making himself a cup of tea when, standing at the counter waiting for the kettle to boil, he suddenly knew that something was behind him. Its head was just at his shoulder, its breath against the back of his neck, cold and fetid. The temperature in the room dropped violently and he shivered, and then he had been at the door, knocking it open and dashing hectic and thoughtless into the hallway, accelerating along it and to the front door and out. Running had been automatic, uncontrollable, driven by something that came before thought, by an unwillingness, a *desperation* not to see the thing behind him.

'And you stopped running at the end of the path again?

'Yes.'

'And when you went back in?'

'Nothing. There was nothing there, no feelings of anything. I made my drink and went to bed.'

'Tell me about your wife,' Becker said.

'Mary? She died,' Pollard said automatically, 'seven months ago.' His standard response, the emotions practiced out of it.

'I know. Did you love her?'

'Yes. I still do.'

'Did you get on well? I mean, were you friends?'

'Yes.' Pollard was unsure were the questions were going, where they were taking him. Becker was leaning forwards slightly now, his hands no longer steepled but crossed loosely over his lap.

'Tell about how the phobia makes you feel.'

'Frightened,' said Pollard. 'Out of control, threatened. In danger.'

'Tell me the three things you miss most about Mary.'

Pollard didn't answer. Thinking of Mary was hard, painful, but he tried and eventually found things he could verbalise. 'Her smell after she'd showered,' he said, 'it was so clean and fresh and nothing else ever smelled that way. Her laugh, how loud it was, too loud for someone so petite but never intrusive. The way she felt when I held her in bed and we talked.'

Becker nodded, as though Pollard had confirmed something for him, and said, 'Please read what's on the paper on the table.' Pollard picked it up, unfolded it and saw, printed neatly in black, THE ATTACKS WORSENED DURING THE WEEK. 'I'm not showing off,' said Becker. 'What you're experiencing is awful but it's also understandable and to some degree predictable. I wonder, why did you have to pause before you could tell me the nice things about Mary but not before you told me about how the attacks feel?'

'I don't know.'

'I do. It's because the attacks are the most important thing for you now, more important than your wife because they're more real, more immediate. All the good memories of Mary are tangled up with the unpleasant memories of her death; thinking of her pulls up not memories of the good times, but of the bad time, the awful time when she died. Those memories are like scabs covering the things you should be able to remember about her without pausing, the things that should be your primary memories of her, the good times and the happiness and the love. In a funny way, the attacks are healthy because they represent the positive memories trying to reassert themselves, trying to regain their rightful place of importance in your brain. In your life.'

'Why are they so frightening?' Pollard said. 'Mary wasn't frightening, I loved her. I still love her, I'm not frightened of her.'

'No,' said Becker, 'but you are frightened of remembering her fully, because doing that means facing fully how much you've lost and how that makes you feel. It means facing the rest of your life without her. You're frightened because the way to stop these phobic attacks is to take control back, to face the panic and pain and fear and the terrible memories of Mary's death, peel them away and allow Mary, the memories of Mary and how she made you feel, to regain their rightful place in your mind and your imagination. Those are the steps you have to take to stop this happening. That's where we have to go, together. Next week, Mr Pollard, we talk about how Mary died.'

'If the paper says 'had an even worse week',' said Pollard, nodding at the new folded sheet lying on the table, 'then it's right.' He felt greasy with tiredness; the attacks had been coming almost daily since his last session with Becker, at all times of the day and night. The previous night's had been repellent, leaving him ragged and queasy with terror and tiredness.

Pollard had been half gone, in that state between sleeping and wakefulness, when his whole body spasmed violently. That, in itself, wasn't unusual; it was a lifelong, though occasional, thing, as though he was walking and had tripped. Mary used to laugh about it and say the startled look on his face as he popped awake was one of the funniest things she had seen. This was harder though, almost painful, a savage jerk that yanked him awake. He rolled, tangling himself in the duvet as he went and then thing sitting on the bed next to him shifted, leaned in towards him.

Pollard remembered screaming. He threw himself from the bed, the duvet clinging to him, and fell to the floor. He was *cold*, terrified, the muscles in his legs jittering spasmodically as he tried to kick away the heavy, tangling duvet, struggling out from under it as behind him something moved across the bed. It was huge, blocking the night's half-light coming in around the edges of the curtains as it came and then Pollard was free of his bedclothes and he ran without looking back.

He had ended up in his back garden, standing at its far end in the shadows of the apple tree that he and Mary had planted when they first moved to the house over thirty years ago. His panic receded in shuddering waves, the world seeming to swim back into reality around him. He was still cold, although not as cold as he had been in the bedroom, and his legs ached from the running but had stopped twitching. Embarrassed, Pollard covered his genitals with his hands and went quickly back down the garden path and into the kitchen. Smells lingered, the residue of his food that evening, a microwave meal from the local supermarket. Suddenly, bitterly, he missed

Mary, missed the smells of her cooking and the times they cooked together, peeling and cutting, chattering, drinking wine. The feeling was almost anger, rage even, hot in his chest.

'And the house? The bedroom?' asked Becker.

'It was fine,' said Pollard. 'I could feel even from down in the kitchen, the frightening thing was gone. I went back to bed, but I couldn't sleep. Although it was gone, every time I closed my eyes I saw it move again, the way it leaned over as though it wanted to get closer to me, to catch me.'

'Let me ask you something,' said Becker. 'Why did you run to the garden?'

'Because I wanted to get out of the house,' said Pollard.

'Did you pass your front door to get to the back door?'

'Yes,' said Pollard. He hadn't thought of that before, had just run.

'So why not go out of the front door?'

'I was naked,' he replied after a moment. 'I didn't want to be naked in the street, people might have seen.'

'So,' said Becker, 'even though you were terrified, the fear of being naked was greater?'

'Yes,' said Pollard. 'No. I don't know.'

'You do,' said Becker. 'It might not feel like it, but you're making progress. The phobic reaction, the attacks, are getting worse, yes, but your inherent rationality is beginning to break through. All of the things you experience can be explained physiologically: you feel cold because your body, having entered an extreme 'fight or flight' reaction, is drawing the blood away from your extremities in order to protect and feed your muscles. The thing you saw moving was your eyes adjusting to opening and the pupils widening very quickly, the movement and change in light being taken in by your eyes being interpreted by your brain, an interpretation fed by fear and adrenaline. We make patterns where none exist; it's why we see shapes in the clouds. The pattern you made was fearful, terrifying, because that's how you were feeling at the moment of interpretation. Consider this, though, Mr Pollard: you went past one potential exit from your home to a further one not because it was a better exit, but because you're starting to take control, to set the attacks within the context of your wider life. You didn't want to be seen naked, so even without realising it you were assessing with the situation, considering your options, acting on them, reducing the possibility of that happening. You may have felt out of control, but you weren't, not really.'

'But it was so real,' said Pollard, remembering the weight on the bed, the shift of the mattress, the cold, the sight of it surging forwards at him as he struggled in his duvet.

'Of course it was,' said Becker. 'The feelings that are causing it, all the pain and fear, all the grief you feel about Mary's death, they're real. You don't want to experience them again, to even remember them; who would? So, unconsciously, you've trapped them down and converted them into this other fear, something powerful but ultimately irrational, an externalised point, a thing to flee from, to allow you a literal running away. The feelings fade when you're run because you've vented them, released some of the pressure, but it builds up again. The attacks are a sign that, whether you realise it or not, you are ready to deal with those feelings now, to get rid of them, to uncover Mary and let her back into your memories. Not as a painful thing but as something good, something positive.

'Tell me how she died.'

The question surprised him, caught him off guard, and Pollard couldn't speak. That day, that miserable, dreadful, awful day, was the most terrible memory he had, and it was scraped and raw when he probed it. Fragments of the day jumbled together inside him, fighting to free themselves, each one bad, worse, the worst; the phone call from the police, the trip to the hospital, the doctor in her white coat with the voice as sympathetic and absolute as cold mercy, being left alone with Mary but not for goodbye, no, for *identification*, to know that she was dead and to be able to confirm for the world that he knew she was dead. Mary, who joked she'd kill him if he went first, Mary who wouldn't eat olives but who loved anchovies, Mary, whose mouth and eyes were open as she lay on the morgue's viewing room table as though she had been caught by surprise, frozen staring into the distance, mid-speech. Mary, who was already going cold when he kissed her for the last time. Mary, who was dead. 'She had a heart attack in the office behind the gallery, unpacking crates,' he said eventually.

'This was an art gallery, yes? She worked there?'

'She owned it. She set it up six years ago, after years of working in a job she hated. She mostly showed contemporary artists, and imported and sold ethnic art. Most of our holidays these last years have been business trips.' He smiled at the memories, Mary excitedly telling him about the new pieces she had found somewhere off the beaten track, of the deals she managed to do. 'She was good at finding things that were unusual, that people liked enough to buy. She was successful, was getting a good name for herself.'

'She had a heart attack?' asked Becker, gently steering Pollard back to the subject he was trying to skirt around.

'Yes,' he said. 'But it didn't kill her, not straight away. She fell. She was unpacking some Inuit pieces at the time, little stone carvings, and they fell with her. Most of them broke on the floor, all except one she was holding. Mary, she ... she rolled in them, and the pieces cut her. She had scratches and punctures all over her arms and face, so many that the police thought at first that she'd been attacked and stabbed. There was an autopsy and an inquest before they decided she'd died of natural causes.'

Pollard took a deep breath, painful and sharp, and said, 'They think she was alive for at least a few minutes after the heart attack. There was a lot of blood and marks like she'd tried to crawl towards her desk, towards the phone. That's the worst of it, I think, the thought of her being alone and scared and in pain for those few minutes. I wish I'd been with her.'

'Yes,' said Becker, 'I'm sure. Have you told anyone that before?'

'No.'

'Then well done. This isn't easy, I know; you're peeling back these layers, all of those miseries, but it's for a good reason. Mary's there at the centre of it all, Mr Pollard, the positive Mary, the good memories. I know I keep saying it, keep repeating it, but I have to know you understand, that you trust me. We're getting there, getting closer.'

'Yes,' Pollard said. He was suddenly exhausted, sick with tiredness.

'Tell me, the object that you wife was holding, do you know what it was?'

'No. The police gave it me back once the inquest was over, but I've never looked at it.'

'Then homework for the week, Mr Pollard, is to look at the object and find out what it is, and tell me about it next week.'

The day before his next session with Becker, Pollard ate his lunch outside. The square in front of his office was busy with businessmen and –women, scurrying, eating, talking, smoking. He liked it here, liked its busyness, the bustle of it. The concrete benches that ringing it faced in, which he and Mary had laughed about that lunchtime all those years ago. 'Business only wants its people to look inwards, at other business sorts,' she had said, 'God forbid they look at the world outside even for a moment!' Pollard, who had worked in finance since he was sixteen and was used to her teasing, had laughed with her and kissed her and poured her another glass of champagne. Sitting here now, he remembered her leaning into him, whispering about the future, the smile on her face evident in her voice. Ah, but he missed her, more every day it felt like.

It had gone cold.

On the other side of the square, something black moved. It was large, stalking behind the curtain of people so that Pollard couldn't get more than a glimpse of it. He had an impression of flanks, of fur sleek with wetness, of a head that swayed from side to side as though sniffing at the floor.

Of eyes as black as obsidian and of teeth the yellow of ivory left in dark places.

It's an animal, he thought, although what, he couldn't tell. It was high at the shoulder, almost as tall as the people around it, none of whom reacted to it. Couldn't they see it? *Feel* it?

It was even colder now, and steam was rising from the thing as it moved around the edge of the square, coming to towards Pollard. A gap opened briefly between two of the hurrying people, allowing him to glimpse a head whose flesh was crenelated and raw-looking. Pollard dropped his half-eaten sandwich and rose, knowing that he had to go, to go *now*, to escape the thing, to not let it any nearer. He heard it, a noise like the snuffle of some giant carnivore scenting its prey, heard a sound like freezing rain hitting glass, and he ran.

'I don't remember much after that until I was in the office,' said Pollard. 'I must have run up the stairs, though, four floors. My legs still ache now.' In fact, Pollard did remember one thing; as he knocked open the door from the stairway onto the fourth floor, startling some of his colleagues, the thing had been at the bottom of the stairwell. It was long and lithe, slipping around the corners with a sinuous grace, peering up at him. In the bright electric light, its black eyes glinted with flashes the colour of burning grass. The sight of it, of those glittering and depthless eyes, made his bladder clench and he had felt a hot splash of urine escape him.

'Did you do your homework?' asked Becker.

Pollard, momentarily startled by the conversation's change of direction but beginning to recognise Becker's tactics, didn't answer. Becker looked at him expectantly, forcing him to speak. 'Yes,' Pollard said. 'I did my homework.' *Homework*, he thought. *Some homework, to investigate the last thing my wife held on this earth.* He had opened the bag the police had given him several nights before, tipping out Mary's purse and phone and the other thing, letting them tumble onto the table in front of him.

The thing was in his pocket and he took it out now, putting it on the table between himself and Becker. It was a small dog, carved out of dark rock. 'It's an Inuit carving of a qiqirn,' he told Becker. 'I remember Mary telling me about it when she originally ordered them. Most Inuit art is stories, they were originally nomadic and didn't have much use for carvings and statues, I don't suppose, so she was excited to find them. Qiqirn are supposed to be malicious spirits, unpleasant, taking advantage of the lonely.'

'A dog?'

'Yes.'

'And the thing you saw, could you say it was a dog?'

'Maybe,' Pollard admitted. 'A big one. It's hard to say for sure.'

'No, it isn't,' said Becker. 'You saw a version of the thing Mary was holding when she died, this Inuit qiqirn, not because it's real and not because Mary was cursed by it, but because it's a representation of her death. Those bad layers, Mr Pollard, they're fighting as hard as they can to stay in place but you're winning.' He gestured to this week's piece of folded paper. Pollard picked it up and read A BAD WEEK IN WHICH YOU HAVE SEEN SOMETHING.

'We're getting closer, Mr Pollard, closer to the heart of it. Closer to Mary, moving through the layers of bitterness and mourning and anger and hurt that surround your memories of her. Those layers have helped protect you these last months, kept you safe until you have the strength to move forwards, but they've done their job now. These attacks are evidence of that, of that fact that the rational, loving part of you is beginning to assert itself, to free Mary from their shackles. Let me take a guess at something: the square in which you saw the qiqirn, it was somewhere that had significance to you and Mary?'

'Yes.' It was where he and Mary had gone after she had signed the lease on the art gallery, where they had had the conversation a year earlier about her quitting her hated job and setting up the gallery. Where they drank champagne at lunchtime and smiled at other and looked forward to the future.

'The kitchen, the bedroom, other places of importance where this thing happens, the qiqirn makes its presence felt in those places because it's a thing of negativity and it can have its greatest affect in places that are most positive for you.'

'It felt real,' said Pollard, not sure which was worse, the idea that the qiqirn was real or that he wanted to it to be real because the alternative was that was holding onto his negativity so tightly that it had made him see things.

'Of course it was, because it *is* real,' said Becker. 'Where our brains are concerned, our perceptions, there are no metaphors or similes, there's simply real and not real. Did it physically exist? No. Was it real? Yes, yes it was, a manifestation of all your unhappiness and loss and sadness and fear.'

'I suppose,' said Pollard, remembering steam rising off grey flanks.

'You're doing well, Mr Pollard, so well. Time for the next stage, I think. All the steps you've taken so far have been around the edges of the attacks. Important, yes, vital even because it's been about helping you to understand what's happening, but now we have to deal with the things themselves. Small steps, Mr Pollard, or in your case, no steps. When the attacks come, try to stand still for a second before you run, for five or ten or thirty seconds, as long as you can manage. Try to stand for longer and longer each time. Take control of them, rather than letting them control you. Will you try, Mr Pollard?'

'Yes,' he said, and thought again of flanks and teeth and eyes that flashed through the darkness of four floors, black and cold and glistening.

'You look tired. I'm assuming this hasn't been a good week?'

'No,' said Pollard, thinking that these sessions were making him monosyllabic. It had been a terrible week, with at least one attack each day and sometimes more. He had tried to stand in the face of them, he had, but they were simply too strong. The fear, the thought of seeing that thing again, the qiqirn, was simply overpowering and he had found himself running within seconds of the attacks starting. He had cowered in his garden, come to a halt in the street, even locked himself in the bathroom once, pushing towels into the gap between the floor and door and knowing as he did so that it was a ridiculous thing to do.

'I did some research on the Inuit, on the qiqirn,' said Becker. 'You were right, they're malicious dog spirits. Most cultures have similar things, from the Native American tricksters to the Japanese *kitsune*, even the Christian devil. They represent all those forces beyond our control, accidents and disasters and bad luck and the like. According to most mythologies, they latch on to someone when they're at a low ebb, when they're mourning or scared or upset, take root, fester. They cause fits, sickness, misery. Does that sound familiar?'

'Yes,' said Pollard. 'It's me. Mary and me, my memories of her.'

'Yes. Qiqirn are supposed to be ugly, bald, vicious, to cause fear and panic and disgust, to carry the cold of their native land with them wherever they go, all the things you've experienced. I found something else out as well: the angakkuq, what I suppose we'd call the spiritual leader of the Inuit group, had advice on how to deal with a qiqirn if you found yourself haunted by one. 'Turn and face it', they say. 'Walk towards it, taking small steps. Be steady. Look it in the eye. Recognise it. Shout its name.' Does that sound familiar as well?'

'Yes. It's the advice you've been giving me.'

'We think of psychology and psychiatry as new sciences, but they aren't, not really. The Inuit have a saying about their mythology: 'We don't believe; we fear'. It's how we cope, by fearing, by putting our fears into shapes that we can categorise, name, understand, and by doing so, we give ourselves the tools to overcome them. Religions, particularly older ones, have always understood that we have to force our fears into view to get rid of them. Each step we take away from them strengthens them; each one we take towards them weakens them. Walk towards it, Mr Pollard, using the smallest steps if you want, but walk *towards* it. This qiqirn, these negative emotions and fears, they exist because you're allowing them to and for no other reason. Keep walking, Mr Pollard.'

'Yes,' said Pollard, feeling a swell of helplessness. Becker made it sound easy, practically sweated confidence, but he hadn't seen it, hadn't heard the noises it made, hadn't felt the numbing fear and the electric twitch in legs that had to run.

'I know it sounds hard,' said Becker. 'It *is* hard, but it's not impossible. Call it a qiqirn, a phobia, a panic attack, whatever you like, but you can defeat it, Mr Pollard. You can.'

Pollard didn't reply. He hoped Becker was right.

Pollard hit the door hard, yanking at the handle, but it refused to open. He had locked it earlier, he remembered, casting his eyes about for the keys. Where were they? He had locked the door and then gone to the kitchen, putting the keys down on the counter by the kettle. They were in the kitchen.

Where the qiqirn was.

The attack had come suddenly, faster than any of the others. Everything was fine, he was getting ready to go to bed, and then it was there, in the kitchen, behind him. He had a vivid, frenzied image of it sitting on its haunches, its black lips curled back in a grin from teeth that were slick with saliva, its bald head a pale, sickly pink, ridges of flesh crawling across its crown, its ears laid flat. The temperature plummeted. Pollard ran.

Hitting the locked door brought him back into himself slightly, the door's solidity and immovability cutting through some of the terror. Pollard heard a moaning sound, realised it was him and forced himself to stop. *This can't go on,* he thought, *I can't keep on like this, it's killing me. I want my life back. I want Mary back, she's dead and I want her back, not this, not this terrible fear.*

He turned, keeping himself pressed again the door. The kitchen was almost dark, the lights off inside, low illumination coming in from the night beyond the window, from the moon and the streetlamps and the stars. From the normal world.

Pollard took a step towards the doorway, his legs shaking so much that his knees actually knocked together. *I wonder if Becker knows that it's not a cliché?* he thought to himself randomly, and took another step.

Another. The thing in the kitchen growled, low and glottal.

No. There was no growl, there was no thing in the kitchen, no qiqirn, no trickster demon feeding on his pain and fear like some fat parasite, there was only air and memories buried under layers of grief and anger and sorrow. He took another step, and the urge to run was terrible, his muscles sick with adrenaline and unspent energy. He reached out, taking hold of the kitchen doorframe, anchoring himself. *I will do this,* he thought, *I will.* In the room ahead of him, claws clicked softly on linoleum as the qiqirn shifted and he imagined it readying itself for him, crouching, bringing its bald, ugly head close to the floor and drawing its lips back even further from its teeth to reveal gums that were flushed and dark, the colour of wet slate.

No.

There is nothing there, Pollard told himself again. *I will step forward into my kitchen, my kitchen and there will be nothing there, no demons except my own and the empty spaces they create.* He took another step, pulling himself against the doorframe. He was cold, the house was cold, his life was cold. More sounds from the kitchen, the spatter of saliva dripping from teeth and tongue to floor in thick, lazy strings, another low growl. I will face it, Pollard thought, and made the last step through the doorway.

In the kitchen it had started, gently, to snow.

LISA TUTTLE

THE THIRD PERSON

WHEN SHE GOT Rachel's text suggesting lunch, Imogen was thrilled into immediate agreement, although the short notice, and her friend's choice of venue, meant a rush, and her colleagues' displeasure that she was taking the full hour for the second time that week.

For once, Rachel wasn't late; eye-catching as ever with her long, red hair and dramatic style, she waved from a booth at the back and announced that she'd already ordered for them both.

'You're going to love the cauliflower cheese soup. And it gives us more time to talk if we don't have to faff around with menus.' She was glowing, radiant, bubbling in a way Imogen had not seen in months. It reminded her of the old days, when they'd shared a flat, before Rachel married Andrew.

Marriage changed everything. Everybody knew how it was: married couples had different priorities, and when they weren't alone together, liked to be with other marrieds. Add to their new status a starter house in a distant suburb and two demanding jobs, and there wasn't much left for their singleton friends. Imogen had thought she might be the exception: after all, the three of them had lived together for nearly a year, so comfortable a threesome that they joked about their Mormon marriage, if too conventional to go farther than flirting with the idea of a sexual *ménage a trois*. Andy's undemanding yet undeniably masculine presence had added a bit of spice to her life, which she missed. She recalled the pleasures of lazy Sunday morning fry-ups over three different newspapers, late-night take-aways and horror movies viewed from the sagging, second-hand couch – even a boring, stupid thing like doing the laundry was almost fun as a threesome. But maybe that was only her. Maybe they would always have been happier without a third person in their life.

She looked at her friend through the steam of soup too hot to touch. 'What's up? I can see you're dying to tell me something.'

Rachel compressed her lips. 'I need you to promise you won't tell anyone.'

She was stung by this distrust. 'Who would I tell?'

'Not anyone. If it ever got back to Andrew . . .'

'Oh my god.'

'Promise?'

Imogen scowled. 'Asking me to promise *now* is a bit stable-doors. You're having an affair?'

Rachel grimaced. She could not deny it, only quibbled over the wording. It was nothing so definite as an 'affair.' Love didn't enter into it. It was just sex.

'But . . . why? Why take the risk?'

'Oh, Immy.' She shook her head and looked chiding. 'I didn't mean to. I didn't go looking for this. It just happened.'

'Yeah? Where, on the bus to work? Oh, I'm sorry sir, it's so crowded, I seem to have impaled myself upon your manly tool. As we've started, may as well continue.'

Rachel nearly choked on her soup, giggling. 'OK, OK. I am a weak and horny woman who cannot resist temptation. I was feeling frustrated and half-dead . . . Andrew, bless him, is just not up for it that often. He's less . . . *driven* by sexual needs than I am. I always knew it might be a problem someday, I just didn't expect it to be so soon. But when Mr. Hotbody came along and woke me up . . .' She gave a fatalistic shrug.

'Who is this Mr. Hotbody?'

'You don't know him,' she said quickly. 'Nobody does.'

'That sounds spooky.'

'Nobody *we* know. There's no reason Andrew would ever hear anything. He's a total stranger I met in a pub.'

Imogen shivered, and took a careful sip of her soup.

'It wasn't a pub I'd ever been in, either. A client had suggested it, and after she left, he came over and offered to buy me a drink. I'd noticed him watching me, and gave him the look . . . it was just like the old days, picking out the sexiest guy in the room, to see if I could pull.'

'So you can still pull. Amazing. Did you tell him you were married?'

'After he put his hand on my leg. He just smiled and said he liked married women the best, because they didn't confuse sex with love, and he sort of walked his hand up my leg, right up to my crotch and started to rub me there, through my pants, looking me in the eye the whole time while he brought me off.'

It was not the heat of the soup that brought Imogen out in a sweat as Rachel continued to describe what followed. 'Sex in the toilet! I don't know what possessed me – I hadn't done anything like that since I was eighteen. And this was much, much dirtier.'

'And that wasn't the end of it?'

She shook her head, eyes glazed over. 'I didn't even know his name. I told Andrew I had to go away overnight, on business, and booked a room in a Travelodge. He met me there. We were at it all night. Never slept. I did things I'd never done before – he made me do things –'

Imogen pushed her bowl to one side, her appetite gone. 'That does not sound good.'

'Are you kidding? It was the best I've ever had.'

'Not good for your marriage.'

'Oh, no, there you're wrong, my friend. Sometimes a bit of danger, the risk of another lover, is just what a couple needs. I went home and bonked the living daylights out of Andrew. He loved it! For a little while, I had my Randy Andy back. Plus, I'm so much nicer when I'm not feeling frustrated. I've stopped being such a bitch at home. What's good for me is good for him.'

'Good for you. You've saved your marriage. End of story.'

'It's not the end.'

'You can't go on sleeping with this guy.'

'I have no intention of sleeping with him, or going out to dinner with him, or knitting little booties, or falling in love. This is just sex. So much spicier than I can get at home. A bit on the side. That's all I want from him.'

'So what do you want from me? A seal of approval?'

'We need a place to go.'

'Oh, no.' Her stomach clenched. 'You can't go to his?'

'He lives with someone. And anyway, I don't want to get involved with his life.'

'So rent a room . . . Travelodge was good enough before.'

'It would be good enough again, if I could afford it . . . or if he could. Please? It won't be very often, I'm sure. Just a few more times, 'til I get him out of my system.'

'Or out of your pubic hair. Where am I supposed to go while this . . . de-lousing . . . is taking place?'

Rachel's face tightened. 'Don't be nasty.'

'You're the one talking about how wonderfully dirty it is.' Before her hurt, angry glare, she caved. 'I'm sorry. I just don't understand why you need to do this thing.'

Her hand was seized and held in a warm, strong grip. 'Of course you don't, my sweetheart, because you're *normal*. This is some kind of madness, but I can't get over it without going through it. And you are the one and only person who can help me, who I can talk to. I don't want to put you out. But you go to the gym and out for a meal with your friends from work every Thursday, am I right? What time do you get home?'

'About nine-thirty,' she said, although ten was closer to the mark.

'I'd want to be on the nine-forty-seven for home anyway,' said Rachel. 'We'd be out by nine-thirty. I promise you, Imogen, you won't know we were there. One evening a week, a time when you wouldn't be there anyway – is that really too much to ask?'

She understood she could not refuse; not unless she was prepared to lose her friendship.

Rachel came by that evening to pick up the spare key, and Imogen was a little stiff with her at first, feeling she had been bullied into abetting a crime, but instead of hurrying away like a guilty thing, Rachel hung around, diffident and awkward, until Imogen thawed and suggested she stay for dinner.

'There's a kebab shop just around the corner; I could run down for something . . .'

Rachel checked the contents of the fridge. 'I'll cook,' she said. 'Spaghetti carbonara sound all right?'

'I don't have any cream.'

'We never did, and I don't recall any complaints in the past, so long as there was plenty of *this*.' With a wicked grin, she produced a bottle of wine from her capacious shoulder bag.

Every remnant of ill feeling vanished as she whipped up a quick supper. It was like old times again. She phoned her husband to warn him she'd be home late, and put him on speaker so Imogen could hear and join in a joking, friendly, three-way conversation. When they were doing the washing-up, Imogen said wistfully, 'We should do this more often.'

'I don't know about you, sweetheart, but I wash up after *every* meal.'

Imogen laughed. 'Idiot. I've missed you. Missed *us.*'

'Me, too.'

Walking through her front door on Thursday night (9:56 by her phone), although it was dark and still, Imogen felt another presence there.

'Ray?' she called sharply. 'Hello?' Her skin prickled; what if it was *him?*

With the light on, she could see into every corner of the sparsely furnished, open-plan living room and kitchen. There was nowhere to hide, unless – looking one-way, behind the half-open door of the bathroom – or, at the other end, in the bedroom. She scarcely breathed until she had checked both rooms thoroughly, even peering inside the built-in wardrobe in the bedroom, and the narrow airing cupboard in the kitchen. But she remained tense, even knowing she was alone, so she phoned Rachel.

'How'd it go?'

'I'm on the train.'

'I wasn't expecting the porno version.' At the familiar sound of her friend's snorting laugh, she relaxed at last. 'I just wanted to check that everything was, you know, all right.'

'Mmm, good question. Not sure what to say.'

Suddenly suspicious, she demanded, 'Is he with you?'

'What? No, of course not! I said, I'm on my way home. There's the tunnel.'

'Catch up tomorrow?' She was talking to a dead phone.

The abrupt end to that unsatisfactory conversation left her feeling on edge, but she went through her usual routines, tidying the already tidy flat, and put herself to bed before eleven o'clock.

She was tired, and her thoughts soon drifted into the

surreal jumble that presaged sleep. Turning on to her left side, she snuggled deeper into her pillow, and caught a faint whiff of Jo Malone's Pomegranate Noir – Rachel's signature scent.

By now her own body-heat had warmed the space between the sheets, and with that warmth, other smells were released from the bedding: body odours that were not her own, sweat and musk and ejaculate, the unmistakable smells of sex.

And then she could hear them – laboured breathing, low grunts, the slap of flesh against flesh – and feel them, too, a woman and a man in bed with her, one on either side of her.

It wasn't real, of course. It couldn't be. If she'd suddenly found herself in bed with two other naked people she would have been repulsed by it, felt disgust, or fear. But instead, half-asleep and knowing she must be dreaming, it was safe to become aroused. These two people, so focused on their own sexual pleasure, stirred desires she kept buried, hidden from her conscious mind. The man behind her was a stranger – it didn't matter who he was. The woman whose soft large breasts pressed against her own was Rachel.

This was Rachel as she'd scarcely dared to imagine her, yet knew she must be, powerfully erotic, sexually voracious. As Imogen allowed herself to be overwhelmed by the power of the fantasy, she heard her friend whispering to her, words she'd actually said once when talking about masturbation:

'You shouldn't feel guilty. That's crazy! It doesn't matter *what* you think about while you're doing it – whatever gets you off is fine, it doesn't matter what crazy, sick thing turns you on, so long as it stays inside your own head. Nobody ever got hurt by a private fantasy. It's the safest sex there is.'

In the morning, though, she was not so relaxed. The first sip of coffee seemed to curdle in her stomach, and she felt sickened by herself, and then angry at Rachel. Why couldn't her friend have followed her own advice, and kept her fantasies locked inside her own head? Why did she have to soil Imogen's bed with them?

She poured the rest of her coffee down the sink and, although there was scarcely time for it, hurried back to the bedroom, intending to strip off the dirty sheets, rather than leave them festering with their alien stains and smells for another day. But as soon as she saw her bed she realized it wasn't necessary. Rachel had changed the bed after using it. The dirty sheets and pillowcases were in the washing machine in the kitchen – a fact she had noticed before going to bed, and then forgotten.

She leaned down and sniffed the pillow. She could just about pick up traces of herself – skin oil, face cream, shampoo – but nothing remotely like Rachel's perfume. When she put her head under the covers she smelled the lavender scent of her fabric conditioner, and nothing else.

Those smells that she thought had triggered an erotic fantasy had been part of the fantasy – part of the dream. It had been a dream, of course, with no conscious desires behind it at all. The knots in her stomach loosened. Dreams were nobody's fault. You couldn't blame yourself for what your unconscious got up to while you slept.

Text messages flew back and forth between Imogen and Rachel over the next few days, but despite reiterated declarations that they must meet, or at least talk, their busy schedules made it impossible before Thursday came around again.

There had been no repeat of that disturbingly erotic dream, and Imogen had almost managed to repress the memory of it until that morning, when she woke up thinking about Rachel and her faceless, nameless lover, who would soon be going at it like knives in this very bed, between her own, used sheets.

She didn't know if knowing his name or what he looked like would have made it better, or worse, but she was tormented by the sense of being unfairly used. Maybe she had no right to judge Rachel for the betrayal of her marriage vows, but wasn't more respect due their friendship? Changing the sheets was the merest gesture; all that frenzied passion must leave traces that could not be easily washed away, a charge in the atmosphere, a kind of miasma in the bedroom that affected her sleep and gave her bad dreams. She wished she had made more of an effort to talk to Rachel; she should have insisted on seeing her. It was too late now, of course, but she decided tonight was the last time. She would ask Rachel to give her back her key.

Mounting the deserted concrete stairs that rose through the large, quiet building at a quarter to ten, Imogen tingled with anxiety, again plagued by the feeling that someone was waiting for her inside. Not even the sight of the clear, empty vista of the main room was enough to calm her nerves, and she was obliged to check out the bathroom and empty bedroom thoroughly before she could relax.

This time, she did not miss the fact of clean sheets on her bed, and deliberately took several deep, calming breaths of the soothing scent of lavender as she settled down to sleep.

But it happened again. As her own body heat raised the temperature within the warm cocoon of the bed, something else was released, as if memories of what had taken place in that space a few hours earlier had left spores ready to blossom into life under the right conditions. All the smells of sex wafted over her and she heard the animal sounds of vigorous fucking, and while a small, civilized part of her was repulsed, and a little frightened, by this activity going on in her own bed, her body was melting, yearning, opening with the longing desire to be a part of it.

They were so close, so close, but at the same time impossibly distant, their desires never meeting hers, so completely focused on each other that they didn't even know she was there. They were all in the same space, but separated by time. And so, although she found herself between them, they were blissfully unaware of any impediment, intent only on satisfying themselves through each other, as if Imogen did not exist, as if she were of less substance than a ghost.

Maybe she was only a fleeting thought passing through Rachel's mind, a weightless fragment of gratitude and guilt, gone before it could be acknowledged, as the other woman hurtled, with single-minded intensity, towards her own satisfaction.

Imogen could not connect. The other two made love through her, without her, and although she was unbearably close to them, forced to witness their coupling, to smell and hear and *almost* feel their moving bodies on either side of her own, she could not make them feel her. She could only join in, steal a share of their pleasure, by pretending. This was no guilt-free dream, no dream at all. They were in her bed, but she was alone, tensing her muscles, arching her back, opening her mouth wide, nothing to fill it, nothing to assuage her emptiness and bring satisfaction but the quick, impatient movements of her own fingers, angry and dissatisfied with her own, too-familiar flesh, but still practiced enough to know what they must do.

She made herself come again and again until at last her bed was empty and she could fall asleep.

She didn't want to see Rachel again. But they were going to have to meet. Rachel had the key to Imogen's flat. Even more importantly, she thought she had permission to use it. Imogen could not be like the evil landlord who changes the locks without warning. Even if she couldn't tell her the real reason, she was going to ban her from using it, and demand the key back. She didn't care if they fell out over it and never spoke again; that would only prove that Rachel had never been such a good friend as she had thought.

They met on Saturday morning, at a Starbucks in a mall, in the middle of a heaving mass of shoppers hunting for a bargain.

'I have to meet Andrew at Ikea in thirty-five minutes, but that should be plenty of time for a coffee,' Rachel said, with a hug and kiss Imogen was not quick enough to avoid. She was as beautiful and bouncy as ever, and Imogen felt like a coward, evading her direct and happy gaze. She ordered a skinny vanilla latte for the look of the thing, but knew by the roiling in her stomach that she would not be able to drink it.

'What's up? Your text was so . . .'

No point wasting time. She blurted it out: 'I want my key back.'

'Oh.' Rachel's shoulders slumped. She stared down at her hands. Her wedding band made its own comment. 'Well. Of course. In fact, I'd already decided . . . decided to end it. It's crazy – I love Andy, we have a good marriage, I don't want to risk everything for a bit of . . . well, *sport.*'

Imogen's tension began to ease as she realized she wouldn't have to argue. 'Good sense wins the day. Did you bring it?'

'Bring what?'

'My key.'

'Oh! God, no, I didn't think – that's not important, is it? I mean, it is a spare, right? And somebody ought to have it, in case you lock yourself out or something happens while you're away – you shouldn't have both keys yourself.'

Imogen recognized the wide-eyed, honest gaze that went with the perfectly logical argument. She'd seen her friend use it on others to get something she wanted. When she was hiding a lie. Her stomach clenched again.

'Ray, this is not about a stupid key. I don't want that man in my flat again.'

'What happened? Did he do something? What did he do? Have you talked to him?'

She felt her ears get hot and prayed she wasn't blushing. 'Talk to him? Of course not! I don't know who he is. You won't even tell me his name.'

'Only because I don't want you involved in this.'

'But I *am* involved. You involved me, by using my flat. You've done it in my bed! You can't do that anymore.'

Something flared in her friend's eyes, and for a moment Imogen thought she'd guessed – somehow she knew exactly what she'd experienced –

'Just once more. Please, darling. I'll finish with him this week. I promise.'

'Good. Break up with him in a pub. Or have your final fling in the Travelodge.'

She shook her head. 'It's not that easy. I can't get in touch with him before Thursday. But this Thursday will be the last, I promise. And then, if you really insist I give your key back . . .'

'I do.'

Rachel made a dramatic gesture. 'Next week, same time, same place. I promise I will bring it. And I can provide all the sordid details you like.'

The following Thursday night, at nine-forty-seven precisely, Imogen turned the key and stepped inside. Refusing to let herself be driven again by the now-expected impression that there was someone else in her flat, she did not waste time looking around, but went straight to the bedroom to put away her gym gear.

The light was on in the bedroom, and there was a man there, kneeling on the floor. He had been crouching, apparently examining the carpet, but when she opened the door he straightened, although still on his knees.

Her mouth dried. She looked past him, to the bed, which had been roughly re-made, but Rachel was not there.

He was not someone she would have picked out as the hottest guy in any pub. He had a muscular upper body, but his face was forgettable, and his thinning grey hair straggled down as if length could make up for what was missing on top. He was older than she had expected, a forty-something clinging rather foolishly to the style of his youth. Most surprisingly, he didn't look surprised to see her, but smiled seductively.

'What are you doing?' She spoke sharply, annoyed at Rachel for leaving this strange man alone in her flat.

He looked down at the carpet again. 'She lost her necklace – chain broke. Gold chain. Had to leave . . . couldn't miss her train . . . but so upset, I said I'd find the missing bit.'

She peered down at the thick pile of the carpet, knowing immediately what necklace it must be, a diamond and amethyst pendant on the finest of thin gold chains, a twenty-first birthday present from Rachel's grandmother.

'She could have asked *me* to find it,' she muttered, and then was startled to notice the man, still on his knees, had moved closer.

He pushed up her shirt and rubbed his face against the bare skin of her midriff. The shock of it froze her in place. She caught a familiar whiff of dried sweat and hair grease at the very moment that his wet, warm tongue darted into her navel.

She opened her mouth to protest, but the incoherent sound emerged sounding more like encouragement. Her arms did not want to push him away. Her muscles seemed to have turned to jelly, and she might have collapsed entirely without his support. She seemed to have fallen into a helpless dream as he touched and rubbed and kissed her from the waist down. When he unhooked and unzipped and pulled down her trousers, she did nothing to help or hinder, and they fell to her ankles, followed soon by her pants, and hobbled her. He carried on with his more intimate explorations as she closed her eyes and surrendered to whatever he would do to her with his hands or his mouth. He sucked and licked, rubbed and poked and prodded, sometimes hurting her with a rough touch, but generally skilful, increasing her arousal to an incredible pitch.

This was no dream. He was doing it all. Doing everything to her that he had previously done to Rachel, things she could only imagine before now. Her own hands, unoccupied, hung at her sides, now loose, now clenched. Her breath sighed and whistled and caught in her throat. She moaned softly and tried to open her legs wider, wanting more, but she was trapped by her own clothes. As she tried to kick free of them, her knees buckled and she almost fell, but he caught her, and lifted her – so easily; his arms were even more powerful than she had guessed. He quickly and efficiently freed her from shoes, pants and trousers, and dropped her on to the bed.

Remembering Rachel's description of how he'd looked into her eyes the whole time he'd caressed her to orgasm that first time in the pub, Imogen waited for him to look at her, but he was absorbed by the task of removing his own shoes and socks and jeans, and when he came back, wearing only his shirt, he stared at only one part of her, so fixedly that she wondered uneasily if he found her hairy pubes disgusting. (Rachel was religious about depilating, but Imogen could not be bothered.) She was disturbed to notice his penis was flaccid, not even half-erect, but that changed as he pulled it, still staring, so it was obviously not a turn-off.

With unexpected suddenness, still without a word or even an affectionate look, he plunged inside her and began thrusting away with an odd, jerky rhythm. She was just starting to get comfortable with it when he suddenly withdrew and ejaculated on her shirt.

She gave a startled, disappointed cry.

He stood up and backed away, looking at her now with a smile that was more of a sneer. 'You slut,' he said, without heat. 'You didn't think I'd let you have my baby?'

He began putting his clothes on. She lay where he'd put her, afraid to say or do anything that might provoke him, and wondering what had been going on inside his head while she'd been caught in her own fantasy. She was grateful when he left without another word, and sat up when she heard the definitive closing snick of the lock on the front door.

She felt sick, and desperate for a wash. She wanted to wash away every trace of that awful man. She stood up. About to cross the room, she saw something glinting on the floor, and bent down to find two gold links, snapped from a chain.

Holding them, looking at the miniscule circles lying in the palm of her hand, she had an image of Rachel's necklace, broken as it was brutally yanked from her neck, and shivered as she touched the skin across her own collar-bone. Then, closing her hand on the tiny bits of gold, she went through to the main room, where she stopped just short of colliding with Rachel.

She only just managed not to scream. Rachel had been in the flat the whole time. She must have been in the bathroom at first – she should have realized her friend wouldn't have left that man here alone – but when she returned to the bedroom – had she seen them? Looked in, and seen Imogen standing with her trousers around her ankles? And said nothing? Was it a total shock, or something she had suggested or engineered, perhaps pursuing her own fantasy of a threesome . . .

If so, it clearly had not turned out as she'd dreamed. She had not interrupted them or tried to join in, and her continued silence now, and the expression on her face, frightened Imogen. She had never seen Rachel with such a terrible, staring face, and such a murderous look in her eye.

'Hey, Ray, ' Imogen said softly, her heart in her throat. 'We need to talk.'

Rachel's fixed, hideous glare did not soften, and Imogen saw something that froze her heart. Yes, that was murder in her eyes. In one hand, half-hidden by her side, Rachel held the longest, sharpest knife from Imogen's kitchen.

'Don't.' The word jumped out, hot and urgent, forced through the lump of ice in her chest, and then she ran for the safety of the bathroom. She slammed the door and locked it; then, leaning her head against the cool tiled wall, she began to cry.

But she soon regained control. She wouldn't risk opening the door, but she spoke through it, yelling at Rachel that she was sorry, but that jerk wasn't worth it, and couldn't they please at least *try* to have a civilized conversation? Nothing at all in reply from Rachel, so Imogen took her time about having a shower. She knew her friend was no killer. Give her a few minutes to calm down, and then they'd talk.

When she came out of the bathroom, reeking of strawberry shower gel, the flat was empty. She knew it instantly, could tell from the atmosphere that she was alone, but went through the motions of searching, just in case. The long, sharp knife was back in the wooden block where it belonged. Rachel had gone without leaving a note.

She slept that night on the couch. It was not very comfortable, but she preferred a broken night of restless dozing to the company of the ghosts in her bed. When she woke at three, four, five and six, she phoned Rachel, and left humble, apologetic messages begging her to call back, regardless of the time.

At seven-thirty, as she dressed for work, Rachel's phone was still switched off. At eight, she rang the landline number, and Andrew picked up.

'Andy, I need to talk to Rachel.'

There was a silence. 'Imogen? I thought she was with you.'

She swallowed hard. 'She left last night. It was after ten, after her usual train, but there's a later one, isn't there? She didn't say, but I assumed she was going home.'

'What do you mean she didn't say?'

'She – she was upset when she left.'

'What was she upset about?'

Her eyes fell on the tiny gold links she'd brought through from the bathroom. 'You know her gold necklace? From her Nan? It broke.'

'She stormed out because she broke her necklace?'

'There was more to it than that, but it was my fault. I couldn't get her to stay and talk about it.' She touched one of the links with the tip of a finger, staring across the counter to the wooden knife-block on the far wall of the kitchen, all four black handles sticking out. 'She was pretty mad – I was sure she'd go home, but maybe she has another friend she stays with sometimes?'

He didn't reply.

'Look, if you see her, I mean, when she comes in, or calls, would you please ask her to call me?'

'I was going to say the same to you.'

She said a rather awkward goodbye, and then, as she broke the connection, felt the hairs rise on the back of her neck, and knew she was no longer alone.

There had been no sound, and the door had not opened, but even before she turned she knew who was there.

Rachel, looking just as she had the night before: same clothes, same ghastly expression, even the knife in her hand, although there had been no time for her to take it from the kitchen. She could only be a ghost.

Then the small, metallic click of a key in the lock, and the door opened. He came in and shut the door behind him, glaring, holding Rachel's black and silver Nokia, which looked ridiculously tiny in his large hand.

'Why'd you keep calling?' he asked. 'You think she'll forgive you for what you did with me last night?'

She realized then that the murderous look in Rachel's eyes, and the knife in her hand, had never been meant for *her*. She could only hope, as she sprinted for the kitchen, that her own attempt at self-defence would be more successful.

SIMON BESTWICK

DERMOT

THE BUS TURNS left off Langworthy Road and onto the approach to the A6. Just before it goes under the overpass, past the old Jewish cemetery at the top of Brindleheath Road and on past Pendleton Church, it stops and Dermot gets on.

He gets a few funny looks, does Dermot, as he climbs aboard, but then he always does. It's hard for people to put their fingers on it. Maybe it's the way his bald head looks a bit too big. Or the fishy largeness of his eyes behind the jar-thick spectacles. The nervous quiver of his pale lips, perhaps.

Or perhaps it's just how pale he is. How smooth. His skin – his face, his hands – are baby-smooth and baby-soft. Like they've never known work, and hardly ever known light.

All that and he's in a suit, too. Quite an old suit, and it's not a perfect fit- maybe a size too large- but it's neat and clean and well-maintained. Pressed. Smooth.

And of course, there's the briefcase.

It's old-fashioned, like something out of the seventies, made out of plain brown leather. He doesn't carry it by the handle. He hugs it close against his chest. Like a child.

Dermot finds his way to a seat and parks himself there. His hands glide and slide smoothly over one another, as if perpetually washing themselves. His lips are slightly parted and behind the thick glasses his pale, almost colourless eyes are fixed on some far-distant vanishing point beyond the bus' ceiling.

After a moment, the man next to him grunts and gets up. Dermot blinks, snapped rudely out of his reverie, then gets up to let the man past. He thinks the man's going to ding the bell to get off but he doesn't, just goes and finds another seat. Another, Dermot-less seat.

Dermot doesn't care.

He sidles up closer to the window and watches Salford glide past him in the thickening dusk, streetlamps glinting dully on in the gathering grey of impending night.

But he gazes beyond what is there to be seen.

And licks his lips as the bus rides on.

'Special Needs . . .' slurs Shires, outside the door. 'Special Needs . . .'

Abbie stops tapping her pencil on the desktop and looks up at Carnegie.

They're alone in the little office, the little dusty old office that never has a proper clean and has phones and a fax machine and a desktop computer that were last updated in 1991. Well, maybe a little more recently in the computer's case, but only that.

They're the dirty little secret. They're the office in the police station that nobody wants to admit is there, nobody wants to acknowledge exists.

That nobody wants to admit there is a need for.

'Special *Needs* . . . Special fucking *Needs* . . .'

Shires is pressing himself up against the door's big frosted-glass pane with its reinforcing wire-mesh. Seen through it, he's blurred but she can make out enough. His arms are up, bent at the elbows and bent sharply in at the wrists, fingers splayed, a parody of some kid with cerebral palsy. He's making

240

that stupid, that *fucking annoying* voice, by sticking his tongue down between his bottom lip and his teeth and gums. It's supposed to make him sound like a spastic.

They have to call their little office something, have to give it some kind of a name, and so they call it Special Projects. Shires and the other lads and lasses in the station who know about it call it Special Needs.

It passes for humour around here.

But it's fear, nothing more. It's not the drab little out-of-date office, caught perpetually in its early-nineties time warp, that they're scared of. It's what it represents.

It's what they have to fight.

And how they have to fight it.

That's the theory, anyway. Abbie knows all about the theory. She knows all about what goes on in here, in theory. She's read all the reports, the rulebooks, the case files. She knows the score. In theory.

But this is the first time she's done it for real.

Carnegie, though, he's different. He's a big guy, solid looking. In his forties, she thinks. Late thirties, maybe, and feeling the strain. Dirty-blond hair, washed-out watery-looking blue eyes and features that all look too closely gathered together in the middle of his face. Black jacket, long black coat, black trousers and shoes. White shirt. No tie. The washed-out watery-looking blue eyes are rolled up towards the ceiling and each new breath is blown out through his lips. Hard. A little harder each time, it seems, Shires lets out his stupid call.

'Special fucking *Neeeeeeeeds . . .*'

Shires slaps and bats a splayed bent hand weakly against the frosted, wire-meshed glass, pressing his face up close against it.

Carnegie grabs the door handle, twists and slams his shoulder back into it. The door opens outwards and the impact knocks Shires flying back into the corridor, arms flailing. There's a heavy crash as he lands.

Carnegie pulls the door shut again. He turns to face Abbie and shrugs.

'Argh! Carnegie you fucking cunt!' Shires' voice is muffled.

Abbie is biting her lips hard so as not to laugh. She has to stop herself doing that because if she starts she doesn't know if she'll stop.

Moaning, groaning and mumbling indistinct threats of revenge, Shires stumbles away down the corridor and out of earshot.

Carnegie spreads his hands in a *what-can-you-do* gesture.

Abbie can't restrain herself anymore and bursts out laughing.

Carnegie starts laughing too.

On the frosted-glass pane behind him, around head-height, there's a splash of red on the outside of the door.

They're laughing.

And then the phone rings and they stop.

They just look at the phone, Abbie sitting at her desk, Carnegie standing by the door, and they watch it and listen to it ring and ring and ring.

Dermot stands patiently before the desk. The desk sergeant is trying to keep his eyes off him, but they keep straying back and every time they meet Dermot feels the thrill of contact, the hatred and the loathing and the contempt like the charge that jolts down a live wire when a connection gets made.

The desk sergeant motions with his eyes to one of the seats in the reception area. The subtext of which is *get the fuck away from me*.

Dermot doesn't care. He'd rather sit down anyway.

He goes to the chair and he sits and waits. His hands flow

over and over one another in their endless washing motions. He hugs the briefcase tightly to his chest. Like a baby.

He licks his lips.

And he waits.

The phone rings.

'Gonna answer it?' Carnegie asks.

'No,' Abbie says.

'Answer it,' says Carnegie.

She looks up at him. The phone rings. She wants to say *you answer it*. The phone rings. Or maybe *you answer it, sir*. The phone rings. Maybe, even, *you answer it sir. Please*. The phone rings. But she doesn't. The phone rings. Because he is her superior officer. The phone rings. And this is her first time. The phone rings. This is her test. The phone rings. This is her rite of passage. The phone rings. And if she fails it, she's out. The phone rings -

She picks it up and answers it. 'Special -' she nearly says *Special Needs*, stops herself just in time; turning tragedy into farce would just add insult to injury. 'Special Projects.'

'He's here,' the desk sergeant says.

Send him up, she almost tells him, but she stops herself again, once more just in time. They won't sully their hands with Dermot. They'll kid themselves they're not involved; leave it to the tainted bastards in Special Needs to do the job.

'I'll be right down,' she says.

There's a loud, definite click as the desk sergeant puts down the phone. He feels Dermot's eyes on him and looks his way. 'They're coming down for you,' he says, managing, just about, not to grit his teeth. Now stop fucking looking at me or I'll break your filthy fucking neck, no matter what you are to them. That's what the subtext is.

Dermot just smiles, a mild, milky smile, and the desk sergeant looks away.

Dermot knows they hate him, but he doesn't care. In fact, he rather likes it.

Because they need him. He knows they need him and they know they need him too.

They have to give him what he wants.

No one in the reception area is looking at him. The lift door chimes and opens. A woman approaches. Girl, really. Trouser suit. Blonde hair. Pretty, rather. If she was his type . . . but she isn't. Pity really.

But then, if she was his type, this wouldn't be all the sweeter. Because it's all the sweeter for the power, and what he can make them do.

She comes over to Dermot. She smiles and tries to look civil, but Dermot notices she doesn't offer to shake hands. There are limits even for the people in Special Projects.

'Sir?'

He nods. He bets it hurt her to call him that.

'Detective Constable Stone. If you'll just come with me?'

Without waiting for a reply, she turns and walks away. The desk sergeant steals a glance at her small, taut behind, rolling beneath the clinging fabric of her trousers, then recoils, blushing, as Dermot catches his eye and smirks.

The desk sergeant's face is red. His knuckles, of the fists clenched on the desktop, are white.

Dermot follows the girl into the lift. No one else looks at him, her, at them. No one else wants to admit they're linked or connected in any way, shape or form.

But they are.

'Have you read my file?' he asks her as the lift ascends.

Abbie starts, nearly jumping, gets it under control. She's stolen a couple of quick glances at him, but that's all. She was hoping he'd stay quiet, stay silent, till she'd got him to the office. Hoped Carnegie would do all the talking with him. She'd just have to make the tea. Not get involved. Not be complicit. Tell herself she wasn't responsible.

Don't talk to me, you bastard, she thinks.

But he does. He has.

And they have to co-operate with him. Have to go softly-softly. Have to give him what he wants.

Even my complicity? Even my soul?

You're kidding yourself if you think you haven't given that already, she tells herself. *You're already part of this. Carry on.*

He's looking at her, eyebrows raised, waiting politely for her answer.

'Yes,' she says.

He nods.

'Then you know all about me.'

It's a statement, not a question, this time. His voice is wavery and weak, with a faint Irish accent. It goes with his pale face and bland features and colourless eyes. With his soft, smooth, hairless hands that have never known honest work.

'Yes,' she says. She doesn't want to reply but she has to. 'Yes, I know all about you.' She tries to keep her voice neutral but can't, not quite. She wishes she could, especially when she sees the look on his face.

He likes this. Making us dance to his tune. He likes this. Almost as much as the other part.

She isn't going to think about the other part. That will come later. She has to get through this one stage at a time, step by step. If she thought about the other part she'd never be able to get this done. And she has to.

The lift chimes, and she'd never have believed that simple sound could fill her with such relief.

'We're here,' she says, and steps out of the lift.

Dermot follows her down the same plain, dusty corridor he's come down how many dozens, how many hundreds, of times before? He doesn't know how many. Even he's lost count. Neither she – the pretty little Detective Constable Stone – nor whichever senior officer awaits him in the room – will know.

Will it be Ryan, or McDonald? No- Carnegie, he thinks. It will be Carnegie's turn now. Carnegie won't know how many times Dermot's come down this corridor and into this room. To perform his thankless task. To receive his grudging reward. But he could find out if he wanted. It will be in a file somewhere. In this country, everything has to go on file.

DC Stone opens the door that Dermot knows so well, the one with the frosted-glass pane reinforced with its wire mesh. Odd. There's a smear of blood on it, slowly drying.

Inside, at the desk, is Carnegie.

I was right, thinks Dermot. *I always am.*

Carnegie smokes.

He doesn't offer one to Dermot. Or to Abbie, for that matter. Not that she cares. She has her own packet of Silk Cut. Carnegie favours Sovereign, a much stronger brand. High tar. There's an ashtray on the tabletop. Fuck the smoking ban.

'We know there's at least one in the city,' he says. 'We need you to tell us where it is.'

Dermot pointedly wafts a hand in front of his face. Carnegie glowers and bashes out his half-smoked cigarette.

'What about my fee?' Dermot asks.

'Fee?' Carnegie spits the word out with loathing.

'My reward, then. For doing my bit. For being such a good boy. For saving so many lives.'

Carnegie's eyes are slits. His hands are clenched, the

knuckles white. His mouth looks like a half-healed scar. Then he breathes out and his face goes slack.

'Your reward's waiting downstairs,' he says. 'When you deliver your side of the bargain. You know what we want. Where is it?'

Dermot smiles, nods, licks his lips. It's the last that Abbie finds the worst. The anticipation in it.

He closes his eyes. Prayers his hands together. Smiles. Parts his lips oh-so-slightly and spit-bubbles go pop-pop-pop.

He opens his eyes and his hands drop. His eyes are bright.

He speaks, rapidly. Abbie's already scribbling, transcribing it in shorthand. Then he's done and she's picking up the phone.

Sirens wail in the night, and three police vans tear up Oldham Road into an area of bleak, functional-looking sixties-era council housing and old mills and factories either abandoned or converted to new purposes. Most of the district's one big industrial estate.

At one point along the roadside, a rank of three shops. The buildings are abandoned, boarded up and covered in geological layers of flyposters. The vans screech to a halt outside them. Armed police officers pile out. Some carry shotguns, other submachine guns.

Doors are kicked in and boots thunder up the stairs.

What they're looking for is on the topmost floor.

All the upstairs rooms of the three shops have been knocked together, creating a huge open space.

Things lie on the floor. Five of them. Still asleep. Waiting to wake up. They are vast. They have long talons. Longer jaws. And worse.

Guns are aimed.

Yellow eyes open. Something wakes, leaps up, howling, screeching, clawed hands aloft.

A dozen guns fire simultaneously. The flat, thundery blasts of shotguns, the staccato splitting cracks of submachine guns. The rearing thing is danced back across the room and collapses to the bare, rotted floorboard, writhing, spurting, and then is still.

Then the guns aim down, at the other things, and they fire again.

They don't stop until nothing is left alive on the floors or walls of that upstairs room.

The phone rings.

Dermot watches Carnegie pick it up. The big man nods and grunts. DC Stone is watching all of this, her eyes darting back and forth from one of them to the other.

Carnegie replaces the handset.

'They found them. There were five of them. Just like you said. They got them all.' He doesn't want to say the next bit, but Dermot has his eyebrows raised and is demanding it, tacitly. Just like he always does. And so Carnegie says it. 'Thank you.'

'You're welcome,' says Dermot. 'Now,' he strives to keep his voice level; to show excitement would be unseemly, 'there's the small matter of my reward.'

'Yes,' says Carnegie thickly, not looking up at him, looking down at the surface of his desk instead. 'Detective Constable Stone?'

'Sir?' says Stone at last.

Carnegie still doesn't look up from the top of his desk. 'Take him down to the cells. It's cell number thirteen.'

'Ah,' says Dermot. 'How apt.'

Carnegie doesn't look up or reply.

Stone's face is ashen. She's even shaking slightly. 'If you'll just come with me,' she says.

All the way downstairs in the lift, Abbie's thinking this can't be real, thinking this has to be a dream, thinking please let me wake up before -

But it is, it isn't, she can't.

The lift doors open in the basement and she heads out, Dermot following in her wake. He's trotting after her, she realises with disgust. Trying to hide his excitement and failing. Miserably.

But who's more disgusting, him or her?

The custody sergeant doesn't look up from his paper at either of them as they pass. Determinedly. He knew they were coming. And he knew, just as well, that he wasn't going to, didn't want to see them.

Abbie leads Dermot down past the row of cells. They're all empty tonight. That's been arranged.

There's a slap of paper, the sound of boots on a tiled floor. She glances round to see the custody sergeant walking out fast. Getting out before the sounds start. Well, there'll be nothing else in here demanding his attention tonight.

She puts the key in the lock and opens the cell door. Light from the corridor spills into the darkness.

'Mummy?' The voice is tiny, thin and blurred. 'Daddy?'

Dermot stands at the threshold, not going in yet.

'Go on then,' she says. He doesn't move.

'Mummy?'

This time she prods his shoulder. '*Go on.*'

Dermot's head snaps round and for a second Abbie is afraid. But he's only smiling. Smiling and holding her with his eyes. Till she drops her gaze.

Then he's moving, tired of the game, and into the cell. Abbie pulls the door shut behind him, but not fast enough to evade a glimpse of the child's face, bewildered and afraid, or shut out the beginnings of her cry.

Dermot hears Stone's footsteps recede down the corridor. He puts the briefcase down on the floor and loosens his tie.

The little girl has backed up against the far wall.

Dermot opens the briefcase and takes his tools out one by one. He puts them on the floor beside the case. And then he starts to undress.

In the pub, afterward, Carnegie is on his third double Scotch and Abbie's forsaken her usual white wine spritzer for a vodka tonic. She's on her third. There's been less and less tonic in each one.

'You did good today,' he says. Thick and slurred, but drunkenly sincere.

'Doesn't feel like it.'

'It's got to be done,' he says. 'They need us. Otherwise . . .'

She knows. Knows what would happen without Dermot to tell them where the latest batch of creatures are incubating, ready to wake to murderous life. Knows you do your time in Special Projects – a year, two, maybe three – and then the world's your oyster, a fast-track to any job you want, or if you don't want one anymore, early retirement on a fat pension. There's a reason for that. A price you pay.

She downs her vodka, digs out her mobile, rings for a cab. She feels bad, a little, about leaving Carnegie to drink alone, but sharing the bar with him just makes her remember what she's now part of.

'What time do you need me in tomorrow?'

'Don't bother. Come in in the afternoon.' His watery blue eyes are bloodshot. 'You passed the test, Abbie. You're in. I'll handle the cleanup.'

Normally, she'd object to being treated like the little woman. But this time around, she doesn't mind.

She weaves out the door to the waiting cab.

Alone now, Carnegie downs the last of his whisky. Without being asked, the barman brings him another.

Carnegie bolts half of it in one, feels it burn its way down. Tomorrow, he'll go to cell thirteen, like so many times before. Dermot will be lying there, naked and pallid as a grub, clothes bagged up in a Tesco plastic carrier, tools already wiped spotless and back in the briefcase.

Carnegie will wake him up and take him to the showers. Get the blood off. When he's clean and dressed, he'll drive Dermot home. But first he'll have to go back into the thirteenth cell, and before they come to hose it down, he'll have to gather the bones.

TYLER KEEVIL

FEARFUL SYMMETRY

THE NIGHT IS freezing and the fierce wind catches her off-guard, cutting through her jacket and raking across her skin. She leaps down from the train, her backpack slung over one shoulder. The doors hiss shut behind her; the brakes wheeze as they release. She looks around. It's too dark to see any station signs. The conductor seemed to be indicating that this was her stop, but his English was about as good as her Russian. Now, as the train lurches into motion, she wonders if she's made a mistake.

The platform is open to the sky and encrusted with ice. There is one other person on it – a tall man standing at the far end. She starts walking towards him, and he comes to meet her halfway. He has a dog with him – a mottled brown Laika that pads along at his side. They stop within a few feet of her. The man has an untrimmed moustache, half-gone to grey, and is wearing a wool watch cap like the one her father used to wear. When he grins, a row of gold-capped teeth glitters in the darkness.

'You are the animal woman?' he says. 'Nicole, yes?'

She smiles back, feeling her lips crack in the cold.

'And you're Vargas.'

They do not shake hands. The dog sniffs around her feet, wagging its tail.

~

His truck is the only vehicle in the parking lot. He's left it running; a plume of exhaust is billowing out from the muddy tailpipe.

'Gas must be cheap up here.'

'Is not gas.'

As they get closer she can smell the odour of burning vegetable oil, like a fast-food joint. Some kind of bio-diesel. There is a gun rack bolted inside the back of the cab. She stashes her rucksack beneath it and climbs into the passenger seat. The dog takes up position between them, idly thumping its tail as Vargas puts the truck in gear. Beyond the station entrance the roads haven't been cleared, but he has chains on his tires and they plough along at a good clip, churning up a wake of snow.

'You stay at our house tonight,' Vargas says. 'Tomorrow I show you where the man is killed, and then you give us permission to hunt.'

She can't tell if it's his accent, or his manner, but everything he says sounds like an order – as if he's accustomed to being obeyed.

'It might not be that simple.'

He scowls and jabs at his cigarette lighter. Driving with one hand, he fumbles about on the dash until he finds a half-smoked cigar, which he fits between his teeth.

'Is a killer. You will see.'

'It could also be a new species. Or endangered.'

'We are all endangered here.'

The lighter pops, emphasizing his point. He raises it to his cigar. As he puffs, the orange coil casts a soft glow across his jaw. She opens her window an inch or so.

'I know you,' he says. 'You Americans. You live in big cities where there are no animals, so you think they are like the cartoons. You want to live with them and play with them. You want to save every single one.'

'I'm not American,' she says. 'I'm Albertan.'

He chuckles. 'Is same thing, now.'

She turns away from him and looks out the window. All she can see is snow smothering the fields, forests and farmhouses. It is greyer here than at home. As grey as the ash Vargas taps from the end of his cigar. Her brief warned her about that. The wording was typically convoluted, but she got the impression that if this area were part of New Europe or the Americas, it would have been deemed uninhabitable.

'Is the cough bad here?' she asks.

'Of course.'

The dog has been poking around among the rubbish at her feet. It drags a tattered magazine onto the seat, and begins to gnaw the corner. Patting the dog, she extricates the magazine from its jaws. It is an old copy of *Hustler*, a special Americas edition featuring models from all the new states and territories. She flips through it. The glossy pages are wrinkled and worn. Near the back she finds Miss Alberta: sprawled on a bearskin rug and draped in an American flag, her legs splayed for the camera.

'You must have a lot of time on your hands,' she says.

He leans forward, mashes his cigar in a coffee cup on the dash. It's difficult to tell in the dark but she thinks his face is reddening.

'Is a gift. A joke.'

'Looks like you got good use out of it.'

He snatches it from her and shoves it back under the seat – the truck swerving to the right as he does so.

From the back his house looks as if it's buried in snow; the only thing that's visible is the peaked roof, poking up like a tent. Around the front, the walk, driveway, and yard have been dug out and cleared. Like most of the houses on the outskirts of town, it is a one-story bungalow with wooden siding and a lean-to garage. The garage door is automatic, but as it shudders up it gets stuck halfway; Vargas has to climb out and duck inside to lift it himself before driving the truck through.

Inside it is warmer, but not by much. Nicole can still see her breath in front of her face. She takes off her toque and gloves but leaves her jacket on. Vargas leads her to the kitchen, where a woman is standing at the stove. He introduces her as his wife, Anya. Anya glances back and smiles and continues stirring whatever it is she's cooking. Her wooden spoon makes a rasping sound against the base of the pot.

'Hungry?' Vargas asks Nicole, and she nods. 'Good. We eat soon.'

They sit at the table. From the next room comes the flicker and murmur of the television. Nicole recognizes the familiar sounds of a hockey game: the crack of sticks, the thud of a puck hitting the boards, the low rumble of excited fans. It reminds her of home, and her father, and a time when she still had both. At one point, Nicole notices a small boy peeking around the doorframe. She does not know how long he's been there, watching her. His skin is pale as flour and his black hair seems unnaturally thin – like a baby's hair. When she smiles at him, he giggles and shirks back out of sight.

Vargas barks something at his wife and she brings them bowls of reddish stew, thick with chunks of meat and cabbage and potato. Whatever it is, it is good. A loaf of homemade bread is placed on the table between them. Vargas grips it in his hands, tears it in two, and motions for Nicole to help herself. His wife does not join them. She waits by the stove, hovering like a servant.

At first they eat in silence. Then, halfway through the meal, the pale boy scampers into the kitchen and whispers something in his father's ear. Vargas grins.

'Her?' he says, nodding at Nicole. 'She has come to play with our tiger.' He adds something in Russian – perhaps repeating his joke – but his son does not laugh.

'I'm Nicole,' she tells the boy.

'Nika,' he says, and beams. He pats his chest. 'I Nicholas.'

She looks at Vargas, surprised.

'Yes,' he says, grudgingly. 'That is his name, too.' Then, as if he doesn't want to dwell on the coincidence, he asks her, 'How long will it take? What you do?'

'If I get a sample at the site, maybe a week.'

He is about to eat a spoonful of stew. Now he lowers it, scowling. He says something, loudly, in Russian, that makes his wife jump. 'More people will die.'

'They should be warned to stay out of the area.'

'They need food to eat. Furs to live.'

She shrugs, helping herself to another chunk of bread. 'That can't be helped. If the animal is rare, or a mutation, the process might go on even longer.'

He crosses his arms, frowning. She takes this to mean he doesn't understand, which isn't a surprise. It's her area of expertise and the legality is so murky that half the time she wonders if anybody understands – or if they make it up as they go along.

'For it to count as a new species, any mutation has to be beneficial.' Still he says nothing, so she continues: 'If it is sterile or infertile, or if the mutation is deemed a disadvantage, the creature is considered invalidated and you'll be allowed to kill it.'

Vargas seems to have stopped listening. He is idly stroking his son's head.

'Who decides?' Vargas asks her. 'Who says what is ... invalidated?'

He pronounces the new word awkwardly – articulating each syllable.

'My bosses at the protection agency.'

Gently, he raises his son's arm, which he has kept tucked at his side until now.

'What about Nicholas?' he asks. 'Would he be invalidated?'

She can see that his hand ends in a smooth, fingerless stump. Like a ball of putty. The boy smiles at her shyly, not understanding the conversation. As soon as his father lets go, he hides his arm again. Nicole lowers her eyes, stares into her stew.

'I'm sorry,' she says. 'I didn't know.'

They continue eating in silence, while Nicole tries to think of something – anything – to say. Eventually she asks, 'You said it's a tiger. How do you know?'

'I know. That is how. Tomorrow I take you to the shack.' He motions to his wife, who has been puttering about the kitchen. She comes forward to clear their bowls, their cups, and wipe the breadcrumbs away. 'We must hike far. If you can.'

Nicole stands up to help, carrying her own dishes over to the sink. 'No,' she says, her expression serious. 'I can't hike. Women don't do that where I come from.'

Vargas doesn't find that very funny, but his wife is smiling.

She awakes in darkness. A phone is ringing somewhere. Her nose and ears are cold, her arms tingling with goose bumps. For a split second she thinks she is back there, in her family's cabin in Northern Alberta. On those mornings when her father took her hunting, she'd learned to wake up early, without an alarm, to impress him. She rolls over, looking around. The mattress squeaks beneath her. She sees glowing stars on the ceiling, a stuffed tiger at the end of the bed. Its black-button eyes glisten back at her. She is sleeping in the boy's bed, since they don't have a guest room.

The phone is still ringing. Then, footsteps. A rumbling voice. She sits up to listen, even though she can't understand. After he hangs up, she hears him coughing, clearing his throat. That is familiar, too. That sound. It echoes throughout the house, making her shudder. It could just be morning phlegm, in his case. She hopes so.

Seconds later, he's pounding on her door.

'I'm up,' she calls out.

She is, too. Already standing, pulling on her jeans.

'We go now,' Vargas says, through the door. 'There is another attack.'

She stops buttoning her shirt, then continues, more carefully.

'No time for make-up,' he says.

'I don't wear make-up.'

He grunts, as if he doesn't quite believe her.

The village where the attack has occurred is half an hour's drive to the east. On the way out of town, Vargas stops at a cluster of apartment blocks – squat and drab as bunkers. At the curbside stands a man in a parka, stomping his feet, his head framed by a cloud of his own breath. Vargas shoos his dog onto the floor, and Nicole shifts along to make room as the man climbs in.

'Is Sam,' Vargas says, putting the truck in gear.

Sam pushes back the fur-lined hood of his parka. He has tan skin, prominent cheekbones, and crow-black hair hanging loose to his shoulders. He is wearing a pair of wire-rimmed glasses, half-fogged over with cold, that sit low on his nose.

'I feel bad that you have to stay with this grumpy bastard,' he says to her. His accent is much softer than Vargas's, his English nearly fluent. 'What did he make you for breakfast? Toast?'

Nicole grins. 'Burnt toast.'

'Come to my place if you want some real food.'

'Yes,' Vargas says. 'The Yuits are very rich – because the government gives them all our money.'

'And your jobs. Right, Vargas?'

'Is right.'

Sam chuckles and removes his glasses, starts polishing them on his shirt. He pauses to hold them up and check the lenses.

'How long have you worked together?' Nicole asks.

'Not together,' Vargas says. 'I am his boss.'

'Sure. For now. I'm just waiting until he catches grey lung. Then I'll get his job.' Sam leans forward, fiddling with the radio. 'How about some music?'

'Radio does not work. Is shit.'

Sam tries anyway, pressing buttons and turning dials, adjusting it through various stages of static, before finally giving up. Instead he snaps and hums to himself, bobbing his head as they drive along. The dog watches him, curious.

'So our cat got hungry, huh?' Sam says.

Nicole asks, 'How do we know it's the same animal?'

Vargas snorts. 'Two attacks, one week. Is the same. We must kill it.'

Nicole considers this, studying the snowed-out landscape. They are passing an abandoned church; the roof has fallen in and the windows are clouded with frost.

'For a conservationist,' she says, 'you're pretty trigger happy.'

Sam guffaws, and Vargas jerks hard on the wheel – fishtailing around an icy pothole. 'My job is conservation and protection. But people must be protected also.'

The village, according to Sam, was once a government-sponsored logging camp – before the collapse of communism. Now it is a ramshackle collection of trailers, cabins, and mobile homes. There are no people in sight, but smoke trickles from most of the chimneys and stovepipes. As they drive through, a three-legged dog hobbles out from a yard to yap at their truck. Vargas's Laika snarls back, teeth bared.

Vargas pulls up in front of a trailer that lists at an angle in the snow – as if the supports on one end have given way. A snowmobile is parked in the drive. It looks new: the bodywork glistening blue, the undercarriage sleek and rust-free. As they get out, Nicole notices a woman standing in the window of the house opposite. She glares at them through the glass, both arms folded across her chest.

'Friendly place.'

'We're not popular here,' Sam says.

They wait as Vargas approaches the trailer. The door opens an inch or so, then swings wide. A bald man stands there, holding a can of beer in his hand. He gestures off to the right – towards the forest the village backs onto. Vargas says something to him, raising his voice, but the man keeps shaking his head. They argue for a while.

'He doesn't want to come with us,' Sam explains.

'Because he's scared?'

Sam shrugs. Eventually, Vargas manages to coerce him. The man trudges out, in snowboots and a hunter's cap – still carrying his can of beer. He leads them into the woods. The snow, as soon as they pass the edge of the village, is knee-deep, which makes the going difficult. For them, at least. The Laika is bred for the terrain, and scampers easily over the snowdrifts, stopping occasionally to let them catch up.

A few hundred yards in, the man says something and points ahead. Nicole sees an army-style canvas tent in the middle of a clearing. By the time they reach it they are all breathing hard.

The snow in front of the tent has been cleared and trampled flat. It is soaked in blood. The dog sniffs at it, wagging its tail. At first she thinks it is the blood of the latest victim. Then she notices a steel wire dangling down from one of the branches overhead. It's the kind you would use to hoist up an animal while you skinned it.

'He was trapping?' she asks Sam.

'Looks like it.'

The man is explaining something to Vargas. He talks quickly, gesturing with his beer can, glancing around all the while. Nicole watches the dog. It is pawing at a pile of snow to one side of the tent. She walks over there and scratches its head.

'What is it, boy?' she asks. 'What have you got?'

She brushes the snow away. At first she's not sure what she's seeing. The fur is frosted, the hide rigid as cardboard. An animal skin. There are others underneath.

'What are you doing?' Vargas says. 'Do not touch things.'

She glances back, lifts one up. 'These are sable skins.'

Silence. The bald man just stares at her. Shrugs. Takes a sip of his beer.

'Yes,' Vargas says. 'He was poaching.'

He doesn't sound surprised. She looks at him, at all of them. Trying to guess what's going on. Sam is pretending to study the snowy ground, not meeting her gaze.

She says, 'Then maybe he got what he deserved.'

She doesn't expect the other man to understand, but apparently he does – he slams his beer can in the snow, spiking it like a football. Then he is approaching her, spitting at her, shouting in her face. She catches one word, which he yells repeatedly: '*Blyad! Blyad!*' She has no idea what it's all about, and can only hold up her hands, palms out, to both protect herself and profess her innocence. Eventually Vargas gets between them; he shoves the man back and points towards the village, ordering him to go. The man does, kicking through the drifts – still yelling at her over his shoulder. His beer can lies in the snow, sputtering foam.

She looks at Vargas for explanation.

'This man is his brother.'

'Oops,' Sam says.

She shrugs. She can't take it back, now.

For the next half hour, the three of them examine the campsite, treating it like a crime scene. Treading carefully. Not touching anything they don't have to. The villagers, according to what the man told Vargas, heard the screams in the night. A few rushed out with rifles, but by then the screaming had stopped; the poacher was gone. They saw and heard nothing else. Or so they say.

While Sam studies the perimeter, she and Vargas check the tent. Inside they find a rug, a pot-bellied stove, and a mattress. The mattress is shredded and ripe with blood. They crouch down on either side of it. Vargas touches the blood; it is frozen.

'Why was he sleeping out here?' she asks.

'So he can skin his hides,' he says, 'without us finding him.'

Leaning closer, she studies the mattress. It has an animal stench to it, of sweat and urine. Among the frozen gore, she spots a cluster of hairs. Maybe human, maybe not. Removing her gloves, she places the hairs in a ziplock bag. It only takes thirty seconds, but by the time she's finished her fingers are numb from the cold.

'What about the body?' she asks.

As they consider that, Sam calls to them from outside. They find him standing at the edge of the campsite, restraining the dog by the collar. It pulls against his hold, its muzzle buried in the snow. There is a track there, wide and blood-streaked – as if something has been dragged into the woods. Keeping the dog on a lead, they follow the trail. Only fifty yards away, strewn across a starburst of crimson snow, they find the remains. Some ribs. A femur. Scraps of clothing. And the head, trailing a rope of spinal cord. The face has been gnawed, the nose and cheeks torn away. Nicole stares at the pieces of flesh, trying to make them fit, trying to imagine them as a man. Off to one side she notices a hand, oddly untouched, still clenching a hunting knife.

'Can I take that?' she asks, pointing.

He looks at her curiously.

'The blood on the blade,' she explains. 'Maybe he cut it.'

The fingers are stiff around the handle. She has to pry them off individually; the knuckles crack and pop and the sounds evoke a shiver of frisson, trickling down her spine. Vargas is watching her as she stands and bags the blade and seals the top.

'What about the remains?' she asks.

'We have coroner,' Vargas says. 'Is his job.'

'Look at this,' Sam says, pointing.

He has found clear prints, leading away from the carcass. They gather around and hunker down to study them. The shape – a rear pad and four claws – is definitely feline. Sam spreads his fingers and holds his palm over the print. It's both wider and longer than his hand.

He whistles. 'Big fucking cat.'

Vargas shakes his head. 'Is too big. Too big for tiger.'

'What else could it be?' asks Nicole.

Then, as they contemplate that, his dog starts barking furiously. It is looking out at the forest, in the direction of the tracks. The three of them stand up. Nicole can see nothing but snow and trees and stillness. Nothing at all.

'Should have brought the guns,' Sam says.

'We go back,' Vargas says. 'Now.'

He mutters to his dog, which stops barking and whimpers once, as if asking a question. Vargas gathers up its lead and they retreat, moving quickly and awkwardly in the deep snow, glancing back like fugitives as they go.

The vodka is cold and numbing and slides straight down her

throat like an ice cube. The aftertaste is unbelievably smooth. No bite, and no cloying bitterness. Nicole places her glass on the table and smacks her lips, accentuating the flavours.

Sam and Vargas watch, waiting for her reaction.

'That's nice,' she says.

'You see?' Vargas says, holding up the bottle with a kind of reverence. It is a plain black bottle decorated with lettering that glitters gold like his teeth. Nicole has never heard of the brand. 'I told you the Yuits have all the money, all the luxuries.'

'It was a gift from my grandfather,' Sam says.

He takes the vodka from Vargas and pours out three more glasses, then places the bottle next to the others they've sampled. They are sitting at the table in his living room. It is cramped and cluttered with Yuit art and paintings, and dozens of stuffed animals frozen in life-like poses. They came back to his apartment so Nicole could use her laptop to scan and upload the samples she'd found at the site. Now it's a matter of waiting, and drinking. Which, in Siberia, seem to be one and the same.

'What next?' Vargas says, eyeing the bottles.

Sam taps a clear bottle without a label, and Vargas groans.

'No – not that Yuit shit.'

'It's a new batch. I filtered it better.'

He fills their glasses. The moonshine looks suspiciously cloudy. As the men bicker about that in Russian, Nicole takes her glass over to the sideboard, where her laptop is set up among stacks of movies – most of them American horror films and creature features. She logs in to check her email again. Still nothing. Straightening, she unzips her fleece and wriggles out of it. Her chest feels hot, her cheeks flushed. Drinking always does that to her. Especially vodka. Just above the sideboard is a shelf with three animals perched on it: a crow, a squirrel, and – in the centre – a ferret. The ferret has two heads. Both its mouths are twisted into a twin-snarl, teeth bared.

'Is this real?' she calls over.

'The ferret? Caught it myself. It had two brains, too.'

'Is nothing,' Vargas says, thumping his chest. 'I killed deer with six legs – and all legs worked. Are many freaks up here. You can make big money from them.'

Sam grins. 'The Chinese go crazy over the body parts. They think it will cure cancer and grey lung, and put a little lead in their pencil. And a lot of other bullshit.'

Nicole nods, takes a tentative sip of her moonshine. It tastes better than she expects. 'Is that what the poacher was after?'

'That,' Sam says, 'and the usual. Rare breeds. Endangered species.'

'Is illegal, but . . .' Vargas shrugs. 'What else is there, up here? No logging, no farming. People must eat. People must live. So they hunt and trap and kill.'

'Which is where we come in,' Sam adds.

Nicole nods. She is standing at the window, now. It overlooks the adjacent apartment blocks, and the rest of town. There's not much to see. Everything is squat and low and buried in grey snow, like ash. Directly below, she spots their truck, and the blue tarp stretched over the bed. It is covering the sable furs that they confiscated.

'What will you do with the hides?'

There is a pause. Then Vargas says, 'Evidence.'

She turns to look at him. He regards her steadily, his eyes heavy with vodka. She almost challenges him about it, but doesn't. That's not what she came here for.

'Anything?' he asks, pointing at her laptop.

She checks it again. 'No.'

He grumbles about that for a while. Then, 'How long?'

'Normally it could be days. But I called in a favour.' Passing behind his chair, she pats him on the shoulder. 'I said: 'my new friend Vargas is in a rush.''

Sam laughs. 'He was in a rush to get out of those woods – that's for sure.'

'So?' Vargas splashes more moonshine into his glass, spilling some on the table in the process. 'You went whiter than me. A snow-white Eskimo.'

'It was stupid to go unarmed.'

Nicole takes her seat at the table again, allows Vargas to top her up.

'Do you think it was out there?'

Vargas shrugs. 'Something. There was something.'

Sam nods, deliberately solemn, then turns his empty glass upside down on the table, like a magician performing a trick. 'You know what my people think?'

Vargas moans. 'They only think about big government cheques.'

Sam waggles a finger at him. 'They think,' he said, 'that Siberian tigers are spirits. They carry messages between heaven and earth.'

'Yes. The message is: I am hungry.'

Sam holds up his hands. 'I'm just saying that's what they believe.'

Vargas grunts. The light in the kitchen is getting dim, now. Behind the layers of smog, the sun must be going down – even though it's only two in the afternoon.

'But it got me thinking,' Sam continues, smiling. 'Say this cat does turn out to be special or unique or whatever. Maybe that means its message is unique, too.'

She can't tell if he's just needling Vargas, or if he's half-serious. Either way Vargas doesn't rise to the bait. He stays silent. Nobody speaks for a few minutes. They sit and sip, wrapped up in the warmth of the vodka. Then her laptop pings, breaking the spell. She gets up to check it, feeling light and loose-limbed as she strides to the sideboard. The men watch, expectant. She scans the email once, re-reads it to make sure. Then she turns to them, trying to decide how to play this.

'We have a saying in English,' she says. 'Don't shoot the messenger.'

She expects anger, but instead the two men burst out laughing. They pound on the table, nearly falling out of their chairs. It takes her a moment to make the connection to what Sam said – about tigers being messengers. Then she laughs, too.

'They say it may be a new species,' she tells them, gasping.

'Whoo-hoo!' Vargas says, raising a bottle in toast.

'And that you can't kill it, until we find out if the mutation is a defect.'

The worse the news gets, the funnier it seems to be, until they are breathless, bent over in hysterics, their eyes watering. Nicole sinks to the floor, clutching her stomach. It aches – actually aches – with laughter, almost like she's broken a rib.

She can't remember the last time she laughed so hard.

The joke has worn off by the time her and Vargas head back to his house. For most of the drive, neither of them says anything. The heating fan rattles intermittently, and through her seat she feels the steady grinding of the tyre chains. The landscape beyond their headlights is drawn in black and grey, like a charcoal sketch. Vargas sits hunched forward, twisting his hands back and forth on the wheel. He is driving more slowly than usual; other than that he shows no signs of all the vodka he has drunk. Every so often, he coughs, clears his throat, and rolls down his window to spit – letting in a blast of icy air in the process.

He says, 'If it kills more people, is their fault.'

'I know.'

'Is *your* fault.'

She doesn't have the energy to argue, or the grounds to

defend herself. The message was clear. The agency won't issue a hunting permit unless they can provide more information. When she asked what was meant by 'more information' the reply came back: *suggest examining site of first attack for further evidence*. She didn't mention this to Vargas at the time, but she tells him now.

'I have gone to other site,' he says, banging the steering wheel. 'I tell you – is same animal. If a freak – so what? Is still a tiger, still a killer. It has the taste.'

'I believe you,' she says, 'but it doesn't matter.'

Back at the house, Vargas gets out a beer and settles on the sofa to watch hockey highlights with his son. Nicole sits cross-legged on the threadbare carpet, her laptop balanced on her knees, studying the DNA analysis the lab sent back to her. Lines of code fill the screen, a maze of genomes and chromosomes, a labyrinth of proteins and nucleotides. Certain sections have been flagged by their technicians.

'What is this?'

Vargas is standing behind her, stooping to peer over her shoulder.

'The genetic sequencing of the animal. By comparing it with a Siberian tiger, they've isolated the differences in the genes. Some of them, anyways. It takes time.'

He blinks at her, his eyes bleary and bloodshot. 'So?'

'None of them are frameshift mutations. Most are transpositions, along with a few point mutations. They still can't tell if any are beneficial or sustainable, though.'

He waves his beer. 'I do not know all this. Speak English.'

Nicholas comes over to join them. He leans against her, clinging to her shoulder in that overly familiar way children do. She can see his face reflected in the screen. She says, 'The main alterations seem to be in size, and bone structure.'

Vargas snorts. 'So is bigger. We know this.'

He goes back to the sofa and slumps into it, changes the

channel to an American comedy dubbed over in Russian. Nicholas stays at her side, watching her work. She smiles at him and adjusts the settings – changing the lines of code into a visual DNA model. The double-helix winds its way up the screen, linked by ladder-rung bases of nitrogen compounds. It turns slowly on the spot, rippling and hypnotic.

'Tiger,' she tells him.

He gapes, awestruck. Then he whispers to her in Russian, tugs her to her feet, and drags her into his bedroom – wanting to show her something. On top of his pine dresser he has an old-style gaming console, and a battered monitor. He switches both on and picks up the controller, using his bad hand to deftly operate the tiny joystick.

'Tiger,' he says, beaming.

It is a hunting game in which you get to select various weapons, various locations, various animals to stalk. She watches him as he plays, eyes fixed on the screen, his mouth slightly parted. His avatar creeps around a tropical jungle landscape while cradling a semi-automatic hunting rifle. It has a scope that allows him to zoom in and aim from afar. When an animal crosses his sights, it always goes down in a spray of blood: boars, baboons and exotic-looking birds. Before he can find her a tiger, though, Vargas appears in the doorway and growls something to his son in Russian. Nicholas drops the controller and scampers out. It's bedtime, apparently.

Nicole yawns. 'We go early tomorrow?'

For some reason, she's started to adopt his curt, broken English.

'Not so early.' He glances at the ceiling, studying the fake stars, as if he's a bit embarrassed by what he's admitting to her. 'Is long hike, but is not safe in dark.'

It takes her a moment to decipher his phrasing, and grasp what he means.

'Because of the animal.'

'We go at dawn, in light. Then, maybe we must stay over-night.'

He nods and strides out, pulling the door shut behind him. Nicole is left alone, sitting cross-legged on the floor like a child. Then, from the monitor to her left, a roar erupts, star-tling her. Claw-marks have appeared on screen, which flickers red before fading to black. Apparently the tiger has found the hunter before the hunter found it.

Nicole squats in the snow, struggling to adjust the straps on her snowshoes. The set is too big but she doesn't want to give Vargas the satisfaction of asking for help. He and Sam are at the side of the truck, unloading rifles from the gun rack. They've come to a forestry commission parking lot, a few miles out of town. According to Vargas, it's the closest they can get to their destination; they'll start their hike from here. The morning light is still dim, the world still locked in mono-chrome. A glaze of smog coats the sky, grey and hazy, so heavy it seems to be weighing down the trees.

Finishing with her snowshoes, Nicole stands up. The two men are in the truck bed inspecting their guns: checking chambers, loading cartridges, adjusting scopes.

'This is still only a research trip,' Nicole says.

'I know.' Vargas tucks an additional cartridge into his pocket. 'So?'

'Isn't that a bit of overkill? All the hardware?'

'Is for protection only.'

Sam smiles at her. 'Don't worry – he's not as trigger-happy as you think.'

The dog bounds up to her, its muzzle coated in snow. She rubs its head, packs down a snowball, and lobs it across the lot. The dog tears after it, snapping wildly.

'Maybe I should have one, too,' she says.

They stop working to stare at her. For a moment, sitting

side-by-side in bulky snowsuits, with their legs dangling off the edge of the tailgate, they remind her of two overgrown boys, playing with toy guns.

'You can shoot?' Vargas says.

'My father taught me.'

Vargas trudges over to the side door, to get a third rifle. She can see that it is lighter and smaller than theirs, and semi-automatic – not auto. But she doesn't bother to mention this. Instead she checks the safety, and takes aim along the barrel, aware that they are watching her. If it's a test, apparently she passes. Vargas grunts.

'Just don't shoot me,' he says.

As they set out, she slings the weapon over her shoulder, so it rests vertically on her back. It knocks awkwardly against her rucksack, which is filled with her food supplies, sleeping bag, and laptop. She hikes between the two men, with Vargas out in front and Sam a few paces behind. Looking after her, no doubt. The dog scampers around, zipping ahead and bounding back, acting as their unofficial scout.

They make good time, padding steadily through the powder. It is well packed and squeaks beneath their snowshoes. Other than that the forest is almost noiseless; the snow dampens any sounds. Visibility is good because the trees – mostly various species of larch – are bare and leafless and spaced relatively far apart. All the branches are coated in an off-white hoar frost that looks like fungus.

'You said it's a full day's hike?' she calls to Vargas.

'Why? You are tired already?'

'I'm wondering what he was doing way out here, alone.'

They walk half a dozen paces before he answers.

'If you asked him, he would say he is hunting wild boar.'

After two hours they take a break. They perch on a fallen tree, without removing their bags or snowshoes. Her calves are burning but other than that she feels good. Vargas looks a bit worse off. He is breathing hard, and his moustache is frozen with snot. Filling a cup from his flask, he offers it to her first. She drinks it down, and nearly gags – it's vodka. She hands it back, trying to take it in stride, but can see him smirking to himself. She gets out her flask of tea and sips that instead.

'Your father,' he says, tapping her rifle. 'He took you hunting?'

'Sometimes. But never for tiger.'

She means it as a joke, but neither of them laughs.

'We have a saying,' Sam says. 'If a tiger wants to eat you, you won't see it.'

He pushes his glasses up his nose, cranes his neck to look around. Nicole finds herself doing the same. Studying the landscape. Trying to imagine just what, exactly, is out there. Then Vargas stands and tosses back the remaining vodka.

'We keep going,' he announces.

By mid-afternoon, the shack comes into view. It is a two-room shanty, with wooden siding and a corrugated tin roof, covered in snow. Long icicles hang like teeth from the eaves and there are small windows on each side, overlooking the forest.

Out front, after they've removed their packs, Vargas tells her about the first attack. Because of the shack's isolation, it went unreported for several days. By the time he and Sam got out there, it had been snowing for hours. At first they thought the trapper – a local man – had simply left. Then the dog unearthed the remains. A few bloody bones, frozen in the snow. That was all. No tracks. No other traces.

'But all his supplies had been used up,' Sam adds.

Nicole looks from him to Vargas, trying to understand. They explain that they think the tiger had him trapped here, in the shack. He waited it out for as long as he could. Then, rather than slowly starve to death, he'd made a final attempt to escape.

'A cat would never normally do that,' she says, 'if it was only about food.'

Vargas shrugs. 'Maybe he shoots at it, and makes it mad.'

Nicole frowns. 'Maybe.'

Afterwards they take her into the shack. It is as cold inside as out, and smells like an old fridge. There is a table in the main room, littered with empty food tins. Mostly canned meat and vegetables and soup. In one corner lies a single mattress, draped in woolen blankets. Opposite it, directly below one of the windows, stands a workbench. The wooden surface is well worn and stained dark brown. Notches – as if from a blade – line the edges. Vargas notices her studying it.

'For scraping hides, cutting meat,' he explains.

The other room is smaller and looks like it was added later. It has been used for storage. Among the clutter she sees paraffin cans, a set of cross-country skis, a few lanterns – the housings smoked black – and some rusty leg traps. A space has been cleared on the floor to the left; in the middle is a mound of shit and toilet paper.

'Because he was scared to go out,' Nicole says, quietly.

Sam grimaces. 'I will be, too. Tonight.'

While Sam takes a look outside, she and Vargas continue to poke around the shelter. It's obvious he doesn't expect her to find anything. She doesn't really expect to, either. But it's what she's supposed to be doing, it's what her office wants, so she does it. On the table, among the food tins, she notices a stack of smut magazines.

She holds one up. 'Looks like he goes to the same bookstore as you.'

'Is not funny,' Vargas says.

As she puts the magazine down, she spots a cellphone half-hidden beneath the stack. She picks it up, turns it on. There's still a bit of charge to the battery.

'No signal here,' Vargas says. 'Or he would call for help.'

She ignores him, examines it anyway. First she scrolls through the picture gallery – mostly more porn – and then checks the videos. There are only a few, all fairly recent. She selects the oldest and clicks 'play.' It shows a man's face, talking into the camera, as if he's holding it at arm's length. He is middle-aged, with a shaved head and a scar above his right eye. He is speaking quickly, in Russian. Obviously agitated. Vargas, having heard, comes over to stand beside her.

'Is him,' he says. 'He is saying – it is still there. Will not go away. It knows . . .' Vargas pauses, startled, then goes on, 'It knows what I have done.'

The second video clip is dark. Too dark to see much, other than the shape of the man's head, lit up by lantern light. This time, he is whispering. Vargas leans in closer to catch it, and translates for her. 'He is saying to listen, listen to it. Is close.'

Nicole adjusts the volume. Faintly – through the tinny speakers – they can hear roaring, like distant thunder. The sound sends prickles along her forearms.

'And next,' Vargas says. He has started whispering, too. 'Is one more.'

The final clip shows the man's upper body – as if he has set up the phone on the table to film himself. He is sitting in a chair, wearing full hunting gear, cradling his rifle. The pale light coming through the window creates a halo-effect around his head. After waiting a moment, he starts to address the camera, struggling for words.

'Is message to his family,' Vargas says. 'He says he has run out of food. He says he is going to try. He says . . .' Vargas trails off. The raw emotion on the man's face needs no translation, no explanation. Then, at the last, the hunter clenches his fist and shouts something, defiant.

'He says he will show it how a Siberian dies.'

The end of the clip is him reaching out towards the camera. Nicole stares at the blank screen for a moment, before carefully placing the phone down.

'It is proof, no?' Vargas says. 'That it stalks him. Is a man-eater.'

She nods, tells him it is. Though she's still unsure what the agency will decide. Man-eater or not, if it's a new species, and sustainable, they'll want to capture and protect it rather than kill it. She is wondering if – and when – she should tell him that, when Sam pokes his head through the door. His glasses are all fogged up again.

'There's something at the back,' he says.

Outside the light is fading; on the horizon the clouds have gone a sickly ochre colour. Behind the shelter, the dog has found a large pit dug in the snow. While they examine it, the dog paces around the edge, sniffing and whimpering. The surrounding snow is dotted with paw-prints – the same over-sized tracks they found yesterday.

'This wasn't here last time,' Sam says.

'No,' Vargas says.

'Why would it come back?' she asks.

The words hang there as the three of them stare into the pit, thinking about it. The back wall is unnaturally flat, as if the cabin has foundations that go deep. Nicole brushes some ice crystals aside – revealing wood, gouged with claw marks.

'It's like it was trying to get into the cabin,' Sam says.

'Or at something beneath.'

Back inside, the three of them shove the table away from the wall, and lift up the tattered rug. Underneath is a small door, with a ring set into the wood, like the entrance to a cellar. It is not locked, and they lift it easily. Below, a stepladder drops into darkness. Vargas digs a flashlight out of his bag, and climbs down first. Then he says something in Russian – short and sharp, like a swear.

'You must see,' he calls up.

The cellar is no bigger than a walk-in closet. It is a tight fit for all three of them together. Vargas waits until her and Sam are down before shining his light around. They are in a kind of makeshift freezer, surrounded by shelving. Each shelf is laden with animal parts. Some in jars, some in plastic bags. She does not recognize all of them but she sees a kidney, a liver, a gall-bladder. There are teeth and claws, too. Tongues. A menagerie of dismemberment. And on the floor, piled practically beneath their feet, are the hides. All neatly folded. The fur tawny and striped. She stoops to touch the one on top. Even stiff with frost, it feels unbelievably soft.

'I don't want to hear,' she says, still crouched there, 'any of your shit about families to feed, or needing to survive. This is a travesty. This is an abomination.'

'Yes,' is all Vargas says.

Sam is perusing the different shelves, like a clerk taking inventory. 'There's sable here, too. And lynx. All rare or endangered. He would have had help. They'd wait until spring, then haul a load out with snowmobiles or four-wheelers. Truckers or loggers would help them smuggle it into China. Risky, but the pay –'

He stops talking; he is standing quite still, staring at something in a styrofoam cooler against the far wall. They wait, expectant, but still he does not say anything. Vargas looks at her, then steps over. She follows. When she sees what he has found, her hand goes to her mouth. In the cooler is a small animal, about the size of a large housecat. Its coat is patterned like a tiger, but the proportions are different. It is stockier, with higher back legs – almost hyena-like. Built for speed and power.

Vargas pans his flashlight along the body. It's obviously a

cub; the feet are oversized, the coat fluffy rather than sleek. The mouth is open, wide, as if it died in pain, or crying out. A leg-trap, probably. Light glints off a pair of wicked-looking eyeteeth. Something about those teeth looks wrong to her. She reaches in, uses both hands to force the mouth closed.

'Look,' she says, pointing.

The eyeteeth come down outside the lower mouth, extending inches past the jaw. Vargas mutters something in Russian again – that same swear word. *Srat*.

'Well,' Sam says, 'now we know what's out there.'

'And why it's pissed,' she adds.

She is sitting in a chair by the workbench with her rifle across her knees. The chair is cold and hard and she shifts around frequently. Beneath the window, a paraffin lamp sputters, giving off smoke. It makes the place stink but the window is open a crack for ventilation. She can see her breath in the light. Aside from their bodies, and the lamp, there is no heat in the shelter. Behind her the other two are stretched on the floor in their sleeping bags. Nobody wanted to sleep on the dead man's mattress.

Every few minutes she opens her laptop, checks her emails. Her inbox is always conspicuously empty. Three hours ago she sent her report to head office, summarizing the videos, the underground storeroom, the cub specimen. Everything they've found. But she hasn't received a reply, even though the satellite link is good.

At one point she thinks she hears something. A sound out there. A low rumble. But it does not come again and when she peers out the window she of course sees nothing. Just blackness, and flakes of falling snow, flickering like tinsel in the lamplight. She stays there, studying the dark, imagining what it contains. It makes her think of that Blake poem her father used to read her – the famous one about the tiger. She can

277

remember most of the first verse, and recites it silently to herself: Tiger tiger burning bright, in the forests of the night. What dread hand, and what dread eye, dare frame thy . . . something. Thy fearful something.

There's rustling behind her. A cough. Looking back, she sees Vargas coming into the light. His hair is tousled, his capped teeth bared in a glittering grimace.

'I have a few more hours yet,' she says.

She knows he gave her first watch as a favour. It's easier to stay up, than get up halfway through the night, or early in the morning.

'I cannot sleep,' he says. 'But maybe you can.'

He pulls up a chair beside her, places his flask on the floor. When he glances at her laptop – closed now to conserve the battery – she expects him to ask about that, but he doesn't. Maybe he's already guessed. Now that the agency has proof of its ability to breed, and the validity of its mutation, there's no way they'll issue a permit to kill it. Instead they'll send up a team of their own to trap it, take it alive. Which may take time. Which may cost lives.

'You have shot animals,' he says.

'Yes,' she says. 'I have shot animals.'

The dog comes up, nuzzles Vargas's palm. He strokes its head, and it sits beside him, thumping out the seconds with its tail.

'This man,' he says, 'is the same as yesterday for you, no? You think he maybe deserved to die. For what he did.'

'I didn't say that,' she says.

'You are thinking it, though.'

He bends forward, picks up his flask. Unscrewing the lid, he pours himself a cup of vodka. His hands are trembling. She can't tell if it's from the alcohol or not.

'I am lucky,' he says, taking a sip, 'to have this job.'

'Yes.'

'I did not always have it.'

She waits. He cradles his cup in both hands, as if drawing warmth from it.

'Before, I was like them. You understand?' He is not looking at her, but rather at a point on the floor – as if gazing right through it to the slaughterhouse below. 'I made money that way.'

She leans her rifle, barrel up, against the workbench. 'And the hides you confiscate,' she says quietly. 'Like the sable fur. You sell those on, don't you?'

In answer, he lowers his head. They sit like that for a while.

Then she says: 'I don't know what you expect me to say.'

'I do not know, either.'

He takes a long drink from his cup. She stands up, nearly knocking her chair over backwards in the process. She's not going to be his priest, give him absolution.

'I need some sleep,' she says.

As she walks away, he mutters something that stops her.

'Maybe it knows.'

He is staring into his cup, which is empty.

'Maybe it does,' she says.

Vargas is gone. Or that's what it looks like, when she wakes up. Sam is still on the floor beside her, and the door is slightly ajar. She scrambles to her feet, startling the dog, and rushes to the window. But no – Vargas is there. Taking a piss in the snow. When he comes back in, the slam of the door startles Sam.

'You didn't get me up,' he says, rubbing his eyes. 'Morning was my watch.'

Vargas only grunts. His face is haggard, his eyes puffy. She knows Sam must notice that, too, but he chooses not to mention it. Working mostly in silence, they put away their sleeping bags, pack up their gear, pull on their parkas. As she gnaws on a frozen energy bar, Nicole notices Vargas staring dully at his snowshoes – like a child who's forgotten how to tie his laces. She goes over to see what the problem is.

'Idiot,' she says, lowering her voice. 'They're on the wrong feet.'

He nods and switches them over. His movements are slow and laborious. The stink of vodka radiates from his pores, like a sickly cologne.

The temperature has risen in the night and it has stopped snowing. Now a mist hangs above the fresh snow. They don't realize how dense it is until they're standing in front of the shelter, ready to leave. Visibility is about thirty yards. Beyond that, the snow blends into the mist, the trees become shadows.

'We could wait until it clears,' Sam says.

'Is fine,' Vargas says. 'We go.'

'Isn't that risky?' she asks.

'Stay if you want, if you are scared. I go.'

Vargas starts off without waiting for a reply, the dog trailing at his heels. Sam and Nicole exchange a glance. 'The stubborn bastard,' she says. 'He's half-cut.'

Sam nods. 'I've never seen him like this.'

They follow. It's either that or let him go. Even drunk, and exhausted, Vargas sets a good pace. Their track has been covered by the snowfall, but he manages to find it. He trudges along with his head down, bulldozing ahead. He does not watch the forest at all. Nicole does, though. She watches the mist, and the way it seems to be moving. Curling about trees, wrapping around branches. Landscape, mist and sky are all a uniform grey. It feels as if she is walking through a dream, the snow soft as cloud beneath her feet. When she looks back, the shelter is already gone – absorbed by the haze. She keeps one hand on the butt of her rifle, slung across her shoulder.

They hike. She doesn't know for how long. Two hours, maybe. Or more. Time is counted by her steps, and her breaths. An endless procession. Only the dog breaks the repetition. Like yesterday it acts as their scout, darting ahead or to the sides, before racing back to rejoin them. Sometimes it goes far enough that she loses it completely in the mist. At one point, she realizes she hasn't seen it for a while.

'Vargas . . .' she says.

From up ahead comes a ferocious yapping, and the dog reappears. It streaks towards them, wild-eyed, trailing trickles of urine in the snow. Its tail is straight back between its legs. Vargas shouts at it, cuffs it, then holds his palm up for them to halt.

Nicole's rifle is already in her hands, even though she can't remember reaching for it. When she moves to slide her finger on the trigger, she finds that her glove gets in the way. She shakes it off, discards it in the snow. Through her inner glove she can feel the chill of the gunstock. She is not shaking. Her hands are steady.

'We can't kill it,' she says, mostly to herself.

Vargas is clumsily removing his rifle from his back. The dog crouches at his side, ears flat back on its head. The mist seems to have thickened, pressing in on them. Nicole looks first one way, then the other. She sees nothing, hears nothing. They are floating in a void. In front of her, Vargas finally has his rifle ready. He turns unsteadily, looking beleaguered and bewildered. She will always remember his face in that moment. Pure terror. As if he's been struck suddenly, inexplicably blind.

'I can't see fuck all,' Sam whispers.

She glances behind her; he is fiddling with his glasses, trying to de-fog them. As she turns back, she hears a whispering sound, and a section of mist seems to shift, morph, as if it's taking shape and coming alive. Then Vargas is gone. Just gone. Off to the left there is a splash of snow; kicked up by the impact of man and animal. The dog is barking insanely; Sam is shouting behind her. She raises the rifle, sights along it, and hesitates. The two figures are tangled together, thrashing around.

In the flurry of white, the fury, it's difficult to tell them apart and she doesn't know what to shoot at, doesn't know what to kill. Then it rears and roars, draws back as if to attack again, and as it plunges down she fires, once, the report resonating right through her body.

Then Sam shouts: 'There!'

His rifle patters, unleashing a drumroll burst. Around the mass of flesh and fur she sees the impact of the bullets – churning up snow.

'Hold it!' she screams. 'Vargas is under it!'

Sam stops firing, the echoes fading away like thunder. Then the only sound is the dog, yapping in panic. Right next to it, directly in front of her, is an empty pair of snowshoes. Vargas was snatched right out of them.

'I didn't even see it happen,' Sam says.

Holding their rifles ready, they shuffle forward. A big furrow has been ploughed in the snow where the animal landed with him. As they approach, she sees that it is not quite as big in length as she expected. But it is broad, especially in the haunches. Its thick hind legs are splayed out behind it, and it is slumped on its right side. In that position, lying limp and lifeless, it looks harmless as a stuffed animal.

'Is it . . .?'

'I think so.'

The fur coat is bloody, riddled with holes. There is blood, too, in the surrounding snow. Beneath it is Vargas. Both man and beast are still, as if they've fallen asleep together. A peaceful repose, of predator and prey. Nicole drops her rifle, kneels and shakes him, shouts his name. No response. But he's breathing.

It's only when she and Sam try to shift the animal off him that they see how oddly the two are interlocked. The cat's mouth is wide open, hungering for him. The barrel of Vargas's rifle is wedged sideways between the animal's jaws, and its extended cuspids are resting up against his abdomen. As far as she can tell he's not injured there. It looks as if, when it attacked, he turned his rifle sideways in defence, submitting to the animal rather than trying to kill it – which is probably what saved his life.

The local clinic is a low brick structure that was once a military barracks, a remnant of the first cold war. The walls and ceilings are encrusted with green paint that is flaking off in palm-sized patches. Vargas has been assigned a private room near the rear of the building, on the recovery ward. When Nicole walks in, the blinds are closed and Vargas is sleeping. He has a neck brace on – from whiplash, apparently – and both his forearms are wrapped in bandages. Several ribs were broken, too, but overall his injuries were relatively light. At the sound of her footsteps, he jerks awake – tugging on the wires attached to his hairy chest, nearly pulling over the heart-rate monitor.

Then he sees her, and sighs. 'Is you.'

She holds her hands up, fingers curled like sets of claws. 'Bad dreams?'

He laughs, weakly, then starts coughing. It goes on a long time and ends with him clearing his throat. He spits into a tissue, folds it up carefully, and tucks it away.

She asks, 'Have you had that cough checked out?'

'Is nothing. Is fine.'

She shakes her head, crosses to the window, and throws open the blinds – letting in a wash of wan light. He shields his eyes and blinks back the brightness.

'So,' he says, his voice still hoarse. 'You save me, Sam says.'

She nods. As it turned out, it was her bullet – that first one – which killed it.

'Somebody had to. It was you or it.'

He tilts his head and squints at her. 'Maybe you wish you have missed?'

'My bosses do. I've been on the phone with them all morning.'

'You are in trouble?'

'I've been temporarily relieved of my position.' When he just stares at her, she's not sure if he understands, so she adds: 'I've been suspended. Fired, basically.'

'Is so stupid,' he says. 'They will save a tiger instead of me.'

'It was more than a tiger.'

'Is very true,' he says. 'So fast. So powerful.' He holds up one hand, and smacks it with the other, acting out the attack in pantomime. 'Like that. You saw?'

'Yes – incredible.'

'And the teeth. This long!' He extends his arms to demonstrate, looking as excited as his son. 'It was – how do you call it? Sword-tooth? Like a sword-tooth?'

She smiles. 'A sabre-tooth. Not quite. But it was similar.'

'It looks at me, you know.' He holds two fingers up to his eyes. 'There. Like that. It sees into me. It came for me. To tell me things. You understand?'

She nods. She is standing over him, hands clasped, gazing down; light from the window casts a cross on his bed. Something about the situation – their postures, the setting, the solemnity – makes her feel like an abbess, taking his confession.

'What did it tell you?' she asks.

He looks down into his lap, and plucks at the sheet tucked across his abdomen. 'That time – it is running out. For us, for it, for everything.' He glances once at her, almost timidly. 'Is hard to say in English. You must learn Russian. Then I tell you.'

'It's a deal.'

He yawns, looking like a tiger himself. 'You leave now?'

'I have a train to catch,' she says.

'Go then – go back to your city. Is safer there, no?'

She reaches over to clasp his hand. He winces, and when

she lets go he shakes it out – pretending that she's hurt him. 'You are too strong,' he says, 'for a woman.'

In the doorway, as she's leaving, she meets his wife and son coming in. The woman – Anya – glances at her, sniffs, and brushes by, almost as if she blames Nicole for her husband's condition. Little Nicholas gets tugged along behind his mother, but he manages to look back at Nicole, raising his bad arm to wave good-bye.

Nicole lingers in the hallway to watch as they converge on Vargas. His son scrambles onto the bed; his wife wraps him up in her arms. She is scolding him and crying at the same time. He murmurs to her in their language, the tones gentle and reassuring. Before they notice her spying, Nicole turns and walks quietly away.

Out front, Sam is waiting in Vargas's truck, ready to take her to the station. He honks twice when he sees her. The dog is in its usual position on the front seat, and the radio is turned up high – blasting out scratchy Russian rock.

'You fixed his stereo,' she says.

'Just a loose wire. I think he broke it on purpose.'

Sam hums along to the tune as they rumble down the highway. The pavement is soaked in slush; the snowbanks at the roadside have shrunk in on themselves. The weather has turned surprisingly mild, almost like a winter chinook back home. They ease past a mud-spattered tractor, and Sam leans forward to turn down the music.

'Think you'll have space for those hides?' he asks.

'Space for what hides?'

'The sable. Vargas didn't tell you?' He jerks a thumb at the rear window, towards the truck bed; she can see the hides back there stacked under the tarp. 'He wanted you to have them, as evidence.'

'I'll make room,' she says.

'Who says a tiger can't change its stripes, huh?'

'What about the haul in the shed?'

'We'll need time to catalogue it. Could give us some leads in tracking down buyers and suppliers. Think your organization would agree to send us some help?'

The dog whines and nuzzles into her lap, its tail going like a metronome.

'They might back it,' she says, idly scratching its ears. 'But I doubt anybody would be stupid enough to volunteer to work with you assholes.' She thinks about it for a moment, and then adds, 'Except maybe me.'

When they both laugh, the dog perks up and cocks its head, as if trying to understand the joke.

ADAM L. G. NEVILL

PIG THING

DARKNESS THEY COULD taste and smell and feel came inside the house. Peaty and dewy with wet fern, it came in damp and cool as the black earth shielded by the canopy of the mighty Kauri trees, as if rising upwards from the land, rather than descending from a sinking sun. The branches in the forest surrounding the bungalow became skeletal at dusk, before these silhouettes also vanished into the black of a moonless country night. Had they still been living in England, it would have been an evening when bonfires were lit. And to the three children, although these nights were frightening, they had a tinge of enchantment in them too, and were never that bad when their parents were inside the house. But tonight, neither their mother or father had returned from the long garden which the enclosing wilderness of bush tried to reclaim.

Dad had ventured out first, to try and get the car started in a hurry, shortly after nine o'clock. Twenty minutes later, her face long with worry, Mom had gone outside to find him and they had not heard or seen her since.

Before their mom and dad left the house the three children remembered seeing similar expressions on their parent's faces: when Mom's younger sister caught cancer and when

Dad's work closed down, just before they all travelled out to New Zealand in the big ship for a fresh start on the day after the Queen's Silver Jubilee. Tonight their parents had done their best to hide their expressions. But the two brothers, Jack who was nine, and Hector who was ten, knew the family was in trouble.

Together with Lozzy, their four year old sister, Jack and Hector sat in the laundry room of the bungalow with the door shut; where Mom had told them to stay just before she went outside to find their father.

Jack and Lozzy sat with their backs against the freezer. Hector sat closest to the door by the bottles and buckets that Dad used for his homemade wine. They had been in the laundry for so long now, they could no longer smell the detergent and cloves. Only in Lozzy's eyes was there still some assurance of this situation becoming an adventure with a happy ending, and them all being back together again. They were large brown eyes, still capable of awe when she was told a story. And these eyes now searched Jack's face. Sandwiched between his sister's vulnerability and the innocence that he could still recognise in himself, and his older brother's courage that he admired and tried to copy, Jack found it his task to stop Lozzy crying.

'What dya reckon, Hector?' Jack said, as he peered at his brother while trying to stop the quiver on his bottom lip.

Hector's face was white. 'We were told to stay here. They are coming back.'

Both Jack and Lozzy felt better for hearing him say that, although the younger brother soon suspected the elder would always refuse to believe their Mom and Dad were not coming back. Like Dad, Hector could deny things, but Jack was more like his Mom and by making their voices go soft he and Mom would sometimes get Dad and Hector to listen.

But no matter how determined anyone's voice had been

earlier that evening, their Dad could not be persuaded to stay inside the house, and had always rubbished their stories about the bush not being right; about there being something living in it, about them seeing something peer in through the windows of the two end bedrooms of the bungalow overlooking the garden and deserted chicken coup. When their dog, Schnapps, disappeared, he said they were all 'soft' and still needed to 'acclimatise' to the new country. And even when all the chickens vanished one night and only a few feathers and a single yellow foot were left behind in the morning, he still didn't believe them. But now he did, because he had seen it too. Tonight, the whole family had seen it, together.

For months now, the children had been calling it *the pig thing*: Lozzy's name for the face at the windows. She saw it first when playing with Schnapps at the bottom of the garden, in the dank shadows where the orchard stopped and the wall of silver ferns and flax began. *It* had suddenly reared up between the dinosaur legs of two Kauri trees. Never had her mother heard Lozzy make such a fuss: 'Oh Jesus, Bill. I thought she was being murdered,' she had said to their Dad, once Lozzy had been taken inside the house and quieted. Up on the hill, east of the bungalow, even the boys, who were putting a better roof on their den, had heard their sister's cries. Frantic with excitement and fear, they had run home, each carrying a spear made from a bamboo beanpole. That was the day the idea of the pig thing came into their lives. And it had returned. It was no longer a children's story.

But this was the worst visit, because earlier that evening, as they all sat in the lounge watching television, it had come right on to the sundeck and stood by the barbecue filled with rainwater to look through the glass of the sliding doors, like it was no longer afraid of their Dad. They could tell, because the pig thing had come out of the darkness beyond their brightly lit windows and momentarily reared up on its bony hind legs to display itself, before dropping and quickly moving back into the shadows of the Ponga trees at the side of their property. It could not have been on the deck for more than two seconds, which had stretched into an unbearable and unbreathable time for Jack, but the power in its thin limbs and the human intelligence in its eyes glimpsed through the glass, frightened him more than coming across one of the longfin eels in the creeks would ever have done.

'Don't. Oh, Bill don't. Let's go together, Bill, with the torch,' their Mom said to their Dad, once he decided to get the car started.

They were so far from Auckland that had either of the police officers based at the nearest station been available that evening, it would have taken them over an hour to reach the bungalow. Their dad had told their mother what the police operator had told him, after he called them and reported an 'intruder', some kind of 'large animal or something' trying to get into their house. He couldn't bring himself to say *pig thing* to the operator, though that's what it had been. Lozzy had described it perfectly. Maybe it took a four year old to *see* it properly. It wasn't quite an animal, and was certainly not human, but seemed to have the most dangerous qualities of each in that moment it rose out of darkness, bumped the glass, and then vanished. But the two police officers had been called away to a big fight between rival chapters of bikers on the distant outskirts of the city. With *it* so close and eager to get inside with his family, because it had looked terribly keen on achieving just that, waiting was not an option even entertained by their father, or open to discussion, after he hung up the phone.

Their nearest neighbours, the Pitchfords, lived on their farm two miles away and hadn't answered their phone when the children's dad called them. They were old and had lived in the national reserve since they were both children; had spent the best part of seven decades within the vast cool depths of the bush, before much of the area was cleared for the new migrants. Mr. Pitchford even had hunting rifles as old as the Great War; he'd once shown Jack and Hector, and even let them hold the heavy cumbersome guns that stank of oil.

After the children's father ended the call, he and their mother had exchanged a look that communicated to Jack the suspicion that the pig thing had already been to visit their neighbours.

Going cold and shuddering all over, Jack believed he might even faint with fear. And all that kept appearing in his mind was the vision of the creature's long torso pressed against the window, so it's little brownish teats in the black doggish hair on its belly squished like baby's fingers on the other side of the glass. The trottery hands had merely touched the pane briefly, but that was sufficient to make it shake in the door-frame. There was nothing inside the house, not a door or piece of furniture, that could be used as a barricade. He knew it. Jack could imagine the splintering of wood and the shattering of glass, followed by his sister's whimpers, his Dad shouting and his mom's screams, as *it* came grunting with hunger and squealing with excitement into their home. He had groaned to himself and kept his eyes shut for a while after the thing disappeared back into the lightless trees. Tried to banish the image of that snouty face and the thin girlish hair that fell about its leathery shoulders.

And then their mother had said, 'Bill, *please*. Please don't go outside.' The children knew their Mom had put her hand on their Dad's elbow as she said this. They didn't see her do it because, by that time, they had been herded into the laundry room where they had stayed ever since, but they could tell by her voice that she had touched his arm.

'Ssh. Jan. Just ssh now. Stay with the kids,' their Dad had said to their mom, but once he was outside no one heard the car engine start. The Morris Marina was parked at the bottom of the drive, under the Wattle tree where Hector once found a funny-looking bone that must have come from a cow. And they had heard nothing more of Dad since he went out to the car.

The sudden gravity introduced into their evening had increased with every passing minute as a stillness inside the house, a heaviness that made them all aware of the ticking of the clock in the hall; it was the very thickening of suspense around their bodies.

Their Mother eventually opened the laundry door to report to the kids. She was trying to smile but her lips were too tight. On her cheeks were the red lines made by her fingers when she held her face in her hands. Sometimes she did that at night, sitting alone at the kitchen table. She did it a lot when Dad was out looking for Schnapps, day after day. And Mom had never liked the new house in Muriwai or the surrounding country-side. Didn't like the whistles and shrieks of the birds, the yelps in the night that sounded like frightened children, the animal tracks in the soil beneath her washing line that spun around in the fierce winds, the fat five-foot eel they had seen by the creek with a lamb in its mouth, the large sticky red flowers that nodded at you as you walked past, the missing dog or the stolen chickens . . . Mom didn't like any of it. Mom doubted she could ever become a Kiwi. She came here for their Dad; they knew that. And now she was missing too.

Holding Lozzy's Wonder Woman torch, because their Dad had taken the big rubber flashlight from the kitchen drawer where the matches were kept, they had heard their mother calling, 'Bill. Bill. *Bill!*' in a voice with a tremble in it, as well as something else trying to smother the tremble, as she went out the front door and then walked past the side of the house toward the garden and the car. Her voice had gone faint and then stopped.

And the fact that both of their parents had vanished without a fuss – no shout, or cry, or scuffle had been heard from outside – first made the two boys hopeful with the possibility that their mom and dad would soon come back. But as the silence lengthened it made their hearts busy with a mute dread that whatever had taken them was so quick and silent, you never had a chance. Not a hope out there in the dark with *it*.

Lozzy had sobbed herself into a weary silence after seeing the pig thing on the sundeck, and had then begun whimpering after her mother's departure. For the moment, she had been placated by each of her older brother's reassurances, their lies, and their brave faces. But her silence would not last for long. Lozzy stood up. She was wearing pyjamas. They were yellow and had pictures of Piglet and Winnie the Pooh printed on the cotton. Her hair was tousled and her feet were grubby with dust. Her slippers were still in the lounge; Mom had taken them off earlier to remove a splinter from her foot with the tweezers from the sewing box. Although the soles of the children's feet were getting harder, from running around barefoot all day outside, the children still picked up prickles from the lawn and splinters from the sundeck. 'Where's Mummy, boys?'

Immediately, Jack patted the floor next to him. 'Ssh, Lozzy. Come and sit down.'

Frowning, she pushed her stomach out. 'No.'

'I'll get you a Tip Top from the freeze.'

Lozzy sat down. The freezer hummed and its lemon glow emitted a vague sense of reassurance when Jack opened the lid. Hector approved of the ice-cream trick. After a deep breath, Hector looked at Jack and then returned his stare to the laundry door. He sat with his chin resting on his knee and both hands gripping the ankle of that leg, listening.

Committed of face, Lozzy tucked into the cone, loaded with Neapolitan ice cream.

Jack shuffled up beside Hector. 'What dya reckon?' He used the same tone of voice before he and his brother crossed a waterfall in the creek, or explored the dark reeking caves up in the hills that Mr. Pitchford had told them to 'steer clear of, lads', or shinned across a tree fallen over a deep gorge in the piny vastness of bush surrounding their house. The forest stretched all the way to the crazy beaches made from black volcanic sand, where the blowholes and riptides prevented them from swimming.

Hector had no answer for his brother about what to do now that he, the eldest, was in charge. But Hector was thinking hard. His eyes were a bit wild and watery too, so Jack knew he was about to *do* something. And that frightened him. Already, he imagined himself holding Lozzy when there were only the two of them left inside the laundry room.

'I'm gonna run to the Pitchfords,' Hector said.

'But it's dark.'

'I know the way.'

'But . . .' They looked at each other and swallowed. Even though Jack hadn't mentioned the pig thing, they had thought of it at the same time.

Hector stood up, but looked smaller than usual to Jack.

Peering between his knees, Jack kept his face lowered until the creases disappeared from the side of his mouth and around his eyes. He couldn't let Lozzy see him cry.

Before his brother left the laundry room and then the house too, Jack longed to hold him for while but couldn't do it and Hector wouldn't want it anyway; it would make his leaving even harder. Instead, Jack just stared at his own flat toes spread on the lino.

'Where's Hegder going?' Lozzy asked, just as a bubble popped on her shiny lips.

Jack swallowed. 'To get the Pitchfords.'

'They have a cat,' she said.

Jack nodded. 'That's right.' But Jack knew where Hector would have to go first before he even got close to the Pitchfords' place: he was going into the forest with the clacking branches and ocean sounds when the wind blew; along the paths of damp earth and slippery tree roots, exposed like bones, that they had run and mapped together; over the thin creek with the rowing boat smells; across the field of long grass, that was darker than English grass and always felt wet, where they had found two whole sheep skeletons and brought them home in a wheel barrow to reassemble on the front lawn. Hector was going to run a long way through the lightless night until he reached the Pitchford's' house with the high fence and the horseshoes fixed around the gate. 'To keep things out,' Mrs. Pitchford had once told them in a quiet voice when Hector asked why it was nailed to the dark planks.

'No. Don't. No,' Jack hissy-whispered, unable to hold back when Hector turned the door handle.

On the cusp of his brother's departure, that Jack knew he could do nothing about, everything went thick and cold inside his chest. Welling up to the back of his throat, this feeling spilled into his mouth. It tasted of rain. And this time, he couldn't swallow. Inside Jack's head was the urgency of desperate prayers trying to find words. He squinted his eyes to try and push the thoughts down, to squash them down like he was forcing the lid back on a tin of paint. Did anything to stop the hysterics he could feel storming up through his entire body.

'Got to,' Hector said, his face all stiff but still wild-looking.

Lozzy stood up and tried to follow Hector, but Jack snatched her hand and gripped it too hard. She winced, then stamped, was tearing up again.

'Jack, don't open the door after I'm gone. OK.' They were Hector's final words.

The laundry door clicked shut behind him. They heard his feet patter across the floorboards of the hall. Then they heard him turn the catch on the front door. When that closed too, the wind chimes clinked together and made an inappropriate spacey sound. There was a brief creak from the bottom step of the porch stairs, and then the silence returned for a while, until Lozzy's sobs made an unwelcome return inside the laundry room.

After comforting her with a second ice-cream cone, Jack unplugged the freezer. Quickly but carefully, so as to make less noise, he removed the rustly bags of frozen peas, steaks, stewed apple and fish fingers. He put the food in the big laundry sink that smelled like the back of Gran's house in England. Then he stacked the white baskets from inside the freezer against the side of the sink. Around the rim of the freezer cabinet he placed plastic clothes pegs at intervals, so there would be a gap between the grey rubber seal of the freezer lid and the base. Then they wouldn't run out of air when he shut them both inside.

'Come on, Lozzy',' he said, hearing some of his Mom in his voice. And he felt a bit better for doing something other than just waiting. He picked Lozzy up and lowered her into the freezer. Together, they spread Schnapps's old blanket over the wet floor of the cabinet so they wouldn't get cold bottoms and feet.

'This smells. His fur is on it. Look.' She held up a tuft of the brown fur the dog used to get stuck between his claws after riffing his neck. Their Mom and Dad had been unable to throw the dog's blanket away, in case he ever came back to lie on it. So the blanket had stayed in the laundry where Schnapps had ended up sleeping at night. Their Dad's idea of dogs sleeping outside became a bad idea after Schnapps began all that barking, whimpering, and finally scratching at the front door every night. 'He's soft,' their Dad had said. But tonight, it all made sense.

After handing the tub of ice cream and the box of cones to Lozzy, Jack climbed into the freezer and sat beside her. She reached for his hand with her sticky fingers. As he pulled the lid down over their huddled bodies, he secretly hoped that the cold and wet of the freezer would stop the pig thing from smelling them. He also wondered if those trotter things on the end of its front legs would be able to push the lid up when it stood up on those hairy back legs, like it had done out on the sundeck. But he also took another small comfort into the dark with him: the pig thing had never come inside their house. Not yet, anyway.

Mrs. Pitchford entered the house through the empty aluminium frame of the ranch-sliding door; the glass had been smashed inwards and collected in the mess of curtains that had also been torn down. She favoured net curtains behind all the windows of her own home; she didn't like the sense of exposure that the large windows gave to the new homes the government had started delivering on truckbeds for the migrants, who were settling all over the area. She also found it hard to even look at the red earth exposed beneath any more felled trees and cleared bush. The appearance of these long rectangular bungalows with tin cladding on their walls never failed to choke her with fury and grief no good for her heart. And who could now say what kind of eyes would be drawn in to these great glassy doors if you didn't use nets? You couldn't then go blaming them who was already here.

All of the lights were still on. It felt warm inside the house too, even though the cold and damp of the night air must have been seeping into the living room for at least an hour after that big pane of glass was put through.

She looked at the brown carpets and the orange fabric on the furniture, was amazed again with what the English did with their homes; all Formica and white plastic and patterned carpets and big garish swirls in wallpaper the colour of coffee. Shiny, new, fragile: she didn't care for it. They had a television too and a new radio, coloured silver and black: both made in

Japan. They mesmerised her, the things these soft-muscled, pale-skinned Poms brought from such faraway places and surrounded themselves with; but anyone could see they and their things didn't fit with the old bush. It had ways that not even the Maoris liked, because there were *things* here before them too.

Glass crunched under her boots as she made her way further inside the house. The kitchen and dining room were open-plan, only divided from the living room by the rear of the sofa.

Unable to resist the lure of the kitchen area, she went inside and stared, then touched the extractor fan over the stove. It was like a big hopper on a petrol lawnmower, for collecting cut grass. She marvelled again at what young mothers considered necessary in the running of a household these days. And here was the food mixer Jan had once showed her. Orange and white plastic with *Kenwood Chevette* printed along one side. A silver coffee pot with a wooden handle; what Jan had called a 'percolator', beside the casserole dishes with their pretty orange flower patterns. Mrs. Pitchford ran her hard fingers across the smooth sides of all the Tupperware boxes that Jan had lined up on the counter; they were filled with cereal, rice, something called spaghetti, bran, sugar. You could see the contents as murky shadows through the sides. Everything in her own home was wood, pottery, steel, or iron. And she remembered seeing it all in use when she was a little girl and helped her mother prepare food. Hardwoods and metals lasted. Whereas plastic and carpet and 'stereos' hadn't been much use to this family tonight, had they?

The sound of the car engine idling outside returned a sense of purpose to her; her Harold had told her not to get distracted. She turned and waddled out of the kitchen, but her eyes were pulled to the sideboard beside the dining table; at all of the silver and ceramic trinkets kept behind its sliding glass doors. Little sherry glasses. Small mugs with ruddy faces on the front. China thimbles. Teaspoons with patterns on their handles. *So special*. She had her own things for special occasions; all a lot older than these things the family had brought with them from England.

They also had a washing machine in the little laundry room beside the 'dining area', and a freezer too. Jan had been horrified to learn that Mrs. Pitchford still washed clothes in a tin bath, used a larder for food, and still preserved things in jars. *The bloody cheek*.

Mrs. Pitchford went inside the laundry room; it smelled of wine, soap powder, and urine. All of the food from the freezer was melting and softening inside the sink. The lid of the freezer was raised and there was an old blanket inside the white metal cabinet that hummed softly. It was still cold inside when she leaned over. And it puzzled her why the food was stacked in the sink, and also how the food inside the plastic bags and paper boxes was even prepared. They had no mutton, no venison, no sweet potatoes that she could see. She looked under her foot and saw that she was standing on a yellow plastic clothes peg.

Inside the unlit hallway that led down to the four bedrooms, she paused for a few moments to get her eyes used to the darkness. It was a relief to be out of the bright living area, but she would need more light to conduct a proper search. Ordinarily, she could have found a sewing pin on the floor by the thinnest moonlight, because around here there were plenty who could see better at night than others. But tonight there was no moon or starlight at all and the curtains in the bedrooms were drawn; it would be terrible if she missed something important. She found the light switch for the hallway.

The family had no rugs; they had laid carpet all the way down the passage and even inside the bedrooms. How did Jan get the dust out of them, or air them in the Spring like she did with her rugs?

Shaking her head in disapproval, she went into the first

room. Jan and Bill's room. Two suitcases were open on the large bed and full of clothes. The headboard was softened with padded white plastic. Mrs. Pitchford reached out and pressed it.

The next room was for the little girl with all of that lovely thick raven hair. Dear little Charlotte. The light from the hall revealed the dim outlines of her dolls and toys, the books on all of the shelves, the bears in the wallpaper pattern. 'Darlin',' she said, quietly, into the darkness. No answer. Some of the teddy bears and stuffed rabbits were on the floor; they had been pulled off the shelves. Mrs. Pitchford had a hunch a few would be missing too.

She carried on, down the passageway to the two end bedrooms: Jack and Hector's rooms. Hector was safe at their home. How he had managed to scuttle all the way to their farm in the dark had surprised her and her husband. But little Hector had come and banged on their door, then fallen inside, panting and as pale as a sheet. She and Harold hadn't wasted a moment and had swept him into their arms, before spiriting him across the yard to Harold's workshop.

'That kid was as slippery as an eel and quick as a fox' Harold had said, his eyes smiling, as he came back into the kitchen from his workshop, and removed his sheep shearing gloves and leather apron before getting their coats off the pegs. 'Come on, mother. Better get our skates on.'

And Hector had been so concerned for his younger brother and his sister when he arrived at their farm, that she and Harold had sped to the bungalow in the old black Rover that someone else had also once brought over from England. Harold had taught himself to drive the car, not long after acquiring it from an elderly couple with those Pommy accents missing the *H*'s in every word.

Harold would dress Hector when they returned with the other two children, if they were still around. That didn't seem likely now to Mrs. Pitchford. The family's bungalow was deserted then, like all of those bungalows on Rangatera Road, waiting for other Pom families, or Pacific Islanders, or even more of those bloody Dutch Dike-Duckies. Poles were supposed to be coming too. *What next?*

The two end bedrooms were empty of life, but she smelled what all life leaves behind. Then she found it on the floor of one of the boy's rooms overlooking the wattle tree. Kneeling down, she tried to scoop it into her salt-white handkerchief. It was ruddy in colour and smelled strong; the fresh stool of excitement, the stool of too much fresh blood gulped down by a very greedy girl. There was too much of it.

She stripped a pillowcase off the bed. 'You've been at it here, my little joker,' Mrs. Pitchford said with a rueful smile. *She* must have hunted right through the house until she'd found the other two kiddiewinks hiding; under the beds maybe, or in that hardboard wardrobe with the sliding doors on the little plastic runners. 'What a rumble you've had my girl.' This kind of house couldn't possibly make a family feel safe; it was like cardboard covered in thin tin. *She'd* at least had the sense to take Jack and little Charlotte outside the house first, like Harold had shown her how to do. Otherwise, they'd have to burn out another of these bungalows to incinerate the leavings, and that was always a flamin' mess. 'One more and it'll smell funny,' Harold had warned after the last one they lit up.

Mrs. Pitchford went back to the laundry room and found a scrubbing brush, detergent, and a bucket. She filled the bucket with hot water from the tap in the laundry, then went back to the boy's room and scrubbed the rest of the muck out of the carpet. While she was doing this, Harold had become impatient outside in the car and sounded the horn. '*Hold* your bloody horses,' she'd said to Harold, who couldn't possibly have heard her.

When she was finally back inside the car and seated, a pil-

lowcase in her lap, the contents wet and heavy, plus three Tupperware containers inside a brown paper bag clutched in her
other hand, she asked Harold, 'You want to check the creek?'

'Nah. *She'll* be right. Long gone. *She'll* be up in them caves
by now, mother.'

Mrs. Pitchford smiled, wistfully. 'She got carried away
again, my love.'

Smiling with a father's pride, Harold said, 'She's a big
girl, mother. You've got to let them suss their own way in this
world. Be there for them from time to time, but still . . . we've
done what we can for her. She has her own family now. She's
just providing for them the best way she knows.'

'We've been very lucky with her, Harold. To think of all
them sheep Len and Audrey lost last year with their girl.'

'You're not wrong, mother. But when you let a child run
wild . . .' Harold rolled his eyes behind the thick lenses in the
tortoise-shell frames of his glasses that he'd taken off the
old Maori boy they'd found fishing too far downstream last
summer. 'It's all about pace, mother. We showed our girl how
to pace herself. A chook or two. A dog. A cat. And if dags like
these Poms are still around after that, well it comes down to
who was here first. And who was here first, mother?'

'We was, dear. We was.'

CONTRIBUTORS'
BIOGRAPHIES

SIMON BESTWICK short fiction has been published in the UK and the States, collected in two volumes; *A Hazy Shade Of Winter* (Ash Tree Press, 2004) and *Pictures of the Dark* (Gray Friar Press, 2009). He's also written for radio. He has written two novels: *Tide of Souls* and *The Faceless*.

JOSEPH D'LACEY is best known for his novel *Meat*, which prompted Stephen King to say, 'Joseph D'Lacey rocks!'. Other published works include *Garbage Man, Snake Eyes, The Kill Crew, The Failing Flesh, Blood Fugue* and *Splinters* – a collection of his best short stories. He won the British Fantasy Award for Best Newcomer in 2009. His most recent novel, *Black Feathers*, is out now. He lives in Northamptonshire with his wife and daughter.

CATE GARDNER is a horror and fantastical author with over a hundred published short stories. Several of those stories appear in her collection *Strange Men In Pinstripe Suits* (Strange Publications, 2010). She is also the author of two novellas: *Theatre Of Curious Acts* (Hadley Rille Books, 2011) and *Barbed Wire Hearts* (Delirium Books, 2011).

CAROLE JOHNSTONE is a Scot living in Essex. Her first published story appeared in Black Static #3 in early 2008, and she has since contributed stories to PS Publishing, Night Shade Books, Gray Friar Press, Morrigan Books, Apex Book Company and many more. She has been reprinted in Ellen Datlow's Best Horror of the Year and her first novella, *Frenzy*, was published by Eternal Press/ Damnation Books in 2009. Her second, *Cold Turkey*, is to be published by TTA Press in 2013, as is her debut short story collection from Gray Friar Press, titled *The Bright Day is Done*. She is presently at work on her second novel while seeking fame and fortune with the first.

TYLER KEEVIL grew up in Vancouver, Canada, and currently lives in Mid Wales with his wife and son. His genre fiction has been published in a variety of magazines and anthologies, including Black Static, Leading Edge, Neo-Opsis, and On Spec. His debut novel, *Fireball*, was longlisted for Wales Book of the Year and received the Media Wales People's Prize 2011. He has a new novel, *The Drive*, due out in August this year. Fearful Symmetry was inspired by the work of documentary filmmaker Sasha Snow.

KIM LAKIN-SMITH's first novel was *Tourniquet: Tales From The Renegade City* and her 1950s' gaspunk short story, 'Johnny and Emmie-Lou Get Married' was published in *Interzone* #222 and shortlisted for the 2009 British Science Fiction Association short story award. She has had many short stories published in anthologies and a variety of magazines, leading to the publication of her second novel *Cyber Circus* which was shortlisted for the 2011 British Science Fiction Association Best Novel award and shortlisted for the 2011 British Fantasy Society Best Novel award. Kim's Young Adult novella, *Queen Rat* was published in 2012.

ALISON LITTLEWOOD is a writer of dark fantasy and horror fiction. Her first novel, *A Cold Season*, was selected for the Richard and Judy Book Club, where it was described as 'perfect reading for a dark winter's night.' Alison's short stories have been picked for the Best Horror of the Year and Mammoth Book of Best New Horror anthologies for 2012, as well as featuring in genre magazines Black Static, Crimewave and Dark Horizons. Her new novel, *Path of Needles*, is out now.

CHERYL MOORE spent part of her childhood in Iran and has one son and four cats. She is writing / illustrating a speculative series of micro stories called *Unbound Boxes Limping Gods: Disconnected Stories*, an experimental series based on the lives of characters in her speculative fiction manuscript. These are published on her website: cherylmoore.wordpress.com.

MARK MORRIS is the author of over twenty novels, among which are *Toady, Stitch, The Immaculate, The Secret of Anatomy, Fiddleback, The Deluge* and four books in the popular *Doctor Who* range. His short stories, novellas, articles and reviews have appeared in a wide variety of anthologies and magazines, and he is editor of both *Cinema Macabre*, a book of horror movie essays by genre luminaries for which he won the 2007 British Fantasy Award, and its follow-up *Cinema Futura*. His recently published or forthcoming work includes the official tie-in novel for zombie apocalypse computer game *Dead Island*, a novelisation of the 1971 Hammer movie *Vampire Circus*, and *The Wolves of London*, book one of the *Obsidian Heart* trilogy, which will be published by Titan Books in 2014.

ADAM L. G. NEVILL was born in Birmingham, England, in 1969 and grew up in England and New Zealand. He is the author of the supernatural horror novels *Banquet For The Damned, Apartment 16, The Ritual. Last Days* and *House of Small Shadows*. He won the August Derleth award for Best British Horror Award 2012 for *The Ritual.*

SAM STONE is best known for her award-winning Vampire Gene Series and the Steampunk Novella *Zombies At Tiffany's*. Stone is an eclectic horror/fantasy writer who loves to blur the genres. Her work can be found in bookstores all over the world and recently her short story horror collection *Zombies in New York and Other Bloody Jottings* was recorded and released by AudioGo as an audiobook. She has received many awards for her work, including Stone's the silver award for Best Horror 2007 for her debut novel *Gabriele Caccini* with ForeWord in the USA and and Best Short Story *Fool's Gold* in the British Fantasy Awards in 2011.

STEPH SWAINSTON has been writing stories set in the Four-lands since she was eight years old. She was the winner of 2004 IAFA Best New Fantasy Writer award (global award) and has published four novels in the Fourlands sequence: *The Year Of Our War*, *No Present Like Time*, *The Modern World* and *Above The Snowline*.

E. J. SWIFT's debut novel *Osiris* is published by Night Shade Books and Del Rey UK, and is the first in a trilogy, *The Osiris Project*. Book 2 – *Cataveiro* – and Book 3 are forthcoming in 2013 and 2014, and will explore the world outside of Osiris. She has a short story in the upcoming anthology *The Lowest Heaven*.

LAVIE TIDHAR grew up on a kibbutz in Israel, lived in Israel and South Africa, travelled widely in Africa and Asia, and has lived in London for a number of years. He is the winner of the 2003 Clarke-Bradbury Prize (awarded by the European Space Agency), was the editor of 'Michael Marshall Smith: The Annotated Bibliography' (PS Publishing, 2004) and the anthology 'A Dick & Jane Primer for Adults' (The British Fantasy Society, 2006), and is the author of the novella 'An Occupation of Angels' (Pendragon Press, 2005). His stories appear in *SciFiction, ChiZine, Postscripts, Nemonymous, Infinity Plus, Æon, Book of Dark Wisdom, Fortean Bureau,* and many others, and in translation in seven languages. His novella *Gorel and the Pot Bellied God* won the Best British Fantasy Award in 2012 and he is the World Fantasy Award winning author of *Osama*. His new novel *The Violent Century* will be published by Hodder in Oct. 2013.

LISA TUTTLE is an American-born author, long resident in the UK, Lisa has written novels, non-fiction and books for children, but short stories are her first love. She lives in a remote, rural area of Scotland with her family. She received the 1974 John W. Campbell Award for Best New Writer; 1989 British Science Fiction Award, Best Short Fiction ('In Translation'); 2007 International Horror Guild Award for Outstanding Achievement in Mid-length Fiction (*Closet Dreams*); 2012 Grand Prix de L'Imaginaire (in France, for *Ainsi Naissent Les Fantomes*), a short story collection. During her career she has been short-listed for the Nebula Award, Hugo Award, Arthur C. Clarke Award, and the World Fantasy Award.

SIMON UNSWORTH is a World Fantasy Award-nominated author of two collection, *Lost Places* and *Quiet Houses*, with appearances in a number of critically acclaimed anthologies including 4 Mammoth *Book Of New Horrors*. He Gained a World Fantasy Award nomination for Best Short Story (2008) and was on the 2012 Edge Hill Prize longlist for *Quiet Houses*.

JON WALLACE lives in Muswell Hill, London. He has recently been published in Interzone, Jupiter Science Fiction, Flashquake and The Fiction Desk, among many others. His first novel, *Barricade,* will be released by Gollancz in 2014. His hobbies include watching the cricket and listening to his wife sing her way around the flat.

ACKNOWLEDGEMENTS

The editor wishes to thank Chris Hamilton-Emery, Jen Emery and Jane Holland.

first published in *Resurrection Engines* (Snowbooks) anthology, Nov 2012, and is reprinted by permission of the author.

'Too Delicate for Human Form', copyright © Cate Gardner 2012 was first published in *Fish* (Dagan Books), Feb 2012, and is reprinted by permission of the author.

'Imogen', copyright © Sam Stone 2012 was first published in *Siblings* (Hersham Books), Sep 2012 and is reprinted by permission of the author.

'In the Quiet and in the Dark', copyright © Alison Littlewood 2012 was first published in *Terror Tales of the Cotswolds* (Gray Friar Press), Mar 2012, and is reprinted by permission of the author.

'The Scariest Place in the World', copyright © Mark Morris 2012 was first published in *Hauntings* (Newcon Press), Sep 2012, and is reprinted by permission of the author.

'Qiqirn', copyright © Simon Unsworth 2011 was first published in *Phobophobia*, Nov 2011 (Dark Continents Publishing), and is reprinted by permission of the author.

'The Third Person', copyright © Lisa Tuttle 2012 was first published in *The Mammoth Book of Ghost Stories* (Robinson), Oct 2012, and is reprinted by permission of the author.

'Dermot', copyright © Simon Bestwick 2011 was first published in *Black Static* (TTA Press), Aug – Sep 2011, and is reprinted by permission of the author.

'Fearful Symmetry', copyright © Tyler Keevil 2012 was first published in *Interzone* (TTA Press), Jan – Feb 2012, and is reprinted by permission of the author.

'Pig Thing', copyright © Adam L G Nevill 2012 was first published in *Exotic Gothic 4: A Postscripts Anthology* (PS Publishing), July 2012, and is reprinted by permission of the author.